EMMANUEL STREET
ST. ANDREW'S STREET
PANTON STREET
DOWNING STREET
BROOKSIDE
TENNIS COURT ROAD
CORN EXCHANGE ST.
TRUMPINGTON STREET
PEMBROKE ST.
BENE'T ST.
FEN CAUSEWAY
LITTLE ST. MARY'S LANE
KING'S PARADE
MILL LANE
GRANTA PLACE
SILVER STREET
SIDGWICK AVENUE
MALTING LANE
WEST ROAD
NEWNHAM ROAD
RIDLEY HALL ROAD

HIDDEN TALES

Riddle of the White Sphinx

To Nicci

Devised by Sorrel May

Written by Mark Wells

Illustrated by Jennifer Bell

Happy drawing
Jennifer Bell

I hope you enjoy your adventure!

Mark Wells

HIDDEN TALES

A special thanks to the families, schools and museums of Cambridge who helped make this book possible.

First published 2019 by Hidden Tales Ltd.

Devised by Sorrel May, *Written by* Mark Wells, *Illustrated by* Jennifer Bell,
Letterforms (book title and hidden code) and Map by Fiona Boyd,
Book Design/Typography by Dale Tomlinson

A catalogue record for this book is available from the British Library.

Printed and bound in the United Kingdom by Lavenham Press, Suffolk.
Typeset in Baskerville.

ISBN 978-1-5272-4012-4

Hidden Tales Ltd
54 Hertford Street
Cambridge
CB4 3AQ

www.hiddentales.co.uk

Supported using public funding by ARTS COUNCIL ENGLAND

Your Quest

Do you have what it takes to enter the dark and mysterious World of Secrets and free the Hidden from their sinister Keeper? If so, read to the end of the book and complete the following tasks.

1. Locate the Secret Portals – the seven Cambridge museums that link our world to the World of Secrets.
2. Identify the Hidden – the historical figures trapped in each museum.
3. Discover their Secrets – the objects on display that bind them there.
4. Crack the Hidden Code – the cryptic messages in each illustration.

There is also a key and a keyhole in each illustration – see if you can spot them all!

If on your quest, you present your book at each museum you will also receive one of seven unique stamps for your passport at the back of the book. Each one contains part of a riddle to lead you to the Keeper's Secret, hidden somewhere in Cambridge. Use the Code to unlock the secret and free the Hidden!

Good luck adventurer!

The Association of Hidden Adventurers (AHA!)
Note: new members seeking advice can visit **www.hiddentales.co.uk**

A Warning!

Stop now, dear reader, this world is not your own
Its ways lie in shadow under darkened skies,
Forgotten the souls who remain here still
Shielded and safe from meddlesome eyes.

We seek not a light to guide our way home
Nor do our words reveal our sad tale,
Our lives are long gone, our fate ever sealed
Do not be tempted to lift the black veil.

Tarry not, walk on and sleep no false dream
Of things that are lost to be sought and claimed,
The safe path is found in ignorance of truth
While fear is the prize for knowledge gained.

I give you fair warning, this is not a threat
It is but a statement of what is and must be,
For we are the Hidden and this is our world
And I am its Keeper, its lock and its key.

Keeper of Secrets

A Hidden Message

NINA stared up at the lion, whose large head looked down on her with cold, hard eyes. Enormous paws curled over the edge of the wall, each one easily heavy enough to crush her. And if that wasn't worrying enough, this creature had a twin, whose massive bulk sat hunched on another outcrop, staring past her as if the presence of a small girl before them was of no consequence.

'Hey, Nina!'

Turning, she saw her brother, Leo, standing some distance away by the bike racks.

'Come on! The entrance is this way!'

'OK!' she replied. 'Just coming!'

The stone lions continued to ignore her. Probably a good thing, she thought to herself. Those jaws could swallow her in one mouthful.

Nina ran over to join her brother, who was waiting with their parents. Leo already looked grumpy. They hadn't really felt like going to a museum on the first day of the holidays. But the alternative was a punting trip on the Cam, and with rain forecast later, the museum seemed the better option. So, with some reluctance, she and her brother had agreed to go along.

'Impressive, aren't they?' said her father, nodding in the direction of the lions.

'I suppose,' she said.

While her Dad headed off to get some museum guides, her mother turned and spoke to Nina using her no-nonsense voice.

'Your father enjoys this sort of thing, so please show some interest. You never know what you might find.'

Nina expected to find the whole thing totally boring, but decided not to share that thought with her mother.

'Can we have an ice cream at the end of the tour?' asked Leo, who had noticed a sign for the museum cafe.

'We'll see,' said their mother, which meant, 'if you behave.'

Their father returned clutching four hand-held devices with headphones attached.

'Here, I got us these,' he said. 'Audible tour guides, so you can go around at your own pace.'

Nina had to admit this was a smart move on her Dad's part. At least now she could look at the things she was interested in rather than the stuff that her parents liked. Leo, who had been scowling since the museum trip was first mentioned at breakfast, already had his headphones on and was examining the controls with an expert eye.

Nina put on hers and looked at her brother. He pointed to a button on the device and gave her a thumbs-up. She pressed it, and after a moment's static, a clear voice said, 'Welcome.'

Leo walked through an archway into the armoury. Every cabinet was packed with an assortment of swords, pikes, spears, and crossbows. There were helmets and shields, flintlock pistols and muskets. Dotted around the floor were full-size suits of armour, including one sitting astride a massive model horse.

'Can you imagine how much that armour must weigh?' he said to Nina, but his sister must have been listening to the audio guide because she didn't respond. Leo scanned the channels to see if he could find the appropriate one for this exhibit, and as he did so, he heard a girl's voice whisper in his ear.

'The horse tells me the armour is rather heavy.'

Leo turned to see who the girl was, but there was no one there. He looked at his sister. Nina was standing absolutely still, staring back at him, her eyes wide. 'Nina, did you hear that too?' he asked.

She nodded. Leo looked around again, but there was no one near them.

'What channel are you on?' he asked.

'Sixteen. You?'

'Nine.' He said, scrolling to sixteen.

'I'm not in there,' came the voice again. 'I'm somewhere else.'

'Whoa!' said Leo, looking at his sister. If it were possible, her eyes were even wider now.

'Leo, there must be something wrong with the headsets,' Nina said.

'Don't you believe me, Nina?' said the voice.

'How do you know her name?' Leo asked.

'The same way that I know yours, Leo,' said the voice, sounding amused. 'I heard you talking together just now.'

Around them, museum visitors moved from display to display, absorbed in the exhibits. Other than Nina, there were no girls among them.

'Why can't we see you?' said Nina.

'I'm a Hidden.'

'A what?' said Leo.

'I am hiding,' the voice replied.

'Who from?' said Nina.

'Someone I'm afraid of.'

'Who?' said Leo, feeling his pulse quicken.

There was a pause before the girl replied, and when she did, her voice was almost a whisper.

'The Keeper.'

There was something about the way she spoke those words that sent a chill through Leo.

'Who is the Keeper?' he asked.

'The one who seeks me here.'

Leo glanced around at the sightless helmets staring back at him.

'Where exactly are you?' he said.

'I can't tell you. If I do, the Keeper will find me. And the others.'

'Others?' asked Nina.

'I am not alone. There are seven of us.'

'There are seven of you here?' said Leo.

'Not here. In the other portals to our world. Places like this that hold secrets from the past.'

'What sort of secrets?' asked Nina. 'They are not something bad, are they?'

'No, nothing like that. A secret possession. Something that meant so much to us when we lived that we could not bear to leave it behind. So, when our time came to move on from your world, we lingered too long and were trapped in this other place.'

'What place?' Leo asked.

'The World of Secrets.'

A door banged open somewhere, making him jump, and he felt a whisper of cold air brush his cheek.

'Why can't you just leave?' asked Nina.

'Some of us want to. To reveal our secret and move on. But the portals are watched by the Keeper's spies. Any who are caught trying to escape are handed over to the Keeper.'

'What happens then?' he asked.

'They are never seen again, their secrets buried with them forever.'

Nina gave Leo a horrified look. 'Why would anyone want to do that?'

'In our world, secrets are power. If we attempt to share them, they will be taken from us.'

'By this Keeper person?' asked Leo.

'Yes, the Keeper of Secrets.'

Without warning, a high-pitched wailing noise split the air, bouncing off the suits of armour around them. Nina grabbed Leo's arm.

'What's that?' she yelled.

'An alarm!' he said, pointing to the flashing red light on the ceiling.

'It's the Keeper!' cried the girl. 'I've said too much.'

There was a flurry of movement as people started streaming for the exits. Leo looked around for his parents.

'I must go!' said the girl.

'Where?' Nina asked.

'Back to my world. The Keeper mustn't find me here!'

Leo could hear the fear in her voice. 'But how do we find you again?' he asked.

'Seek the seven portals. Find those, and you will find us, and our secrets!'

Leo spotted their parents hurrying towards them. They were out of time.

'Can't you just tell us yours?' he said.

'No, then the Keeper will know me, and my secret, and I will be trapped for eternity. All I can do is leave you clues.'

'Clues? Where?'

'In your dreams.'

'What?' said Nina. 'I don't understand.'

'It's a fire alarm, children,' said their father, reaching them. 'We have to go to the assembly area outside.'

'But Dad…?' began Leo.

'No buts, we have to go,' said their father.

'Your father's right,' said their mother, 'we can come back another time. Come along children!'

Reluctantly, Leo and Nina hurried towards the entrance lobby, accompanied by their parents and the other fleeing guests.

'Look for me in your dreams…' the girl's voice called out. 'Follow the clues…'

And then she was gone, drowned out by the shrill wail of the siren.

The mouse darted behind the suit of armour and scurried across the floor. Her black button eyes spotted a gap in the forest of moving legs, and she dodged between the stampede of humans. Reaching the edge of the room, she raced along the skirting board, her nose sniffing the air for the scent of her point of entry. Up ahead, she caught the tell-tale smell of the other world seeping through the hole behind a display cabinet, and she sped towards it, aware that another presence would be able to sense it too.

In her peripheral vision, the mouse saw a feline shape bounding towards her. With an involuntary squeak of alarm and her paws scrabbling on the polished floor, she covered the last few inches in a blur. Darting through the gap, she felt her whiskers brush against the hole's rough edges and then there was an explosion of pain as claws raked her hindquarters. Squealing in agony, the mouse pushed herself through the hole and dived into nothingness.

Down she fell, the wind rushing past her tiny body as she twisted and turned in the darkness. Above her, the light of the museum faded into the distance, and as it did so, the mouse started to change. The grey fur covering her skin began to thin, her legs stretched and her back straightened. Her long nose shortened, as did the prominent front teeth, retracting into gums now wrapped in full-bodied lips. Pale arms reached upwards, and a long cotton dress slipped over her head and shoulders. A heavy cloak wrapped itself around her thin frame, its material flapping behind her like bat wings in the night.

Gradually, her descent slowed, and the whistling of the wind was replaced by the caress of cold, damp air that clung to her skin and hair.

Still, it was a shock when she landed, the Girl's feet hitting the cobbled street and pitching her forwards to fall in a heap on the floor. Fresh pain erupted from the wounds in her back where the claws had raked her. A reminder, if she needed one, that she was being hunted. Grimacing, she scrambled to her feet and lurched into a run.

The alleyway was dark, and a dense mist hung in the still air. A faint glow emanated from the portal behind her, but this faded with each step as the shadows closed in. The Girl felt her way along the wall, fingers scraping over the rough brickwork for the gap she knew must be there.

Behind her, something large and heavy landed in the alleyway, blotting out whatever light was coming from the portal. The Girl came to a halt and stood motionless, clinging to the wall, not daring to breathe.

Utter silence.

Then came the unmistakable sound of heavy footsteps moving with slow deliberation in her direction. Stifling a cry, the Girl stumbled on, not daring to look over her shoulder as she groped along the wall, her torn fingers frantically feeling for the opening. Up ahead came the sound of voices, muffled in the mist.

'Come on you lot, this way! The Keeper's after one!'

The Girl froze. That could only mean one thing. Watchers! The Keeper's spies must have been warned she was coming. Now they were bearing down on her, eager to block off her escape.

'Hurry up. We don't want to miss all the fun!'

'I wouldn't want to be in that one's shoes!'

Above the din of the mob, the Girl could still hear the steady tread of footsteps approaching from behind. She was trapped!

In a final desperate effort, she reached along the wall and almost fell as her hands grasped empty air. Stifling a prayer of thanks, she slipped into the opening and crouched down as a press of bodies rushed out of the mist and past the place where she had been standing only seconds before.

The shouts of the Watchers rose to a crescendo before their cries were cut short. In that eerie silence, all the Girl could hear was her heart thumping like a drum in her chest. She willed it to be quiet.

A screech of anger tore through the night, so loud and piercing that it set her teeth on edge. The wail of terror that followed was accompanied by the sound of many footsteps fleeing back towards her.

The Girl didn't wait to hear what happened next. Turning, she fled down the steps to the safety of the catacombs buried far below the city's streets, her bare feet padding over the well-worn surfaces as silent as a mouse.

Nina was woken the next morning by a sliver of sunlight that drew a line from the gap in her curtains to the duvet tucked under her cheek. Wrinkling her nose, she kept her eyes tight shut and lay there for some time, enjoying its warmth on her face. That was when the dream started coming back to her. As if she'd seen the world through someone else's eyes.

Her thoughts were disturbed by a quiet knock at her bedroom door. It creaked open a fraction to reveal Leo, still in his pyjamas, peering in from the landing. Raising herself up, she waved at him to come in, and he slipped into her room, careful to pull the door closed behind him. Even in the dim light, she could see the frown on his face.

'Hi,' she said, 'what are you doing up so early?'

'I couldn't sleep. At least, not after I woke up.'

That wasn't like him. Leo could sleep till lunchtime if their parents let him. 'What's up?' she asked.

He sat on the edge of her bed and examined the rope of his dressing gown.

'I don't suppose you...' He paused.

'Had a weird dream?' Nina suggested.

His head jerked up. 'Yes!'

'With a sphinx chasing a mouse?'

'You saw them too!' he said, eyes bright.

Nina nodded, remembering the sight of that claw reaching out for her. She shuddered.

'It was the Girl, Nina, I'm sure of it!'

'She did say she would visit us in our sleep, I suppose.'

'Exactly! And that she'd leave us clues!'

Nina reached for a pen and her diary next to the bed. 'Come on then, let's write it all down before we forget.'

For the next half hour, they sat together on her bed sharing their visions of the dream. It was like trying to remember the details of a painting, the setting, colours, characters, and objects before they faded away. Nina was glad Leo had come straight away because he mentioned things, like the owl, which she was beginning to forget, and she reminded him about the little Egyptian people.

Nina was sure that if they went back to the museum, they could follow the trail of objects from the armoury through the various halls to where the Girl was hiding. Once there, they just had to find an object that could tell them who she was.

'But what about the piece of paper?' Leo asked.

'It's some sort of message,' said Nina.

'I don't recognise the letters.'

'Maybe it's in the Hidden's language.'

'Or a code perhaps?' asked Leo, sounding excited. 'Remember when Dad took us to Bletchley Park. You know, where the codebreakers cracked ENIGMA in the war!'

'Yes, but they had hundreds of people working on that. How are we supposed to solve this one?'

'Didn't they start with single letter words and go from there?' he suggested.

'You're right!' said Nina, thinking of the strange script from the dream. 'Come on, let's give it a go.' She began jotting down the symbols on a piece of paper and trying different letters under each one, noting where the same one appeared twice.

By the time the children heard their mother calling them from the kitchen for breakfast, they had already identified a number of letters and had some theories about what the secret treasure might be. Now they just needed to find the Girl.

'So, you want to go back to the museum?' their Dad asked, looking up from his newspaper.

'If that's OK with you,' said Nina, careful not to sound too excited. They had decided it wasn't a good idea to tell their parents about the dream. 'We'd only just got there when the alarm went off, and it looked really interesting. I thought I might take a look at some of the china.'

Leo nodded his agreement. 'Yeah, and I wanted to see the stuff they had from Ancient Egypt.'

'Hmm,' said their father, looking from one to the other before turning to their Mum. 'What do you think? I'd be happy to take them if you have things to do.'

She studied them over her cup of coffee. 'I don't see why not? As long as you are all back in time for lunch.'

'Oh, we will be!' promised Nina, getting up.

Leo rose too, leaving his toast untouched. 'Thanks, Mum.'

Nina felt a buzz of anticipation as she headed for the door, exchanging a look of excitement with her brother. Neither had any understanding of the dangers that lay ahead. If they had done, they might not have been so eager.

In a dusty cellar, concealed deep within the catacombs under the city, the Girl sat on the upturned back of an empty coffin. In the dull orange glow of an oil lamp, she stared at the bandages covering her torn fingers. Next to her squatted a much taller figure, his broad shoulders hunched and his head bowed to avoid disturbing the cobwebs that hung from the ceiling.

'I'm going back, Brave Bird,' she said.

'Are you sure you are strong enough to travel?' he asked.

The Girl flexed her back. The claw wounds were still painful, but she could move freely.

'It is time. The children will be looking for me.' She looked up at him. 'Last night I visited them in their dreams and laid out a trail of clues.'

'Did you give them enough?'

She shrugged. 'I couldn't show them too much or…'

'…the Keeper would have found you.'

She nodded.

'But I did leave them a message telling them what I am.'

She saw the look of alarm on his face.

'Don't worry, I wrote it in the script of the Hidden.'

'How will they know what the symbols mean?' he asked.

'If they are clever, they will work it out.' At least, that is what she hoped.

'And your secret?'

'When they find me, they will see it,' she said, her fingers straying towards her throat before she noticed what she was doing and returned them to her lap.

Brave Bird didn't say anything and instead looked down at his massive hands.

'If we're going to break the Keeper's power,' he said, 'the children will need to find all of us, not just you.'

The Girl knew he was referring to the Cypher, the prophecy that was known to all the Hidden, despite the Keeper's efforts to suppress it.

'Seven souls to find a key,' she began.

'To pick the lock and set us free,' he finished.

Though each of the Hidden knew those words, few, if any, dared utter them aloud. It was how the Girl had found the rest of the Seven. They alone had mustered the courage to invoke the Cypher. Once spoken, there was no going back.

'We do it one at a time,' she said. 'Each of us will use a different portal. The Keeper can't keep an eye on all of them at once.'

'What about the Watchers?' he said. 'After last night, they will be looking for us. They won't want to let another one slip through their fingers.'

'We'll just have to be careful,' she said. 'Keep to the shadows. Use the rooftops and tunnels. Once we reach a portal, only the Keeper would risk following us in there.'

The big man studied her for a long time, his forehead creased in a frown. She held his gaze, knowing that they had no other choice. At last, he nodded.

'Very well. I will tell the others.'

'Thank you,' she said, reaching forward and hugging him. She felt his hand rest on her closely cropped hair, careful to avoid the wounds on her back. They sat there for a while, the Girl not wanting to leave but knowing she had to. Finally, she released him and stood up. The huge man eased himself up, careful to avoid the low ceiling.

'Take care Little Mouse,' he said.

'And you Brave Bird.' She looked up into his hooded eyes. 'When you've told the others, promise me you will follow.'

Brave Bird stared down at her. He had probably never run from anything in his life. In his tribe, he had told her, you stayed to protect the weak and infirm. But he wasn't with his tribe any more. He was here in this other world. And she needed all of the Seven to break the Keeper's hold over the souls trapped here.

'Brave Bird?' the Girl asked again. 'You will come, won't you?'

'I will,' he said. 'When I've told the others.'

Feelings of relief and gratitude threatened to overwhelm her as she looked at his strong, proud features. He would not let her down. Knowing that made it easier to leave.

'Remember,' she said, her voice thick with emotion. 'Seven souls to find a key…'

'To pick the lock and set us free,' he finished.

The Girl nodded, and before he could say anything, she turned and headed for the door without looking back. As she ducked under the archway, she used the back of her bandaged hand to wipe her wet cheeks before fleeing up the stairs.

A Night Call

THE TILES were slick from the residue of the evening's fog as the hooded figure moved over the uneven rooftops of the higher dwellings. After the Girl had left him, Brave Bird had made his way here, using the safest route for tracking down the next of the Seven, scattered as they were all over the city. Navigating through the forest of twisted chimneys, he avoided the Watchers roaming the maze of narrow lanes and alleyways below. Even those patrolling the upper levels would struggle to see his cloaked form through the blanket of thick, grey smog that spread from the soot-stained chimney pots.

Nearing his destination, he dropped onto one of the wooden walkways that crisscrossed the gaps above the streets, stitching together the buildings with a patchwork of precarious routes that threaded their way over the city. Moving with a lightness of foot that belied his size, he crossed the span to the building opposite and stepped through an archway to emerge onto Lofty Lane, the name given to a passageway that ran beneath the rooftops of some of the city's tallest structures.

There he paused for a moment, waiting for a cry of alarm or the sound of boots running up the rickety stairway that clung to the external walls of the building like long-dead ivy. When none came, he headed along the landing, weaving around refuse barrels and ducking under timber trusses that disappeared into the pitched roof above. His destination was a nail-studded door to a tiny dwelling, set back in an alcove, half concealed from view. As he approached, Brave Bird noted the well-kept iron hinges and intricate lock mechanism that fixed the door to its thick oak frame.

Once more, Brave Bird checked up and down the landing for signs of movement, but nothing stirred. Satisfied, he faced the door, raised his fist and gave seven sharp knocks. No response. The visitor was not surprised. In the World of Secrets, gatherings were frowned upon, and anyone turning up at your door this late at night could only mean trouble.

He knocked again. 'Tinker!' he whispered.

A floorboard creaked inside the room.

'Tinker, it's me, Brave Bird.'

Metal bolts scraped back, and the mechanical click of a key turned in the lock. The door opened a fraction, and the illicit glow of an oil lamp escaped through the crack, reflecting off the lenses of a pair of glasses.

'What are you doing here?' The sharp voice made no attempt to hide its irritation.

'I have a message for you.'

'What sort of message?'

'One that cannot be spoken of through the crack of a door.'

The highly polished lenses stared at him for a moment longer before the door swung open silently on its well-oiled hinges.

'Come in then,' said the voice, 'but be quick about it.'

Brave Bird dipped his head under the lintel and stepped inside the room. The door was closed behind him and the lock and bolts secured fast. A small, rotund figure stepped around him and headed towards a workbench in the centre of the room where an oil lamp stood on an elegant brass stand. Brave Bird glanced towards the window and saw that heavy black drapes had been hung over the opening, blocking the light from any Watchers in the street below.

Despite the frostiness of its owner, the lamp's orange flame cast a warm glow over the room, which Brave Bird could see was as bare as any in this city. There was a camp bed in the corner, with a small wooden table beside it. A wardrobe stood against the far wall with its door ajar. Next to this was a threadbare armchair tucked in a corner by the shrouded window, its seat cushion faded and worn.

The one item of interest in the room was the workbench, over which the Tinker was now fussing, his back to his visitor as if to hide its contents. From what Brave Bird could see, it was covered in a bizarre assortment of mechanical drawings and devices with their inner workings laid bare.

'So, what is the message you've come all this way to tell me?' asked the Tinker, his balding head bent over a device of concentric silver circles.

'It's from the Girl,' said Brave Bird.

'The Girl, eh? What does she have to say for herself?'

The man peered through his spectacles at a drawing while holding a set of small brass cogs in his delicate fingers. He showed little interest in what his visitor had come to say and gave every indication that he wished to be left alone to play with his toys.

'Seven souls to find a key,' said Brave Bird.

The figure in the centre of the room became quite still. Then, with great care, he placed the cogs back on the workbench and laid his hands flat on its surface as if to support his weight. For a while he just stood there, breathing slowly, the only movement in the room coming from the flickering flame of the lamp.

'So, it is time?' said the Tinker quietly.

'It is,' said Brave Bird.

The man's head sagged between his shoulders for a moment, as if weighed down by this message. Then, with a sigh, he straightened and turned to face his visitor. The blue eyes peering through their round lenses were softer now. The grey-flecked eyebrows had lost the frown that had greeted Brave Bird on his arrival.

'I take it, the Girl has found someone.'

'She has. Two children.'

The Tinker nodded. 'Of course.'

'She wants each of us to leave them a message.'

'In their dreams, I assume.'

Brave Bird nodded. 'She's gone back to her portal to wait for them.'

'And the Keeper?'

Brave Bird shrugged. They both knew the Keeper would be hunting her even as they spoke.

Then the Tinker did something Brave Bird hadn't expected. He smiled.

'In that case, it is time we created a distraction.'

'A distraction?'

The small man reached across his workbench and picked up a piece of paper and two spherical objects, which he slipped inside his jacket pocket.

'Naturally,' said the Tinker. 'Something to divert the Keeper's attention from the Girl.'

'And what would that be?' asked Brave Bird as the little man strode across the room towards the wardrobe.

'Why, open another portal, of course,' said the Tinker as he pulled open the door and retrieved a grey cloak.

'You are ready to leave, then?' asked Brave Bird.

'Oh, I've been ready for a while,' said the Tinker, casting his eye over the workbench. 'I've kept myself busy, but now the wheels are in motion, it is time for action. Besides, this particular portal is very dear to me.'

He stared at Brave Bird, a twinkle in his eyes that didn't come from the lamplight. 'Are you coming with me, my feathered friend?'

'The Girl asked me to tell the others. When I've done that, I will follow.'

'Of course,' said the Tinker, the hint of a smile on his lips. 'She's quite something, that Girl.'

'She is,' said Brave Bird.

They stood looking at each other, and Brave Bird realised, for the first time, that the Tinker understood more than just mechanical hearts.

'Right!' said the little man, clapping his hands together before striding over to the heavy blinds and throwing them open with surprising force. A cloud of dust billowed into the room, illuminated by the orange light which streamed through the dirty window onto the building opposite.

'The Watchers!' said Brave Bird. 'They will see the light!'

'Precisely!' said the Tinker. 'Time for us to leave!'

'But what about your things?' Brave Bird asked, pointing towards the workbench.

'What? Those?' said the little man, smiling. 'Complete nonsense. I thought I'd leave a few diversions to occupy the Keeper for a while.'

Brave Bird stared at the myriad of objects and drawings as their owner busied himself with the door bolts. When he turned, his host was standing by the open doorway.

'Shall we?' said the Tinker. 'Only, I think we can expect some unwanted visitors before very long.'

Brave Bird stepped out onto the landing, and the Tinker followed him, closing the door and locking it behind them. Then he crossed to the dwelling opposite and lifted the lid on its soil barrel. Recoiling from the smell, he reached out and dropped the key into its stinking contents before replacing the cover.

'That should keep them busy,' said the Tinker, wrinkling his nose.

As if on cue, a cry of alarm rose up from the street far below, followed by a chorus of angry voices. The Watchers had spotted the light from the window.

'I take it you are not coming with me?' asked the Tinker, ignoring the commotion.

Brave Bird shook his head. 'My path lies in another direction.'

'Over the rooftops?' said the little man.

Brave Bird nodded. The sound of voices was getting louder, and he could feel the building tremble from the stamp of many feet pounding up the stairway.

'It seems it is time we went our separate ways,' said the Tinker, offering his hand.

Brave Bird took it and was surprised by the firmness of its grip.

'Fly, my friend,' said the Tinker with a smile. And with that, he pulled up his hood and hurried off along Lofty Lane, his diminutive form soon lost among the roof beams.

Brave Bird watched the figure go. Then he turned and headed in the opposite direction towards the opening over the street. When he reached the archway, he peered down the outside of the building. An angry mob was scrambling up the staircase, too busy jostling and cursing to notice him for now.

Time to go, he thought.

Taking two steps back, Brave Bird spread his arms and leapt into the air. For a few heart-stopping moments, he flew across the gap between the buildings before landing neatly on the walkway on the other side. By the time the Watchers had reached the top of the staircase, his shadowy form had melted into the night.

'I'm so sorry children,' said their father.

Leo stared at the sign over the museum entrance. CLOSED.

'But Dad, I don't understand.' Leo had been so excited on the way there and had never imagined their morning's adventure would end like this.

'It must be something to do with yesterday's alarm,' said their father. 'I wonder what set it off?'

Leo exchanged a look with his sister. The Keeper!

'I'll tell you what, children, why don't we pop down the road to Fitzbillies and get ourselves a Chelsea bun. I know another museum, just around the corner from there.'

Leo wasn't so sure. After the dream he and his sister had shared, it was this museum they really wanted to visit. But a Chelsea bun was a Chelsea bun, after all.

A little later, their hands still sticky with sugar, they emerged from Fitzbillies, and their father turned right to lead them down a narrow alleyway between a church and a row of cottages. At the end of the lane, they came to another street, and their father pointed at a pair of oak doors with a crest above them. 'There it is!'

'Are you sure this is a museum, Dad?' Leo asked, thinking it looked more like a fire exit.

'Trust me,' said his father, pushing the doors open. 'I think you might be surprised.'

Leo glanced at his sister, who shrugged, so they followed their father through the doorway and found themselves in a small entrance hall. Immediately on the left was a glass window with an attendant sitting behind it, tapping away on a computer.

'Which is the way to the museum?' asked their father.

'Up the stairs and turn left. Or, if you want the library, turn right,' said the man.

'There's a library too?'

Leo knew his father loved libraries even more than museums.

'Yes, but you'll need to sign in, first.'

'Right, of course.' Their Dad turned to Leo and Nina, his eyes bright. 'Listen, children, you go on up, and I'll follow you shortly.'

'What do you think?' said Leo to his sister.

'Might as well,' she said.

There didn't seem to be any harm in having a look, so they set off up the stairwell. At the top, Leo did as the man said and turned left through a set of doors.

'Wow!' he said.

They were standing in a vast, barn-like room, its ceiling rising far above their heads supported by massive timber cross-beams. Tall wooden cabinets lined the walls, and glass display cases were dotted around the floor, each housing some of the most bizarre-looking objects Leo had ever seen.

'I didn't expect this,' whispered Nina.

'Nor me,' said Leo, staring around in amazement.

His eye was drawn to a large wooden telescope on a tripod at the back of the hall, and a giant mechanical clock in a glass case, its distinctive 'Tick, tock, tick, tock,' echoing through the cavernous space. In a nearby cabinet, an assortment of highly polished brass microscopes looked as good as new, though he suspected they probably dated back centuries. Other devices looked like they were designed to measure things, but what exactly and how they worked was beyond him.

For the next ten minutes, they wandered around a series of interconnected rooms, looking at globes, astronomical instruments and other intricate mechanical devices covered in dials and tubes whose function they could only guess at. In one cabinet, Leo came across a gruesome collection of body parts made out of wax, and in another, he came face to face with a dissected human skeleton whose lidless eyeballs gave it a permanently surprised expression.

Searching around for Nina, he found her standing by a wall cabinet filled with what appeared to be row upon row of oversized dentures. He went over to join her and stared at the strange display.

'Nife teef!' he mumbled, using his fingers to pull his lips apart.

But Nina wasn't smiling.

'Oh, come on Nina, it wasn't that bad.'

'Leo, don't you hear it?'

SCHOOL LANE

'What?'

'The ticking,' she said. 'It doesn't sound right.'

Leo listened.

'Tick, tick, tick… tock, tock, tock… tick, tick, tick.'

Odd, he thought and looked over to where the sound came from. The mechanical clock stood in its own glass cabinet on the far side of the hall. The sequence of sounds reminded him of something, but he couldn't quite work out what it was.

'Tick, tick, tick, tock, tock, tock, tick, tick, tick,' he said out loud, hoping it would jog his memory. And then it came to him.

'Nina! I know what that is!' he said. 'We learnt it at Scouts. It's Morse code. It means S-O-S. Save Our Souls!'

'Very good,' whispered a man's voice.

Nina turned, expecting to see her father, but he was nowhere to be seen. The museum was deserted. Nina looked at Leo, and by the expression on his face, she knew he had heard the voice too.

'Err… hello,' she said.

'Hello, children.'

'Excuse me for asking, but where exactly are you?' she asked.

'If you are the two children I think you are,' said the voice, 'you'll know I cannot tell you.'

'Because of the Keeper?' asked Nina.

The chime of the clock striking the hour made them both jump.

'Shush,' whispered the voice, 'it doesn't pay to use that name around here. The portals are being watched.'

'The portals?' asked Nina.

'The doorways between our world and yours,' said the voice. 'The places where we can cross over.'

'So, this is a portal?' asked Leo.

'It is my portal, in more ways than one.'

'What do you mean?' asked Nina.

'In another life, I spent a great deal of time here. Many of these objects are very dear to me. But one, in particular, is the reason I am still here.'

Nina looked around at the displays. 'Which one?'

She heard a chuckle. 'That would be telling.'

'Can you give us a clue?' asked Leo.

'Look for a mechanical map which is missing two astronomical objects that were only discovered after it was made. I set out to make models of these distant orbs and find a way to incorporate them into its design. I have both with me now, in my pocket in fact.'

'So, they are your secret?' Nina asked.

'They are indeed. Discover their names, and you will free me from the World of Secrets.'

Nina was about to ask what he meant by this when she heard a door open behind her, followed by a breath of cold air on her cheek. Leo must have felt it too because they both turned and looked at the museum entrance, just in time to see the door swing closed.

'What was that?'

'I don't know,' said Leo. 'Was it him? Has he just left?'

'Hello?' Nina called out. 'Are you still there?'

'Shush!' said the voice.

Nina and Leo stood still, not daring to move. The room was silent apart from the rhythmical ticking of the giant clock. Then, between those regular beats, Nina heard another noise.

'Clack.'

'Leo, was that you?'

'No,' he said, frowning.

'What was it then?'

'I don't know.'

'Clack, clack.'

'Whoa! Did you see that?' said Leo, pointing at the cabinet.

'The teeth moved!'

Nina looked at the display.

'Clack, clack, clack!' Three sets of teeth slammed shut.

'Leo?' said Nina, edging away from the cabinet.

More rows of teeth began to chatter in unison.

'Clack, clack, clackety, clack!'

'It's the Keeper!' said the voice. 'I must go!'

'Wait!' said Nina as the noise intensified. 'We still don't know what we are looking for?'

'Clackety, clack, clackety, clack, clackety, clack!'

Straining to hear the response over the din coming from the cabinet, she could just make out, 'In your dreams… two missing…' before the racket drowned out his fading voice.

'CLACKETY, CLACKETY, CLACKETY, CLACKETY, CLACK, CLACK, CLACK!'

'Come on Nina!' cried Leo. 'Let's get out of here!'

They turned and fled, running straight into the arms of their approaching father.

'Ooof!' he grunted, staggering backwards under their combined weight. 'What's all this noise about?' he asked.

Nina looked up at him. 'You heard it too?'

'I heard you both cry out,' he said. 'I thought you must have seen a ghost!'

'A ghost?' Nina turned to her brother, but Leo wasn't listening. He was staring, pale-faced, at the cabinet. Unable to stop herself, she followed his gaze.

The rows of teeth sat on the shelves, perfectly still and silent. Not a single clack escaped from their toothy grins. The only sound that could be heard in the cavernous hall was the steady 'Tick, tock, tick, tock,' of the old mechanical clock.

An Open Cage

THE NEXT morning before breakfast, Nina sat on the end of Leo's bed as they talked about the dream that they had shared the night before. This one had been very different from the first, and they were sure it came from the voice they heard in the second museum.

The children carefully wrote down all the things they had seen in the dream. But Nina didn't feel like going back there just yet, not after the chattering teeth. They had really spooked her.

'I don't like this Keeper,' Leo said. 'Anyone who tries to scare people like that can't be very nice.'

'Yeah,' she agreed, thinking back to last term when her brother had been picked on by some other boys in his year.

They fell silent, and Nina felt something hot grow inside her. It was anger. She didn't like bullies.

'Leo, you know these Hidden. I think we should help them escape.'

'I was thinking the same,' he said. 'But that means finding the other portals. How do we go about doing that?'

Nina thought for a moment.

'What have the two portals had in common so far?'

'What, apart from strange voices and weird things happening, you mean?'

'No, the places themselves,' she said.

Leo frowned. 'They were both museums?'

'Exactly,' said Nina. 'Remember what the girl said about places that hold secrets from the past. Well, museums are full of secrets, aren't they? Maybe the portals to the World of Secrets are all in museums!'

'Could be, I suppose. But even if you are right, Nina, there are loads of museums in Cambridge!'

'I know, so choose one. What would you like to see first?'

Leo thought for a minute, then his face split into a grin.

'Dinosaurs!'

The cobbled lane descended towards the murky river that snaked its way through the city. The hooded shape moved from building to building, keeping to the shadows of the workshops and storehouses that lay empty at this time of night. Its silent progress went unnoticed until a startled rat burst from the gutter and scurried behind a discarded pile of old crates and barrels, causing the figure to come to an abrupt halt.

Brave Bird stood there motionless, his breath condensing in front of his hidden face. When nothing else stirred, he continued on his way, eyes scanning the shadows for any other signs of movement.

At the end of the lane, a fog bank marked the location of the river more clearly than any sign could do. The impenetrable wall of mist drifted like a ghost beyond the edge of the cobbled wharf.

Peering around the corner of the lane, Brave Bird could make out the irregular line of masts from the vessels moored along the quayside. The only sound to be heard was the occasional creak and groan of a hull, rubbing gently against the jetty wall.

Turning right, he headed along the wharf, staying as close as he could to the timber-framed buildings which leaned forward as if their upper floors were peering over the water's edge. Brave Bird counted down the doorways until he came to a weathered oak door with a brass knocker in the shape of a dog.

The eerie quiet was shattered by a sudden crash as a door was swung open further down the quayside. Light spilt onto the street, followed by the roar of laughter as a group of figures staggered out onto the cobbles. Brave Bird flattened himself against the doorway, hoping they hadn't spotted him.

'You should have seen the stuff!' one of them sneered. 'Desk was covered with all sorts of machinery. Looked really technical, so we brought it all to the Keeper.'

'What did the Keeper make of it?'

'Took one look and hurled it across the room. Smashed it to pieces!'

'What did the Keeper do then?' asked another.

'What do you think? Turned on the nearest Watcher and bound him, just like that!' He clicked his fingers. 'Ain't seeing him no more. Nothing left but his shoes. Still, one less for us to watch, eh?'

More laughter.

Brave Bird knew that if any of them turned his way, they would see him, even in their present state. Feeling the brass knocker pressed against his back, he gave the door seven quiet knocks with his knuckled fist.

One of the Watchers separated from the group and took a few faltering steps in his direction. Brave Bird's body tensed under his cloak, and he held his breath, ready to run. The figure swayed for a moment before tripping over a bucket and falling in a heap on the cobbles. Loud jeers filled the air.

Brave Bird took his chance and tapped against the wood another seven times, louder this time. Without warning, the door swung open behind him, and he fell backwards onto the floorboards of a darkened room. Immediately, the door was swung shut, and Brave Bird found himself staring up at the pale face of a young man who was holding a finger to his lips.

The sounds from the street grew louder as the Watchers headed up the quayside towards them. The commotion reached a crescendo right outside, and both of them jumped when something slammed against the doorframe. This was followed by some cursing and another chorus of laughter as whoever had stumbled against the building staggered off to follow the rest of them into the night. Inside the room, both figures remained motionless until the sounds had faded away. Finally, the young man standing by the door smiled at Brave Bird and offered him a hand.

'Sailing close to the wind, my friend,' he said.

'Thanks, Cabin Boy,' Brave Bird replied as he pulled himself to his feet.

The young man nodded at a chair over by the far wall.

'Stow yourself there, while I make a brew.'

Brave Bird went over and sat down in the sturdy, mahogany seat, which took his weight without so much as a creak. Pulling the hood of his cloak back, he was greeted by the sound of chirping. Glancing around, he spotted a tall brass birdcage hanging from one of the roof beams in the corner of the room. Inside, two little birds with distinctive orange beaks peered out at him through the bars.

'Good evening to you too,' he said.

While the young man busied himself in the kitchen area, Brave Bird looked around at the rest of the room. Books and storage boxes were stacked neatly on shelves alongside an extendable brass telescope. An old, battered sea chest stood on the floor, its leather carrying handles worn from use, and near the birdcage, a sailcloth hammock hung from two iron rings fixed to the roof joists. Everything looked orderly and ship-shape, thought Brave Bird.

The pot began to bubble, and the Cabin Boy poured steaming

coffee into two tin mugs. These he brought over to the table, putting one down in front of his visitor before settling into the chair opposite. Brave Bird bent forward and sniffed the coffee.

'Brazilian?' he asked.

'Old habits,' said the young man, smiling. 'So, what brings you down to the docks at this time of night, my friend? I thought you preferred loftier quarters.'

Brave Bird waited for a moment and then began.

'Seven souls to find a key.'

The Cabin Boy hesitated, the mug halfway to his lips, before completing the verse.

'To pick the lock and set us free.'

They stared at each other for some time.

'So, you know what to do?' Brave Bird asked.

The young man peered at him through the steam rising from his cup and nodded.

'Am I the first?'

'No, and you won't be the last,' Brave Bird said. 'The Girl asked me to spread the word.'

His host took a sip from his cup and closed his eyes before placing it back on the table.

'I'm glad. I've been holed up here too long. It would seem that the tide is finally turning. Time to venture forth again. Who am I to rendezvous with?'

'Two children.'

The Cabin Boy raised an eyebrow. 'In that case, let me see if I can give them some assistance.'

Getting up, he crossed the room to a small desk by the window, where he retrieved a pen and a piece of paper on which he wrote a message in the Hidden's coded letters. Slipping the piece of paper in his pocket, he headed for a set of pegs on the wall and unhooked a long, oilskin cloak. Brave Bird rose and went to wait by the door while the young man retrieved the brass cage, the birds chirping in excitement.

'You're planning on taking them with you?' Brave Bird asked.

'Can't leave them behind,' said the Cabin Boy. 'Old shipmates, you see.'

Brave Bird unlocked the front door and, after checking the way was clear, stepped onto the street. His companion followed him outside and held up the cage.

'Time to cast off, my friends,' the Cabin Boy said, opening the door of the cage.

The two birds hopped back and forth and angled their heads to peer first at their owner and then at the open doorway. The Cabin Boy waited patiently until, with a sudden flutter of wings, one of the birds shot through the gap. The other followed in a heartbeat, uttering a final chirp as it disappeared into the darkness.

'Goodbye, my friend,' said Brave Bird, holding out his hand.

The Cabin Boy took it. 'Bon voyage,' he replied with a smile.

Pulling up their hoods, the two figures parted company and disappeared into the night.

Leo and Nina followed their mother as she led them through the iron gates and under the tall archway. They found themselves in a large courtyard with an area of lawn and a huge tree, surrounded by tall buildings.

'You would never think from the street there was a tree in here,' said Leo.

'It's amazing what you find in places like this,' said their mother. 'Come along, it's this way.'

They turned left and walked along a rack of bicycles towards a curved staircase guarded by two stone bears, draped over the handrails.

Leo patted one on the head as he passed, and his sister gave him a funny look.

'What?' he said. 'I like bears!'

They followed their mother up the steps and turned left through a set of double doors. Emerging into a long hall, they were greeted by a towering dinosaur skeleton, its neck disappearing into the rafters some 20 feet above them.

'Yes!' Leo said, delighted.

'I'm just going to have a look at the books in here,' said his mother, pointing to the wood-panelled museum shop opposite the entrance, where an attendant sat behind a desk.

'No problem,' said Leo, who had already begun reading the information panel by the foot of the skeleton.

'So, what is it?' asked Nina, who was standing a few steps behind him.

'An *Iguanodon*!' he said, reading. 'Believe it or not, it's a vegetarian. Whereas that little guy there,' he pointed at a skeleton standing on top of a cabinet. 'He's most definitely a meat eater!'

His sister turned and stared up at the dinosaur that was about their height.

'That's a *Deinonychus antirrhopus*!' he said.

'A what?' said Nina.

'Also known as Terrible Claw. You see that hooked talon on its middle toe? It uses that to rip into its prey. A bit like an eagle would today. In fact, they think old Terrible Claw may even have had feathers. How cool is that?'

And before his sister could answer, something else caught his eye.

'Wow, Nina!' he said, hurrying over to the huge glass cabinet. 'A *Tyrannosaurus rex*! Get a look at those teeth!'

But when Leo turned to see her reaction, he found that his sister was making her way towards the other end of the hall.

What's got into her? he thought.

'Teeth!' muttered Nina. Of all the museums we could have visited, Leo had to choose the one filled with row upon row of razor-sharp teeth. 'Just brilliant!'

Deciding to put as much distance as she could between herself and the carnivore exhibits, Nina headed for the area where the skeletons had nothing more threatening than antlers or horns. As she approached this end of the hall, she noticed a handsome bronze bust mounted on the far wall and stared at the name on the plaque.

'Charles Darwin,' she said.

'You've heard of him, have you?' asked a voice behind her.

'Hasn't everyone?' Nina replied, turning around and finding herself quite alone. A prickle of excitement ran up her spine as she looked for Leo, but he was nowhere to be seen. So, taking a deep, calming breath, she said, 'Hello.'

'Ah. I see you were expecting me.'

'Well, yes. We thought we might find one of the Hidden here.'

'You know about us then?' said the voice.

'The girl told us,' said Nina. 'Me and my brother.'

'So, I take it you've come here to find out who I am and what secrets hold me here.'

'Secrets?' she asked. 'Are there more than one?'

'There are three. My Master and I found them, and we brought them back here together.'

Nina started looking around at the many cabinets and drawers lining the walls, and her heart sank.

'Somewhere among this lot?'

'Yes, safely stowed away from prying eyes.'

'From the Keeper, you mean?'

Nina felt a faint shift in the air, and the voice fell quiet.

Then came an urgent chirping noise from overhead, and Nina looked up to see a little bird with an orange beak standing on top of the bronze bust. There was more chirping nearby, and craning her neck, she spotted another one fluttering back and forth beneath the vaulted ceiling. Both looked very agitated as if they weren't happy about something.

'I think it's time for you to go,' said the voice.

'What do you mean?' she asked.

But before he could reply, she heard Leo yell from the far end of the hall.

'Nina!'

She turned and saw him rushing towards her, face white, hand pointing upwards. 'The Keeper's here!'

And that's when she saw it. Springing effortlessly from cabinet to cabinet, Terrible Claw bounded towards her. The black-boned nightmare covered the length of the hall in seconds, its stunted foreclaws knocking aside light fittings in its haste to reach her. With a final leap, it landed on top of the display closest to her, its claws digging deep grooves into the mohogany to arrest its momentum.

Moments later, Leo arrived, skidding across the polished museum floor and slamming into her.

'Ow!' she cried.

'Sorry!' he said.

They looked up and stared into the empty eye sockets of the prehistoric predator peering down at them. Nina watched in horrified fascination as the creature opened its mouth, revealing needle-sharp teeth before emitting a bone-rattling screech that shook her to the core.

Then, out of nowhere, one of the little birds swooped past the dinosaur inches from its nose, and an instant later, its companion did the same. Instinctively, Terrible Claw's head reared up and whipped around as it snapped at the fleeing birds. Undaunted, they continued

OPEN ME!

to wheel in and out of the dinosaur's reach, sometimes even diving between its legs to escape its thrashing tail.

'Nina!' Leo gripped her arm. 'We need to get out of here!'

'What about the birds!' Nina said.

'Buying you time,' said the voice. 'Now, go!'

Terrible Claw screeched and leapt into the air, its snapping jaws missing one of the birds by inches before the dinosaur fell back down, landing on another display case right beside them. Leo gasped, and the creature's head turned towards them. The sickle-shaped talon in the middle of the creature's foot arched backwards ready to strike.

'Run!' yelled the voice as a third bird buzzed their attacker, buying them precious seconds.

Nina needed no more persuading. Yanking her brother's hand, she sprinted for the exit. Behind her, she heard clawed feet scrabbling for grip on the glass surface. The beast howled in frustration as it tried to scramble after them. A thump followed by a horribly fast clicking noise told her that it had leapt from the cabinet and was in hot pursuit.

Not daring to look back, she and Leo dodged between the cabinets, weaving in and out of the exhibits in a deadly game of cat and mouse. Leo narrowly avoided crashing into a display stand, and Nina sprinted past him, heading for the museum exit. They had almost made it too when she heard the birds chirping wildly in alarm just behind her. Instinctively she looked over her shoulder to see what it was and...

'Wham!'

Nina ran straight into somebody who had appeared out of nowhere. Reeling, she tried to get away, but only succeeded in staggering sideways into a door marked 'TOILETS'.

'What on earth are you two doing?' said her mother as Leo skidded into her too.

Gasping for breath, they both turned, expecting to see the dinosaur careering towards them. Instead, the museum remained quiet and still, except for one of the hanging lights, which swayed gently back and forth like a pendulum from the ceiling.

'But, the birds...' Nina began, looking across at her brother, who had his hands on his knees, his face pale.

'Oh, you must mean the finches,' said the museum attendant, coming out of the shop. 'Cheeky little things often sneak in through the windows. They make a terrible mess at times.'

'The ones with orange beaks?' Nina asked.

The woman looked surprised. 'You must be mistaken. I haven't seen any like that. Still, I'll go over and have a look. See if I can chase them out.'

The attendant headed off down the hall.

'I didn't know you were frightened of birds, Nina,' said her mother.

'I'm not, it was the...' she was about to say dinosaur when she saw something that made her blood run cold.

Terrible Claw was looking down at them from its display stand, the obsidian skeleton posed as before with its talon extended. To Nina, the model's empty eye sockets appeared to be staring straight at her, its jaws clenched together in a wicked grin. And lodged between the teeth, she could just make out the broken quill of a feather.

A Frosty Reception

BRAVE BIRD stood at the locked gate and stared at the house that rose out of the fog like a tombstone emerging from the underworld. From the upper levels, darkened windows peered over the forecourt like the empty sockets of a long-dead skull. Even in the World of Secrets, the misery that hung over this place was like a funeral shroud, enough to deter the most intrusive of Watchers.

The building was surrounded by a high wall crowned with jagged shards of glass. Frost-covered brambles protruded from the mist that hovered over the neglected garden. Brave Bird looked down at the lock and noticed the icicle hanging from the rusting keyhole. He leaned his shoulder against the bars and began to push. The lock held for a moment before its brittle casing disintegrated under his weight. The gate swung open, its iron hinges squealing at this unwanted intrusion.

Ignoring these futile protests, Brave Bird wrapped his cloak around him and strode through the freezing mist. Crossing the forecourt, he climbed the stone steps that led to the front door. Reaching down, he gripped the brass bell-pull protruding from the crumbling stonework and gave it a firm tug.

From deep inside the house there was the tinkling peal of a bell, like shards of glass disturbed by a chill wind, before silence descended as before. Brave Bird waited for a few moments, listening for the sound of movement before tugging the knob again. The bell sounded once more, and as its pitiful jingle faded away, silence returned. He was about to pull a third time when a distinctive click came from the lock. Resting one hand against the peeling woodwork, he pushed the door open and stepped inside.

Brave Bird stood in a dark hallway that was empty save for a candelabra that hung like an ice sculpture from the high ceiling. Looking around, he noticed there was frost here too. It covered the floor, the furniture, even the balustrade of the wide staircase that disappeared up towards the shadowy landing above. All the doors off the hallway were closed, save for one next to the stairwell, opening onto a narrow passageway leading to the back of the house.

Brave Bird headed towards it, his footsteps crunching on ice crystals under his feet. He proceeded down the narrow corridor, his shoulders disturbing cobwebs that clung to his cloak like finely embroidered lace. Up ahead was an open doorway, and he felt the cold grow in intensity as he approached. By the time he reached the entrance, his breath had formed a white mist in front of his face. Brave Bird paused and waited for the fog to clear, and when it did, the figure waiting for him was revealed.

The woman was sitting in a rocking chair facing a large window, through which a pale light shone from a shrouded moon. Wispy white hair framed her head as she stared out of the window overlooking the empty garden. Her bony hands lay on her lap over the folds of a black linen dress, dusted with the same frost that clung to the small side table next to her.

'Hello Brave Bird,' she said.

'Hello Widow,' he replied and stepped into the room.

The old woman didn't move or look in his direction, her gaze over the garden as still as the frozen air of her parlour. Brave Bird stood watching her.

'Why do you come here to disturb my peace?'

'Are you at peace?' he asked.

Her blue lips tensed. 'This is a peace, of sorts.'

Brave Bird looked around the room. Light reflected off the icicles hanging from the fireplace, mocking the empty grate below.

'Is that what you call it?' he said.

The Widow shifted, and the rocking chair creaked.

'You still haven't answered my question,' she said.

'You haven't answered mine,' he replied.

The dress rustled as the old woman's head turned.

'Peace is all I have left!'

The bitterness in her voice was meant to cut him, but Brave Bird knew that the only person hurting in this room was sitting in that chair.

'You have memories,' he said. 'Good memories of a life before this,' he gestured around the room, 'this undeath.'

'What do you know of memories?' Her voice was sharp as flint, but he could sense the spark of anger growing hot, melting the ice that had formed around her heart.

'I know the memories of a younger woman whose love was lost in a frozen ocean,' he said, 'and who has spent a lifetime waiting for news that never came.'

The Widow's eyes blazed, and Brave Bird knew it was time.

'Seven souls to find a key,' he said.

'Seven…?' Her voice faltered.

'Seven souls to find a key,' he repeated, knowing now that he was finally speaking to the woman within.

'To pick the lock and set us free,' she replied.

Brave Bird watched as warm tears formed and began rolling down her face, tracing lines through the frost, revealing the pale pink skin underneath. He stepped towards the woman and held out his hand. She looked at it, her eyes blinking in the moonlight.

'Come,' he said. 'It is time to find the thing you gave up and now holds you here. Only then will you truly be at peace.'

The Widow raised a shaking hand and placed it in his. It was still cold, but Brave Bird gently closed his fingers around it, and as he did so, he felt the embers of warmth kindle beneath her skin. As his hand enveloped hers, the colour began to seep back into her wrist, her arm, and along the coal-black material of her dress as the frost melted away. The halo of white hair crumbled into a flurry of ice crystals, revealing a head of glossy brown locks. The colour flowed across her face and into deep, dark eyes, now looking back at him with the first dawn of hope.

'Time to go,' he said. 'People are waiting for us.'

'Who?' she said.

'Two children.'

The young woman smiled, and leaning on him for support, rose stiffly to her feet. There she stood for a moment, marvelling at the movement in her limbs before retrieving a slip of paper from the side table and tucking it inside the cuff of her dress. Nodding at Brave Bird, she followed him from the room, leaving behind the chair that rocked back and forth in farewell as the lady of the house departed for the last time.

The night after their encounter with the dinosaur, Nina and Leo shared a dream in which a young man took them on a remarkable journey across oceans and continents, returning with the ship's holds full of samples, from exotic birds to rocks and fossils. Once again, the children noted down everything they could remember before it faded from memory.

Once they had finished, they looked at each other.

'Are you OK?' he said. It had been Leo's idea to go to the dinosaur museum, not realising how dangerous it was going to be.

'Yeah, let's just steer clear of places with lots of sharp teeth,' she said.

'We must be getting close, Nina. Otherwise…' but he didn't finish the sentence.

'The Keeper wouldn't have attacked us?'

He nodded, looking guilty.

Nina thought for a moment. 'How many voices have we heard so far?'

'Three.'

'Well, if the girl was right, that means we need to find four more.'

'So, you think we need to go to another museum?' her brother asked.

'No, Leo,' she said.

'No?'

'We need to go to four more.'

He grinned.

'Only this time, I'm choosing the next one,' she said.

'Agreed!'

They didn't have to wait long as it turned out. Later that day, they were cycling with their father towards the swimming pool when Nina spotted a neat little building by the side of the road. When she read the museum's sign, she asked her Dad if they could pop in on the way home and he enthusiastically agreed. An hour later, their hair still wet, they pulled up at the museum's cycle racks. While their father locked their bikes together, Nina wandered over to a sculpture standing on the lawn outside. It looked a bit like a stick man, only made out of large blocks of stone, crudely cemented together with elongated legs, stunted arms, and a blank rectangular face.

'Hey, Nina! Look at this!'

Leo was standing behind a massive harpoon gun, its metallic surface oxidised to pale green, aiming the barrel at the stone giant.

'Fire!' he yelled.

Nina rolled her eyes.

'Come on you two!' said their father, striding towards the entrance. 'We only have time for a quick look. Mum will be expecting us home.'

He led them round to the front of the building where they passed another statue, this one cast in finely polished bronze.

'What type of dog is that?' Leo asked, approaching the squat, powerful animal standing resolutely on its granite plinth, guarding the entrance.

'A husky,' said Nina, reading the inscription. 'You know, for pulling sledges.'

'You wouldn't want to mess with him,' said Leo. 'Come on, let's go inside.'

Her brother headed after their father inside, leaving Nina trying to imagine what it must be like to be on a sledge in a frozen wilderness being pulled by a team of animals like that. Dogs that would battle through blizzards and snowstorms to take you to the very ends of the earth. Some animals were amazing, she thought. They do all that for us and expect nothing in return. She reached out and patted the creature's head.

'You brave boy.'

With that, she turned and followed her brother into the museum.

The first thing that struck Leo when he stepped through the doors was how light it was. All the walls were painted a bright white, so he had to squint against the glare as he looked left and right at the photographs and exhibits at either end of the entrance lobby. He heard his sister arrive a few seconds later.

'Wow, Leo! Look at those!' she said.

She was craning her neck to stare up at two large maps of the Arctic and Antarctic painted on the ceiling.

'Nice,' he said, though geography wasn't really his thing. So, he left his sister admiring the maps and walked towards a pair of frosted glass doors, which slid apart to reveal the main exhibition hall.

'This is more like it,' he said and stepped inside.

The first display comprised an assortment of kayaks, tools, and clothing used by the native tribes of the Arctic regions. Reading the information panels, Leo discovered that the indigenous tribes of the Arctic spent their lives venturing out on its freezing waters in flimsy sealskin canoes to hunt seals, walruses, and even whales. He looked around for his father, but he was chatting to the museum attendant. Of Nina, there was no sign.

'Are you waiting for someone?' a woman's voice asked.

'Just my sister,' said Leo, looking around but seeing only an assortment of ceremonial outfits standing in glass cases. He felt a sudden chill in the air.

'Your sister?' said the voice. 'Are you close?'

'Err, yes, I suppose so,' he said, thinking, but I wish she were a bit closer now!

'It is sad to lose someone you love,' said the voice. 'I lost someone too.'

'I'm sorry to hear that,' he said, looking around for Nina and noticing his breath begin to mist in front of him. 'So, who was that then?'

'My husband.'

'Oh, what happened to him?' said Leo.

'No one knows. Many searched,' said the woman, 'but he was never found.'

A thought struck Leo.

'Is… is he the thing we are supposed to find?'

'No, child, it is too late for that. He has passed on. I know that now.'

'So, what is it exactly that is keeping you here?' he asked, realising he was going to have to do this on his own.

'A token of my love for my husband, which I gave away to another.'

'What sort of token?' said Leo, feeling excited.

'You know I can't tell you.'

'Because of the Keeper?'

Somewhere a door banged, and an icy wind swept through the hall. The hairs rose on the back of his neck and the voice fell slient.

Leo looked around. 'Hello? Are you still here?'

And that was when he saw Nina. She was standing over by a cabinet, her face pressed against the glass.

'Nina!' he hissed. 'Did you hear her? The voice I mean?'

His sister looked up and nodded. 'I heard it all. And what's more Leo,' she said, her eyes bright with excitement, 'I think I know who she is!'

'What? You do?' But before he could say any more, the woman's voice cut across him.

'Too late, children! The Keeper is here!'

With an enormous crash, the cabinet behind Leo exploded in a cloud of glass, its display of model ships flying through the air and scattering in all directions across the polished marble tiles. He leapt clear, but his shoes slipped on the broken glass, and with a cry, he fell to the floor, the impact knocking the wind out of him.

Groaning, Leo rolled onto his back in time to see the hulking shape of the stone giant stride through the debris and tower above him.

The enormous statue may not have had eyes carved into its crudely fashioned head, but at that moment, Leo felt the unforgiving gaze of the Keeper on him. They stared at each other for what seemed like an eternity before the giant stepped forward and lifted its massive foot above his prone body.

'No!' Nina yelled and rushed forward.

But before she could reach him, a bronze dog came out of nowhere and barrelled into the giant's midriff. The loud clang of metal against stone resounded around the hall as the statue was knocked off balance and gravity did the rest. The giant toppled backwards and crashed to the floor, marble tiles splintering under its enormous weight.

Immediately, the dog was on it, its teeth gripping one of the stubby arms and shaking it viciously from side to side. Leo began scrabbling backwards from the frantic struggle playing out just beyond his feet. He felt Nina grab him from behind and hoist him up.

'Leo! Are you alright?'

'Yes,' he said, shaken, 'I think so.'

There was a crunch of glass as the giant tried to get back to its feet, the dog clinging desperately to its arm, snarling as it tried to keep the monster off balance.

'Quick!' said the woman's voice. 'This way!'

Leo looked around and saw a sign marked 'EXIT'.

There was a heavy thud, followed by a yelp of pain from the dog as it slid across the floor and slammed into a wall.

'Come on Leo!' pleaded his sister, tugging him.

'But the dog!'

'Leave that to me,' said the woman's voice. 'Now go!'

There was another crash, and Leo looked across the room to see the stone giant stomping over the wooden ships towards them.

And then something extraordinary happened.

Without warning, the temperature in the room plummeted, and the walls of the museum began to shimmer as ice crystals formed on every surface. Leo looked around in amazement as a wind came out of nowhere and, screaming like a banshee, tore the ice from the walls and flung it at their attacker. The ferocity of the blizzard buffeted the stone giant, slowing its progress as the newly formed snow rose up in drifts against its legs.

'Leo, come on!' yelled Nina, dragging him towards the exit.

Needing no more encouragement, Leo turned and followed his sister through the doors and out into the fresh air.

'There you are!'

Leo and Nina turned and saw their father standing outside admiring a lifeboat on a display stand.

'Fascinating story about this boat,' he said, pointing to an information panel on the wall. 'Are there other boats inside?'

'I don't think so,' gasped Leo. 'At least, not anymore.'

'Oh,' said their father, sounding disappointed. He looked at their pale faces. 'You two must be cold after all that swimming.'

Leo glanced at his sister. 'Frozen.'

Nina laughed, and somewhere in the distance, in a place beyond their world, Leo thought he might have heard the answering howl of a dog.

Green Shoots

BRAVE BIRD tumbled out of the portal, sprawling onto the muddy lane. Blood ran from his mouth, where the stone arm had yanked itself free. He tried to push himself off the ground, but pain erupted from his ribs where the giant had kicked him, and he collapsed groaning onto his back. Lifting his head, he looked up at the gateway above him. Emerald light glowed from the gap between two stone pillars, turning the fog that flowed around the entrance a sickly green colour.

The Keeper would be coming for him now. He knew it. Any moment, Brave Bird expected to see that dreaded figure emerge from the mist and bind him here forever. He had to move. Once more he tried to rise, but the pain was so excruciating that he collapsed back onto the damp earth, screwing his eyes shut and gasping for breath.

That's when he felt, rather than heard, the tread of approaching footsteps. Slow, heavy strides, that shook the ground and sent ripples across the puddles around him. Helpless, Brave Bird just lay there, unable to move as they came closer, finally stopping inches from his head. Blinking away the sweat from his eyes, he looked up and saw a dark shadow looming over him, blotting out the grey sky above.

'You!' he said before huge hands reached down for him. Brave Bird cried out as pain exploded through his body. He was lifted into the air like a rag doll before a piercing white light blinded him, and he knew no more.

When Brave Bird awoke, everything was dark. He lay still for a while, wondering if this was what being bound by the Keeper felt like. If so, perhaps it wasn't too bad after all.

Gradually, the darkness receded, and he became aware of his other senses returning. First, the gentle whisper of his breathing, then the rise and fall of his chest against his shirt. The touch of linen against his fingers and the softness of the pillow beneath his head. Eventually, he tried to open his eyes, but pain blossomed behind his temples and he closed them, wincing.

'Steady now,' came a deep voice. 'I'd take it easy if I were you. You're safe for now. But there are all sorts of folks looking for you. Though it'll be a while before they venture out here, I reckon.'

There was something familiar about the voice, but he couldn't place it.

'Where is here?' he asked

'I don't go in for city life, which is why I brought you to this place. From here you can see the city, but it can't see you, unless it has a mind to, that is.'

'So, we are outside the city?'

'We are, and good riddance too, I say.'

Brave Bird heard the footsteps recede, followed by the sound of running water.

'You said that someone was looking for me?'

'I should think so too, after all that rumpus you've gone and created. Still, I expect you know who it is that's after you?'

'The Watchers.'

'Goes without saying,' said the figure, his footsteps returning. 'And the Keeper too, by all accounts.'

Brave Bird flinched, remembering the stone giant.

'You've stirred up quite a wasps' nest, you have, and make no mistake. Here, take a sip of this.'

Brave Bird tried squinting through his eyes and could make out the shape of a tin mug. Slowly, he raised himself up, feeling a dull ache from his ribs, which he realised now had been wrapped tight in bandages. Leaning his head forward, he sniffed the contents of the mug and recognised the smell of vegetable broth. He managed a sip, wincing as the hot liquid touched his swollen lip, and eased himself back down, finally understanding where he was.

'Thank you, Gardener,' he said.

'Good lad. I wondered when you'd remember. You've been asleep such a while.'

'How long?'

'Four days, by my reckoning, since the first revealing that is.'

'The what?' said Brave Bird, starting up and stifling a cry of pain.

'Steady now,' said the Gardener, laying a firm hand on his patient's shoulder and easing him back down. Brave Bird let out a long breath as he rested his head against the pillow.

'You... you said there had been a revealing?'

'The day I hoisted you out of that muddy lane. A great big light appeared from that portal. Never seen a light like it in this city before.'

'The children found the Widow's secret!' cried Brave Bird, feeling elation replace the pain in his body.

'The children? What children?'

Brave Bird remembered the boy sprawled on the floor and the girl dragging him clear.

'A boy and a girl. They were with me in the portal.'

'Then they've been busy those two,' said the Gardener. 'Very busy.'

'What do you mean?'

'Come and see for yourself. If you can stand up, that is.'

The giant reached forward, and Brave Bird felt huge hands lift him upright with surprising gentleness. Leaning heavily on his host, he managed to straighten up into a standing position. The Gardener pointed a thick finger towards the window in the far wall.

Brave Bird squinted at the bright light shining through the mud-smeared glass until his eyes grew accustomed to the glare. Gradually, he was able to make out the distant towers and rooftops of the city, silhouetted against the dark sky. His jaw dropped in wonder at the three beams of light shining towards the heavens like searchlights in the dark.

'As I say,' said the Gardener, 'looks like they've been busy, those children. By my reckoning, that leaves only four more to find.'

'Seven souls to find a key,' murmured Brave Bird.

'To pick the lock and set us free,' finished his host, 'which means it's time for me to go.'

Brave Bird looked up at him. 'You are ready?'

'Sitting here watching over you these past few days, I've had time to think about things,' said the Gardener. 'I've been hiding away here too long. I left something dear to me back there in that city and moping around here is not doing me any good.'

'Let me get my things,' said Brave Bird, turning towards the door and stumbling before the Gardener caught him and eased him back upright.

'Now, don't you go hurting yourself after all I've been doing to patch you up,' said the Gardener, guiding him back towards the bed. 'I think it best if you wait here a day or two. As I said, they'll be looking for you, so I'll be better off travelling on my own. No offence meant, mind you.'

Brave Bird couldn't argue as he lowered himself down onto the straw mattress. He was in no shape to travel.

The Gardener strode across the room and retrieved a coat the size of a small tent from one of two hooks on the back of the front door.

He stared at the other peg for a moment and chuckled to himself before picking up a piece of paper from a potting bench.

'Mustn't forget that,' he said. 'Been working on that these past few days, while you've been sleeping.' He slipped it inside his waistcoat.

'What if the Watchers stop you?' Brave Bird asked.

'Oh, they don't pay me much attention,' said the giant. 'They see me bringing my vegetables into the city now and again.' He reached down and grabbed a heavy sack in his meaty hand, swinging it up and over his shoulder as if it were a feather pillow. 'For some reason, they don't seem to want to bother me much.'

'Funny that,' said Brave Bird.

The Gardener opened his front door and turned to face his guest, his massive frame filling the doorway.

'I expect I'll be seeing you, Brave Bird. On the other side, I mean.'

'You will, my friend. And thank you.'

The Gardener smiled and, adjusting the sack on his shoulder, set off towards the lights of the city.

Nina came down to breakfast to find her mother reading a letter and her father making tea.

'Morning, Nina,' said her father. 'Sleep well?'

'I suppose so.'

There was the sound of footsteps clomping down the stairs, and a few moments later, Leo slouched into the kitchen.

'Morning Leo.'

'Morning.'

Her brother slumped down at the kitchen table, looked across at Nina and shook his head. That meant he hadn't had a dream either. That was four days now, and Nina was beginning to wonder if they would ever have another one. The night after escaping from the stone giant, the woman had appeared to the children in their dreams, and Nina had guessed correctly who she was and what her secret object had been.

Encouraged by this breakthrough, they had spent the next few days camped out in her room, trying to figure out what the other dreams had meant. They had a stroke of luck one evening when Leo had overheard their parents talking about something his mother had discovered in the dinosaur museum about the voyages of Charles Darwin. Then Nina had noticed a book on astronomy lying open on her father's desk, and that had given her an idea which solved another mystery too. That left only the girl in the first museum, and despite their best efforts, they had both drawn a blank. Since then, they had waited in vain for another dream, but none had come.

Nina glanced at her brother, who was playing with his cereal, looking fed up. She decided it was time to pick up a new trail. Taking her spoon, she began tapping it quietly on the side of her bowl. Tap, tap, tap, tip, tip, tip, tap, tap, tap.

Leo looked up and Nina raised an eyebrow. Her brother's face broke into a grin, and he nodded.

'Mum?' asked Nina. 'I was wondering if we could go to another museum today.'

They parked their bikes and Leo ran ahead of the others towards a building with a large museum sign painted on its wall.

Stepping through an iron gate, he emerged in a tiny courtyard, which was filled with a multitude of different objects scattered around its uneven flagstones. A line of stone spires stood like chess pieces on one side of a square, as if ready to do battle. Nearby, commemorative plaques were arranged like discarded shields from jousting knights. An ancient iron wheelbarrow sat rusting in a corner next to an abandoned horse trough overflowing not with water, but with an assortment of colourful plants.

'This place is old,' said Nina, who had caught up with him and was staring around at a traditional shop front, filled with a collection of antique objects and clothing.

'Yeah, feels promising,' he said.

'Come on, you two,' said their mother, 'the entrance is this way.'

They followed her under an archway and through a low door that opened into the museum's reception area. Everything was smaller and more cramped than Leo had expected. The walls bulged, the ceiling sagged, and the timber joists were twisted and gnarled. It was like stepping into a fairy-tale inn.

While their mother paid for the tickets, he and his sister went down a narrow passageway leading into a room dominated by a massive open fireplace. A wooden seat ran around one wall.

'This is cosy,' said Nina, who sat on the bench, holding her hands and feet up to the grate, pretending to warm herself by the empty fire. Leo tried to picture the scene. What sort of people would have sat in that chair? Travellers perhaps, or even a highwayman seeking out his next victim to rob. His eye was drawn to an ancient flintlock rifle that hung from the chimney breast, its barrel longer than he was.

'Take a look at that gun, Nina. Who on earth could lift that?'

'It's not so hard when you get the hang of it,' said a voice.

Leo and Nina exchanged looks. Her face said it all. A mix of fear and excitement. She nodded for him to continue.

'So,' Leo said, 'you've used one of them before have you?'

'Now and again,' said the voice, its tone deep and mellow, like loamy soil. 'For hunting duck.'

'They must be big ducks.'

There was a strange booming noise, like a big bass drum, and it took Leo a moment to realise it was laughter. Smiling, he turned to his sister and saw that she was too. It was hard not to with this voice.

'Did you once live here?' Nina said.

'Not far away. I'm a local lad.'

'Why are you here?' asked Leo.

'There's something of mine here that I'm rather attached to,' said the voice. 'Too much so, as it turned out.'

'Your secret,' said Nina.

'That would be telling, and I can't do that as you both know.'

He and Nina looked around the room. It was packed with all sorts of tankards, jugs, and bottles. They could spend all day here, guessing which item belonged to the voice and still be no closer to the truth.

'You're going to have to give us a clue,' he said.

'You're cold,' said the voice.

'Not now,' said Nina. 'It was a bit chilly on the bikes, maybe.'

Again, the booming noise, but this time it seemed to come from the next room.

'Hey, don't go!' cried Leo, getting up. 'Quick, Nina, we don't want to lose him!'

They hurried across the room and ducked through a low doorway, emerging into a farmhouse kitchen piled high with pots, pans and utensils.

'Warmer,' said the voice.

'Oh, I see,' whispered Nina. 'It's like that game we used to play at parties.'

'Got it,' said Leo, nodding and beginning to look around the room. At the far end of the kitchen, there was another doorway. He crossed over to it and tried the handle, but it was locked.

'Colder,' came the voice.

'Leo, here!' said Nina, pointing to a narrow staircase on the other side of the fireplace. He went over to join her, and they peered up a narrow circular staircase.

'Warmer,' confirmed the voice.

Leo looked at his sister.

'You first,' she said.

Leo began to climb, the worn wooden steps creaking and groaning under his trainers. When he reached the top, the stairwell opened out onto a low-ceilinged room with a small cot-like bed along one wall. Looking around, he saw another fireplace, much smaller than the one downstairs, and in a corner was a wall cupboard with its door slightly ajar.

'Anything?' asked Nina, emerging from the stairwell behind him.

Leo pointed towards the cupboard, and his sister nodded. Reaching for the handle, he pulled the door open and saw a faceless head staring back at him.

'Aaagh!' he yelled, jumping back.

'What is it?' Nina yelled, ready to run.

Leo stared wide-eyed at the shape, expecting it to lunge at him or worse. Instead, it remained completely still, and as his initial panic subsided, Leo realised he wasn't looking at a head at all. He let out a long sigh.

'It's OK, Nina,' he said, moving back to inspect the curly white-haired object, resting on its stand. 'It's just a wig.'

There was a deep, booming chuckle.

'That one's a bit too small for me, I'm afraid. But you are getting warmer.'

Encouraged, they resumed their search, and Leo spotted another doorway which led to an old Victorian parlour. This room was much grander, filled with bookshelves and cabinets. Portraits hung above the mantlepiece, and a circular dining table stood in its centre. For a few minutes, he and his sister poked around the various items on display, but the voice remained silent.

In one corner of the room, there was another doorway, which opened onto a landing with more rooms off it and a stairwell leading to what could only be an attic. Leo saw Nina look nervously up the stairs and back at him.

'I don't think we should go up there,' she said. 'Something doesn't feel right.'

'What? The Keeper you mean?'

Somewhere in the building, they heard timbers creak.

'Leo!' she whispered. 'Don't say that word!'

'Sorry,' he said, peering up the twisting stairwell, 'but the secret must be here somewhere, and an attic is just the sort of place I would hide something.'

His sister looked up into the dark. 'I don't know.'

'Listen, let me check the attic,' he said. 'You check the other rooms. If either one of us hears the voice say we are getting warmer, we just yell, OK?'

'OK,' said Nina, not sounding convinced. Leo gave her what he hoped was a reassuring smile and began to climb.

Like the first stairwell, this one was old and rickety, twisting like a corkscrew back on itself. When Leo reached the top, he found himself standing in what must have been a children's playroom. Everywhere there were toys and books, stacked in boxes, on shelves, or scattered around the floor.

In one corner, there was a display cabinet with an assortment of dolls, the largest one in a white lace christening dress, her big baby eyes staring blankly at him beneath long eyelashes. Nearby, there were three large dolls' houses complete with furniture, carpets, and paintings. And in an old trunk, he found some rusty tin cars and a wooden box filled with toy animals.

Leo began sifting through all of them, hoping at any moment to hear booming confirmation from the voice that he was 'Very warm!' Instead, all he heard was a creak on the stairs behind him. Turning, he expected to see his sister, but the stairwell appeared empty. Odd,

he thought, he could have sworn that he heard someone using them. Leo looked around the room, checking if she was hiding somewhere, but everything seemed to be the same. Everything except… except the doll in the dress was missing.

'Warm,' came the deep voice from the floor below.

'Nina,' Leo murmured, a horrible feeling in his stomach.

'Very warm,' repeated the voice.

'Nina?' Leo called out, getting to his feet and hurrying across the room.

'Hot!' boomed the voice.

Leo had reached the top step and was about to start down when he heard his sister scream. Flying down the stairs, he bounded onto the landing before charging into the next room, where he came skidding to a halt.

There was Nina, her hair dishevelled, backing away from a tiny figure in white, standing in front of her, its arms outstretched.

'Leo!' she said. 'That doll, it attacked me!'

Before he could say anything the doll's head began to turn, slowly, deliberately, until its face had twisted all the way around to stare back at Leo, its big eyes boring into his.

'That's not a doll, Nina,' he said, his voice shaking. 'That's the…'

But he never finished. Out of nowhere, a large boot swung into view and kicked the doll across the room.

'Run!' came the deep, booming voice, anything but playful now.

Leo reached forward and grabbed his sister, dragging her out onto the landing. Veering right, they ran through rooms filled with pianos, desks, and sewing machines as a great thumping and crashing noise erupted behind them.

'Leo, there!' cried Nina, pointing to a sign at the head of a flight of stairs: 'TO SHOP AND EXIT'.

The children rushed down the stairwell, not daring to look back as the dreadful din above them grew even louder. At the bottom, they darted through a doorway and rushed out into the museum shop. There was their mother, standing in front of one of the displays, browsing through a selection of traditional children's games and puzzles.

'Hello, you two.' she said, looking up. 'What have you been up to now?'

Leo was panting, so it took him a while to gather his breath. But as he did so, he realised that the sound of fighting above them had ceased. He glanced at the flushed face of his sister, who shook her head.

'Just playing…' he said.

'With some dolls,' she added.

'Hmm,' said their mother, 'I didn't know you still liked that sort of thing.'

'I don't,' said Nina and Leo in unison. And somewhere above them, they thought they could hear the echo of a deep, booming laugh.

Into the Underworld

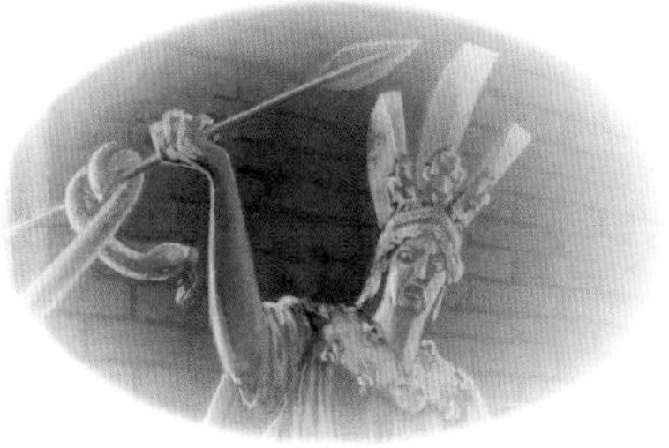

'PLINK! PLINK! PLOP!'

The drips of water echoed down the tunnel, their sound fading into the gloom as Brave Bird stood motionless in the shadows.

Few dared to enter the labyrinth of sewers that spread like a subterranean spider's web beneath the city. It wasn't just the damp and the filth; it was the overpowering stench that rose from the streams of waste running through the murky arteries of this hidden world. And that was why Brave Bird had chosen to use this route to find the next one of the Seven.

He had set out from the Gardener's hut earlier that day, after a fourth green light had lit up the sky above the city, joining the other three beacons signalling the children's progress. The frenzy of activity caused by these revelations had meant it was no longer safe to travel above ground with roving gangs of Watchers patrolling the streets.

Brave Bird had entered the sewer network on the outskirts of the city via a neglected outlet that fed waste into the river. Wrapping a cloth over his nose and mouth, he had made his way through the tunnels, bending his head low to avoid the stalactites of slime that hung from the curved ceiling of bricks above him. After what seemed like miles of painful progress, he had entered the central system, where the tunnels were large enough for him to stand upright and move more quickly. Until now.

Moments earlier, Brave Bird had thought he heard the faintest of noises behind him and stopped dead, waiting for the tell-tale tread of a boot or the murmur of hushed voices. He stood there for what seemed like an age, but the only sound was the occasional drip of water.

'Plink! Plink! Plop!'

Unsettled, Brave Bird began moving again, heading deeper into this filthy underworld. The passageways twisted and turned, and every now and again an opening would appear in the wall, leading to the dwellings above. At each of these, he would run his fingers over the stonework, feeling for an impression in the surface. At last, he felt the outline of a V and two vertical lines roughly carved into the stonework.

Glancing back over his shoulder, the tunnel appeared empty as far as he could see, but Brave Bird hesitated, unable to shake the feeling he was being watched. He waited for any sign of movement, any ripple across the surface of liquid waste, but there was nothing. It couldn't be helped, he decided, this was his destination, and he hadn't come all this way to turn back now. Brave Bird ducked through the opening and began the long climb to the surface.

As his hooded form disappeared from view, there was a disturbance in the stream a few feet from the walkway. A flat, serpentine head rose from the sewer, rivulets of slime running down its pale, scaly skin. Red eyes peered at the opening and the symbols carved into the stonework. A pink tongue emerged from the slit of its mouth, tasting the air until it caught the scent of its prey. Then the albino body slid back beneath the surface with only the faintest of noises to indicate its departure.

'Plink! Plink! Plop!'

Minutes later, Brave Bird emerged at the top of the stone staircase and headed across a small landing to a stout-looking door. Raising his fist, he knocked seven times and was relieved to hear the approach of footsteps on the other side. A key turned in the lock, and the door swung open to reveal a girl dressed in a simple brown dress, her blond hair partially covered by a woven headscarf, held in place by thin bands of fabric. She smiled when she saw who it was and ushered him in, though he noticed her nose wrinkle at the smell as he entered the dwelling.

Brave Bird found himself standing in a rectangular room with woven rugs on the floor and tapestries on the walls. The furniture was simple but elegant and neatly arranged around a kitchen table, lit by the orange glow of a fireplace in the corner.

The servant girl offered to take his cloak, and Brave Bird saw the relief on her face when he declined.

'I don't plan on staying long. I have a message for your Lady.'

'A message? How intriguing!' came a velvety voice from the other side of the room. Brave Bird turned and saw a woman sitting on an ornately carved chair, her sandaled feet resting on a matching footstool. She wore a long robe, the material tied at the waist and flowing like water over her body. The curls of her dark hair were held in place by bands of gold and gathered at the back in a scarf of deepest red. She stared ruefully at long, elegant fingers, and when she looked up, her green eyes sparkled like emeralds in the light of the fire.

'Hello my Lady,' he said.

'Brave Bird,' she replied, her delicate lips parting in a smile as she rose in one fluid movement from her chair and glided over to the fireplace. 'Come, you must be cold after your journey.'

Brave Bird crossed the room to join her, conscious of how filthy he must seem. If the woman noticed, she said nothing and stood looking at the flames, a picture of calm.

'So, you have come at last,' she said.

'I have.'

'You have been busy, I see.' She indicated the window, where a thin line of green light stole through the crack in the curtains.

'I had help. Two children.'

'Children? Why would they choose to help us?'

'The Girl asked them.'

The Lady smiled. 'Ah yes, the Girl. And where is she now?'

'She has passed over.'

Her keen eyes turned to look at him.

'Are you sure?'

Brave Bird wanted to say yes, but something in her look made him hesitate. He thought back to when he had first seen the lights shining above the city from the window of the Gardener's hovel. He had assumed, or, rather, hoped, that one of those lights came from the Girl's portal.

'Seven souls to find a key,' said the Lady, interrupting his thoughts.

'To pick the lock and set us free,' he replied.

'All of us must be revealed Brave Bird,' she said. 'I will be next, and then you will follow. Is that not so?'

'Yes.' But now there was doubt in his heart.

'Six souls will not be enough,' she said. 'How can we be sure that all seven will be found?'

Brave Bird looked at the Lady and thought of the Girl. Had she been hiding in her portal all this time? The children had to go back for her!

'I will see to it,' he said.

The Lady nodded and turned. 'Bring me the box.'

The servant girl appeared at her side holding a wooden casket edged in polished metal. The Lady lifted the lid and, from among the glittering objects stored within, retrieved a handwritten piece of paper, which she slipped inside her robe. Replacing the cover, she caressed the cheek of the girl in farewell.

The peace of their parting was disturbed by a commotion from the street outside. The noise of many footsteps was followed by the sound of a heavy fist banging on the front door.

'My Lady, we must go!' he said. 'You too!' he added to the girl, who stood wide-eyed as the knocking intensified. Brave Bird strode over to the cellars and pulled open the door. The sickly smell of sewer water wafted into the room.

'Come, my dear,' said the Lady, gathering cloaks for herself and her servant and ushering the frightened girl towards the cellar entrance. Brave Bird waited until they were through the doorway and then headed back towards the fireplace. Something heavy crashed against the front door, rattling its hinges. Grabbing a poker, he levered the hearth of burning logs over the floor. Flames spread rapidly across the carpet to the tapestries on the wall.

Shielding his face against the heat, Brave Bird ran for the cellar and, slamming the door behind him, led the Lady and her servant down the stairwell into the dark.

Despite their scare at the doll's museum, the children had no problem the next morning identifying the voice and his secret item from their latest dream. Nina realised she had been right next to his secret object when the doll attacked her. As Leo pointed out, that was probably why the Keeper had intervened – to stop her discovering the voice's identity.

'If it's any consolation, the madder the Keeper gets, the closer we must be,' he said.

'I suppose so, but it doesn't make it any less scary,' said Nina. 'We've found four of the objects, which means we are more than halfway there. What will the Keeper be prepared to do to stop us finding the next three?'

'Do you think we should tell Mum and Dad?'

Nina had been wondering about this too.

'I don't know, Leo. I'm not sure they'd believe us. Besides, every time adults appear, things go back to normal. I'm not sure the Hidden would speak to us when grown-ups are around.'

'Why is that?'

'Maybe you have to believe in the Hidden to hear them.'

Leo looked at her. 'So, it's down to us then?'

She nodded. 'I think it has to be.'

'Nina? I've just noticed,' he said, looking around. 'Have you done something to your room? It feels different.'

'I got rid of my old dolls,' she said. 'I'm donating them to a charity shop. That Keeper's got a lot to answer for.'

After breakfast, Leo thought the next museum they should try was one they had visited before on a school trip. But with their father busy that day, they first had to accompany their mother, who had to drop some books off at the library she worked at.

'I won't be long,' said their mother after they arrived in the entrance lobby to a low-rise, red-brick building. 'But while you're waiting, you might find upstairs interesting.' She pointed to a sign by the staircase.

Nina read it and turned to her brother. 'There's a museum here?'

Her mother nodded. 'As I said, I'll only be a few minutes.' She disappeared through a set of doors as the children headed for the stairs.

When they reached the top, they turned a corner and found a life-size sculpture of a woman lying on her side, apparently asleep. There was a sign below the statue: 'PLEASE DO NOT TOUCH'.

'Funny place to take a nap,' said Leo as Nina opened the museum door and stepped through.

A tall Egyptian-looking statue, its arms and feet frozen mid-stride, stared down at them. And it wasn't the only one. Everywhere they looked, there were more figures, each of differing height, build, posture, and condition. All were cast in the same white plaster, which looked like bleached bone against the blood red fabric that lined the display area. The walls themselves were covered by horizontal friezes, intricately carved with horses, chariots, warriors, and citizens.

'Look, Leo. It goes all the way back there!' she said, pointing down a walkway that led right to the back of the vast exhibition hall.

'This is a find, isn't it?' he said.

Sun shone through a skylight that ran down the length of the pitched roof, reflecting off the pale-skinned statues. Down the middle of the hall, a partition wall had been erected, dividing the space into two long galleries. Crammed into every nook and cranny were hundreds of statues, busts, and friezes.

'All the time Mum's been working here, and she never told us this place existed,' said Nina.

'A hidden gem,' agreed Leo.

'It's not the only thing hidden here.'

It was a woman's voice, but as far as Nina could see, they were the only ones in the museum. She exchanged a look with Leo, who gave her a thumbs up. Without intending to, they had stumbled across another Hidden.

'Hello,' said Nina, peering around at the statues.

'Hello children,' came the voice. 'I've been expecting you.'

'So, you know about us?' asked Leo.

'A little bird told me that you might be coming.'

Leo grinned. 'That's good.'

'You've come to uncover my secrets.'

'Secrets?' asked Nina.

'Two items that I valued very much.'

Leo looked at the nearest statue, which had lost both its arms. 'Not your hands, by any chance?' he suggested.

'Leo!' hissed Nina.

'What?' he said. 'She might have?'

'No, but my hands once held them.'

'And they are somewhere here in this hall?' asked Nina, looking around.

'As am I,' said the voice.

'Any clues where?' said Leo.

The voice was silent, but Nina thought she could hear a strange dripping noise in the distance and an unpleasant smell wafted through the hall.

'We've been followed!' said the voice.

'We?' asked Nina. 'There are more of you?'

'My servant and me. We must hide.'

'Wait, please!' asked Nina

'Find us children, but hurry!'

In the silence that followed, Nina looked at her brother.

'There are an awful lot of statues, Nina,' said Leo. 'How are we going to check them all?'

'We'll split up. I'll take this side, and you take the other. We'll meet up at the far end of the hall.'

'I'm not sure splitting up is a good idea,' said Leo, and Nina realised he was thinking about the last museum, when his decision to split up had led to her being attacked by the doll.

'We don't have any choice. Besides, Mum said she would be up in a minute. Come on!'

Leo took the left-hand aisle of the exhibition hall. The first thing he saw was a statue of Hercules standing with his legs crossed, leaning on an enormous club.

There were no female statues nearby, so he moved onto the next section. This was filled with busts of famous emperors and gods. Each one stared at him in silence as he walked down the aisles between the exhibits, and he couldn't shake the feeling that some of those blank eyes were following him.

In the next section, one statue stood out from the rest. It was a Roman boxer, cast in bronze, who was sitting on a rock, his heavily strapped fists folded in front of him. The boxer's face was battered, with a broken nose, bruised lips, and cauliflower ears.

'Looks like you've been in the wars,' he said to the impassive face.

The statue didn't respond, remaining stoic and unmoved.

Leo clenched his fist to his chest in salute and continued down the aisle. He passed a collection of female statues in a variety of frozen poses. Some were goddesses, tall, proud, and beautiful. Others were mortals, weeping or mourning lost loved ones. At each one, he whispered 'Hello? Is that you?' But he was greeted by a stony silence.

Before long, Leo had seen all the statues on his side without a flicker of a response. Wondering how Nina was doing, he went to the end of the hall, where one more figure stood in the passageway between the two halves of the building. He realised it must be the largest statue in the museum. The goddess stood over three metres tall and was armed with a circular shield, a long spear and a triple-crested helmet. Leo read the information panel on the plinth.

'Athena,' he said and glanced up at the imposing figure. She was flanked by two animals. On one side was an owl with huge, unblinking eyes staring straight at him. On the other, rising up as if preparing to strike, was a pale-skinned snake.

'Psst!'

Leo turned and saw Nina peering at him from the corner of the partition.

'Any luck?' she whispered.

He shook his head. 'Not so far. I asked all the statues on my side.'

'Asked?' she said. 'You mean you spoke to them?'

'Well yes, what else was I supposed to do?'

'What about the wall carvings?'

'What do you mean?'

'There were loads of women in the wall carvings on my side. Did you check them too?'

Leo looked back down the hall. He'd been so focused on the statues, he hadn't paid any attention to the friezes that lined the walls. He looked at the nearest one and felt a thrill of excitement as he turned to his sister. But then he spotted something that made his blood run cold.

'Err… Nina?'

'What?'

'What happened to the snake?'

Nina looked around. 'What snake?'

Leo heard the hiss moments before it struck. He just had time to pull his sister clear as the creature lunged from the shadows, its pale head darting forward, the razor-sharp fangs missing Nina by inches.

'Run!' he yelled.

Nina hated snakes and needed no more encouragement. She set off after her brother, racing past statues and displays that looked on impassively as they rushed past. There was another angry hiss, and Nina glanced over her shoulder. That's when she stubbed the toe of her shoe on the edge of a carpet tile and fell headlong to the floor.

In an instant, Leo was at her side, grabbing her arm and dragging her up. Nina looked back to see the snake slithering towards them, its powerful body covering the ground at a frightening speed, blank eyes locked onto hers. Terrified, she scrambled to get away and knocked into her brother, who stumbled and fell, tripping her again in the process.

The snake glided over the last few feet and came to a stop a few inches from their feet. It coiled its body, raising its fat, ugly head to strike.

And then something unexpected happened.

The snake jerked backwards, hissing and spitting in alarm. It convulsed again, and before Nina knew what was happening, the creature was flying through the air, its long serpentine body wriggling and thrashing to escape the tall bronze figure that was gripping its tail. Like a circus master, the statue began spinning the snake around its head with dizzying speed before slamming it against a stone plinth with such force that it fell senseless to the floor.

'Go, Boxer!' Leo yelled in triumph as he and Nina struggled to their feet. The statue nodded towards them and began dragging the stunned serpent by its tail back down the gallery. But then, the colossal figure of the goddess Athena jumped down from her plinth and landed with a heavy thud that shook the floor. Before the Boxer could react, she knocked him aside with her shield, sending him crashing into one of the walls.

'No!' yelled Leo.

The goddess looked across the hall towards them. Her face was expressionless, but Nina could feel malice there.

'Leo?' she said, 'I think it's time to get out of here.'

'Too right!' he agreed.

But before they could turn and run, the goddess planted her feet and pulled back her arm, ready to throw the massive spear.

'Out of the way, children,' cried the Lady, as a bronze deer leapt over their heads and bounded towards the armoured figure, its head lowered.

Faced with the charging animal, Athena hesitated for a split second, just long enough for something long and white to whip through the air and wrap itself around the spear shaft. Nina gasped as she saw the Boxer yank the snake's lifeless body taut as a bowstring, tearing the spear from its owner's grip.

A moment later, the deer leapt up at the warrior queen, who had to raise her shield to fend off the flailing hooves.

Knocked off balance, the goddess stumbled sideways, her plaster foot smashing against the edge of a display stand, and unable to arrest her fall, the enormous statue came crashing to the ground. The impact caused a collection of busts to sway and then topple over covering her in a pile of broken limbs and torsos.

Through the cloud of dust that rose in the air, Nina saw the bronze deer and the Boxer standing at the end of the hall, the limp tail of the snake still held in one hand.

Slowly, the deer bowed and the bronze figure raised a fist above its head in salute. Nina saw her brother raise his own in response, and instinctively, she did the same. They stood there, looking at each other across the field of battle, fists held high until something shifted among the debris, and Nina saw a damaged helmet rising from the dust.

'Time to go,' said her brother.

'Agreed,' Nina replied.

Turning as one, they set off to find their mother, and later that night, the Lady visited them in their dreams.

To the Eyrie

BRAVE BIRD ran, weaving through the chaotic maze of alleyways, swerving around soil barrels and ducking under archways. Whichever way he turned, whichever alley he took, he heard the sound of footsteps, tracking him like a bloodhound, only his pursuer was the Keeper, and the scent of blood was his own.

Since escaping from the Lady's portal, he had kept to the labyrinth of tunnels beneath the city, now mercifully free of their serpentine Watcher. But Brave Bird had known he would have to return to the surface at some point to reach his own portal, and then the hunt would begin again. Sure enough, no sooner had he emerged above ground and started making his way through the back streets than the sound of those dreaded footsteps, faint at first, but becoming more evident over time, had begun stalking him once again. Now, as Brave Bird hurried to stay ahead of his pursuer, he felt that if he could only get to the rooftops, not even the Keeper would be able to catch him there.

Up ahead, he spotted an unguarded staircase that ran up the side of a crooked building and disappeared into the murky grey smog of the upper levels. Brave Bird sped up, his feet racing over the cobbles towards what he knew was his best means of escape. But just as he thought he would make it, a group of Watchers turned into the alleyway ahead of him. He barrelled into the lead rank, sending bodies flying like skittles, but not before he tripped over a flailing leg and tumbled after them.

His fall was broken by one of the Watchers, who was unlucky enough to have Brave Bird's full weight land on top of him, forcing all the air out of the man's body. His breath smelt rank, but Brave Bird had no time to worry about that. Instead, he pushed himself off the floor and scrambled over the sprawling bodies, desperate to get past them before the Keeper arrived.

He almost made it too, but at the last moment, a hand reached out, grabbing his ankle, and he fell. Brave Bird struck out with his foot, hearing a yell of pain as his leg came free. But already, the other Watchers were getting to their feet, murder on their faces.

'That's going to cost you!' said a vicious looking brute, advancing on him.

'Behind you!' said Brave Bird.

The Watcher sneered. 'You think I'm stupid enough to fall for that one.'

His colleagues laughed. But then the unmistakable sound of heavy boots could be heard approaching, and with that came a flicker of doubt on their faces. Brave Bird shrugged.

'Don't say I didn't warn you.'

The footsteps stopped, and all heads turned, save one.

Brave Bird knew what was coming down that alleyway, and he didn't need to wait to see who it was. Even as the Watchers' cries of alarm rang out, he was already running, intent on getting as far away from the Keeper as possible.

Leaping for the staircase, Brave Bird took it two steps at a time and reached the first landing before the Watchers realised he had gone. Not daring to stop, he continued up the next flight of stairs, and as he arrived on the second landing, he looked down at the street below. The Watchers parted as a tall figure strode out of the alleyway and stood in the middle of the road, casting a shadow darker than night.

Its hooded head looked up towards the stairwell, and Brave Bird felt baleful eyes glare at him from beneath the cowl. He had to reach for the handrail to steady himself as a gloved finger appeared from under the folds of the cloak and pointed directly at him above the heads of the mob. All heads turned towards him, and at that moment his resolve faltered, drained by the malevolent will that demanded he remain and resist no more.

But then, a blinding flash of light lit up the street and the surrounding buildings. Brave Bird flinched, fearing a lightning strike, but the answering rumble of thunder never came. Squinting, he opened his eyes, and there, above the city, the fifth beam of green light shone towards the heavens. That could mean only one thing. The children had revealed the Lady!

Hope surged within him, and he looked down at the street. The figure was still there, but it was no longer pointing, shielding its eyes against the light now streaming through the alleyway. The words of the Cypher came flooding back to him, and Brave Bird raised his head to bellow his defiance.

'Seven souls to find a key,
To pick the lock and set us free!'

Below him, the Keeper snarled in frustration and lashed out at the surrounding Watchers, driving them towards the stairwell.

Brave Bird didn't hesitate. He turned and leapt up the steps towards the rooftops. This was the final leg of his journey, and no Watcher or Keeper was going to catch him now. His own portal was waiting, and tonight he would deliver his message to the children.

Nina sat bolt upright in bed, her heart racing. The dream had been so vivid, as if she had actually been there, standing on that high place looking down from a great height. Kicking off her duvet, Nina ran to the door of her bedroom. No sooner had she swung it open than she saw Leo emerge from his room on the other side of the landing.

'Did you see him?' he asked.

'Yes! It looked as if he was flying!'

'Yeah!' he said, 'and you know what the best thing is?'

'What?' she asked.

'I think I know where he's going!'

It didn't take much to persuade their Dad. When Leo described the museum that his class had visited before the end of the term with its collection of local archaeological finds, their father could hardly contain himself. He told them that he had worked on plenty of local digs in his youth after reading a book called Masquerade about finding buried treasure. He would have gone on more about it if their mother hadn't told him he was using up valuable visiting time.

It wasn't long before the children were parking their bikes and hurrying after their father as he strode through the frosted glass doors of the museum. Once inside, Nina spotted a cartoon-like carving of two squat figures holding hands, similar to the one she had seen on the museum entrance. Next to this was a life-sized figure of a tribesman, his head fashioned out of shells and pieces of animal horn, both of which she remembered from her dream. She turned to her brother. 'Leo, what about the other things we saw?'

'We haven't been upstairs yet.'

'There's an upstairs?'

He nodded, pointing towards a lift by the entrance. 'Just going upstairs Dad,' he said to their father, who gave them a distracted thumbs-up before returning his attention to the contents of a stone coffin.

Leo led his sister into the lift. 'Are you ready?' he asked.

'As ready as I'll ever be.'

Her brother grinned and pressed the button for the top floor. When the lift doors opened again, they stepped out into a vast hall, bathed in sunshine from the glass roof far above them. Dotted around the walls were cabinets containing old bits of pottery, water urns, and glass storage jars. In the centre of the hall was an oval-shaped atrium with a balcony rail running around its circumference. Nina headed over to the railing, looked down and gasped.

The lower hall was filled with displays and cabinets containing costumes and artefacts that seemed to come from all over the world. She could see intricately carved masks, feathered head-dresses, beaded ceremonial robes, and a polished black suit of Samurai armour.

In the middle of the floor were the larger exhibits, clearly too big for standard cabinets, including full-length canoes and exotic statues of gods or spirits. Some of the items she recognised, including a full-size model of a shark made from what appeared to be bamboo.

'Nina, over here!' called Leo.

Her brother was standing under an enormous dug-out canoe that must have measured the entire length of the upper hall and was suspended above their heads from heavy iron hooks set into the wall.

'What is it?' she asked, heading over to join him.

'Look there,' he replied, pointing towards the ceiling.

Nina had to shield her eyes against the bright sunlight shining through the glass roof. Squinting through her fingers, she saw the shadow of an eagle perched high above them.

'Hello children,' came a deep voice.

Nina glanced at her brother.

'It's him,' he said. 'The one from the dream.'

Nina nodded. Together, they looked up at the eagle.

'Hello,' she said.

'Hi, there,' said Leo.

'Hello, children. Thank you for coming for me. For all of us, in fact.'

'Are you the last?' she asked.

'The seventh, yes, though not all of us are found.'

'What do you mean?'

'You must go back to where it all began.'

Nina thought back to when they had heard the first voice in the headphones.

'The Girl, you mean?'

'She still waits for you,' said the voice. 'You must return and finish what you started.'

'So, you want us to go back there?' asked Leo.

'I do.'

'Hold on,' said Nina. 'What about you? We're not leaving here until you are free too.'

'Yeah,' said her brother. 'The Girl said we had to save all seven of you.'

There was a long pause, and all Nina could hear was the sound of her heart beating in her chest.

'Very well.'

Nina and Leo grinned at each other.

'So,' she began, 'if we are going to find you and your secret, where do we start?'

'You must look high... and low.'

Nina noted how deliberately he said those words and peered up at the vaulted ceiling. Other than the eagle, there didn't seem to be anything else of note. What about below? Moving over to the railing, she stared down at the various exhibits in the lower hall.

'What is it that we are looking for?' she asked.

'An object I once sold that tells my ancestors' story.'

Nina frowned and was about to ask what he meant, when she noticed her brother had his eyes shut. 'Leo? Are you OK?'

'I'm trying to remember the dream from last night,' he said.

The dream, of course! Nina closed her eyes and tried to picture the objects and the message written in the Hidden script. Understanding dawned on her and she opened her eyes.

'Leo! I've got it!'

'What? Where?'

'There!' she said, pointing. 'It has been in front of us the whole time!'

Her brother's mouth fell open, then he peered over the balustrade. 'And I bet his name is written on that display panel down there! Come on, before the Keeper gets here!' There was a gust of wind that ruffled Nina's hair as she looked down to where he had been pointing. That's when she noticed a gap in one of the nearby displays.

'Nina let's go!' said Leo, who was already running for the lift.

Nina heard the lift doors slide shut on the floor below and the humming noise as it began to ascend.

'Err, Leo? I don't think we should use the lift.'

Her brother turned to look at her. 'Why not?'

Nina saw the lift indicator flash above her brother's head as it reached their floor.

'There's something not right,' she said, desperately trying to recall what object was missing from the display. The lift bell rang and its doors were already sliding open, when Nina remembered.

'Leo!' she yelled. 'Shark!'

If it hadn't been for Nina's warning, Leo would have had no chance. He just had time to throw himself to one side before the creature launched itself out of the lift. Seconds later, a blur of teeth, fins, and tail swept past him and over the balcony, the long tail thrashing from side to side as the shark propelled its torpedo-like body through the air.

Craning his neck, Leo tracked its progress as the predator twisted this way and that searching for its target. It passed over where Nina had been standing moments before, but she was nowhere to be seen. Leo scanned the hall and caught sight of movement to his left. His sister emerged from behind a railing, crawling on hands and knees towards the safety of the stairwell.

The shark must have sensed her too because its dorsal fin turned in the air, and immediately it began heading back towards them from the other side of the hall. Its speed was incredible, and Leo could tell his sister wasn't going to make it to the stairs in time. So, he did the only thing he could think of. Scrambling to his feet, he jumped up and began waving his arms above his head like a drowning swimmer.

'Hey! Jaws!' he yelled. 'Over here!'

The shark jerked its head towards Leo. Moments later, Nina made it to the stairway doors and stared back at him.

'Go!' he yelled. 'Find him!'

Wide-eyed, his sister nodded and barged through the door as the shark lunged at her and missed. It circled back over the balcony, its black eyes looking for prey, and when it caught sight of him, the wide mouth split into a toothy grin.

That's not good, Leo thought.

With a flick of its tail, the creature sped across the hall. Leo looked around for somewhere to hide and saw that the lift was still open. The shark must have seen it too because as he ran for the gap, it changed course to intercept him. Putting on an extra burst of speed, Leo dived for the doors, sliding the last few feet on his stomach as the shark swept over him, missing him by inches. Leo slammed into the far wall of the lift compartment.

'Ow!'

Looking back through blurred vision, he saw the pale grey shape circling around the far side of the hall readying itself for another attack. Reaching for the control panel, Leo jabbed the button for the door and heard the welcome sound of the lift bell ring. So too did the shark.

Its tail beating hard, the creature flew through the air towards the lift. The doors started to close, but the shark accelerated, crossing the last few feet in a blur. Leo could only stare in horror as the approaching mouth opened wide, revealing rows of serrated teeth.

'WHAM!'

The eagle's claws slammed into the side of the shark, smashing it into the closing lift door. Splinters of wood exploded into the air as the bamboo body bounced off the frame, the tremendous impact shattering one of its fins. The eagle's talons dug deeper into the shark's damaged flank, and with powerful beats of its broad wings, the bird began to drag its stunned prey back from the doorway. Leo watched in stunned silence as the eagle's noble head turned towards him and looked into his eyes.

'Find the girl!' said the voice.

'I... I will,' Leo promised as the lift door slid shut, and its motor whirred into life.

For the few seconds it took to reach the lower level, Leo just sat there in shocked silence. When the doors opened, his sister was standing outside, a look of concern on her face.

'Leo! Are you all right?' she said, reaching down and helping him to his feet.

'The eagle saved me,' he said.

'Well, now it's our turn to save him.' And before he could say any more, Nina revealed the identity of the brave bird and his secret.

'Good work, Nina,' he said. 'Now we just need to find the Girl.'

'Let's go and get Dad,' she said and was reaching for the button when he grabbed her hand.

'Nina, do you mind if we take the stairs?'

'Oh, OK.'

Leo followed his sister as they passed a museum attendant and headed for the exit, ignoring the black stare of the bamboo shark following their progress from its central display.

Cat and Mouse

HIGH above the World of Secrets, a shaft of green light shot towards the heavens, piercing the thick grey carpet of cloud. The hooded figure staggered backwards, boots slipping on ancient flagstones, arms raised to shield itself from the glow that told of another revelation, another failure to keep what was once hidden a secret.

For the Keeper, the pain of that humiliation was worse than the physical pain caused by the eagle's talons, coming out of nowhere to save the boy and his meddlesome sister. Six times those children had slipped through the Keeper's fingers, and if the ancient Cypher was to be believed, they only needed one more secret to be able to pick the lock and set this city free. That could not be allowed to happen.

The seventh portal was not far from here, and if reports from the Watchers were to be trusted, the remaining Hidden was still hiding there. Trapped and with no interfering bird to protect her, the Girl was on her own. Only the children could save her now. If the Keeper could get to her before they did, there would be no seventh soul to find the key to set this or any other city free.

Turning from the light, the Keeper broke into a run, heavy boots pounding over the cobbled streets, making a sound like thunder. This time, there would be no escape, not for the last of the Seven, or the children.

Leo pedalled behind Nina as they cycled across the city, his sister's bike light blinking up ahead as they avoided potholes in the road. He heard the rattle and thump of his father's bike bouncing along a few feet behind him, struggling to keep up with the pace Nina was setting.

'Almost there Dad!' Leo called over his shoulder.

'All… good…' came the breathless response.

It hadn't been easy to get their father to leave after finding him still engrossed in the local archaeology section.

'Please Dad,' Nina had said. 'You always said you would take us back there.'

'I suppose we could,' their father had agreed. 'But I'll have to call your Mum to let her know we might be late back.'

Minutes later, they were on their bikes, racing across town. Already Leo could see their destination up ahead, an imposing stone building set back from the road and guarded by iron railings. Above its tall classical columns, dense black clouds were swirling around the sky, converging on the museum.

A powerful rumble of thunder greeted them as they entered the museum grounds. It sounded to Leo like a warning growl.

'That's odd,' his father said, looking up at the heavens. 'I don't remember a storm being forecast.'

Leo glanced over at his sister, and he could tell by the anxious look on her face that she was thinking the same as him. This was no ordinary storm. It was the Keeper. Moments later, the first drop of rain splattered on his head. This was followed by another and another in quick succession, and by the time they had found a space for their bikes, it had turned into a deluge.

'Quick,' said their father. 'We need to get inside.'

As Leo struggled with his bike lock, a blinding flash and deafening bang rocked him backwards, his ears ringing and a strange prickling sensation fizzing over his skin. After that, everything seemed to move in slow motion.

Dazed, he looked around and spotted his father crouched over a shape lying on the ground. For a horrible moment, he thought it must be his sister before another fork of lightning snaked across the sky and he saw it was an elderly woman. His father looked up and shouted something to Leo, but he couldn't hear anything over the ringing in his ears.

Someone grabbed his shoulder. He turned and saw it was Nina, peering at him through strands of wet hair plastered over her face. Another fork of lightning lit up the front of the museum, and she flinched. Then she was yelling something at him, but he couldn't hear the words.

Nina began pulling him towards the entrance of the museum as the rain hammered down on their heads. Leo did his best to follow, though his legs were slow to respond, and he found it hard to see where they were going.

Once they reached the entrance, the museum staff ushered them inside. Nina headed over to the reception desk, and Leo found he could just about make out what she was saying as the ringing in his ears began to subside.

'There's been an accident,' she said to a member of the museum staff. 'A lady outside has collapsed. My Dad is with her, but I think they need some help.'

Immediately, one of the attendants pulled on her high visibility jacket and headed for the door. The other picked up a phone to call for an ambulance.

Nina turned and led Leo over to a bench by the wall.

'Leo?' she said. 'Can you hear me?'

He nodded.

'Are you alright? Only, your hair is standing up.'

Leo reached up and flinched as a spark of electricity pricked his fingers. There was another blinding flash outside, followed by a tremendous clap of thunder that made them both jump. The lights in the museum flickered and gave off a strange buzzing noise. The attendant standing behind the desk paused in his phone conversation and stared nervously around.

Worried visitors began pouring into the foyer from other parts of the museum, crowding around the information desk. It wasn't long before the room was filled with people milling about and peering out at the rain lashing against the windows.

'Leo, this storm…' began Nina, but he interrupted her.

'I know. It's the Keeper trying to stop us, isn't it?'

'That's my guess,' she nodded. 'If you think you're strong enough, we need to go on before they shut the museum again.'

Leo knew she was right. He was beginning to feel a bit better now, and the buzzing in his ears had almost gone. Besides, they had made a promise earlier today to find the Girl.

'I'm fine,' he said, easing himself to his feet. 'Let's finish it.'

Taking his sister's arm, they began edging their way slowly through the crowd and had just made it into the first hall when the museum attendant made an announcement.

'Ladies and gentlemen, we appear to be experiencing…'

Another bright flash lit up the crowded foyer, followed by a massive clap of thunder that shook the building. Then, the lights went out, and people started screaming.

'Come on!' said Nina, dragging Leo behind a cabinet full of swords and shields as the crowd surged towards the exit. They crouched down and waited until the stragglers had passed before heading out across the empty exhibition space and into the next gallery.

'Where now?' Leo asked.

'I don't know,' said his sister. 'I was hoping the voice would be here to guide us.'

A flashlight beam shone across the room, and they ducked down behind the statue of an unusually large owl as a museum attendant hurried past, heading for the entrance foyer. Leo waited until the footsteps had died away before turning to his sister.

'What if she's not here anymore?'

'She must be,' said Nina. 'Why else would the Keeper be trying to scare everyone away?'

'Hello, you two,' said the Girl. 'I was wondering if I would see you again.'

They both looked at each other. She had found them!

'I'm so sorry it has taken us so long,' said Nina. 'We've been helping the others.'

'The others?' Leo could hear the excitement in her voice. 'How many?

'You're the last one,' said Nina.

'Yeah,' he added, 'a rather large bird made us promise not to leave you behind.'

The Girl went silent for a few moments. When she finally spoke, Leo could hear the emotion in her voice.

'That... that was good of him.'

'But, we're not the only ones looking for you,' said Nina.

'We think you-know-who followed us here,' Leo added.

'In that case,' said the Girl, 'you had better follow me.'

Leo looked around at the dark exhibition hall for any sign of her. 'OK, but where exactly are you?'

'Leo!' cried Nina, grabbing him.

'What?'

'Something ran over my foot!'

He looked down and caught sight of a small shape running across the polished wooden floor.

'There!' He pointed.

Another flash of lightning lit up the hall, and in the archway ahead of them, he saw a mouse standing on its hind legs looking back at them. It sniffed the air for a few seconds before darting across the floor into the next gallery.

'Come on!' he said. 'We can't lose her now!'

They ran after the mouse as lightning flashed and thunder rumbled around them, but they paid it no heed, their footsteps echoing down the empty corridors. Nor did they see or hear the other creature emerge from the darkness, and watch them disappear before padding along silently behind them.

Nina ran after her brother through a long gallery filled with hundreds of porcelain figurines staring out at them from the maze of glass cabinets. Leo paid them no attention, so intent was he on keeping track of the scurrying creature, skittering across the floor in front of him. But Nina was dazzled by a flash of lightning and narrowly avoided colliding with a display containing a china elephant

'Wait up Leo!' She called out as he sprinted into the next gallery. Nina ran after him into a large room whose windows were covered with blinds, making it hard to see where she was going. By the time she made it into the next room, Leo was nowhere to be seen.

Panting, Nina looked around. Ahead, she could just make out two rows of columns disappearing into the darkness, the space between filled with a bewildering assortment of statues and sculptures blocking her path.

'Leo?' she called out. 'Where are you?'

There was no response other than the fading sound of footsteps somewhere up ahead. Nina was about to follow when she heard another noise, a soft padding sound behind her. Spinning around, she stared into the gloom. The room was silent, and nothing stirred.

'Nina!'

Leo's shout made her jump. Turning, she could just make out her brother's hand waving from behind a group of statues. Nina hurried to join him, unable to shake the feeling that she was being watched.

'What kept you?' he said.

'I thought I heard something.'

'The voice?'

'No, something else.' She looked over her shoulder. 'Leo, I don't think we are the only ones here.'

He peered back into the darkness. 'In that case, we need to keep moving. I followed the mouse into a room at the end of the hall, but it was pitch black, and I couldn't see her anymore. You don't have a torch or something?'

Nina felt in her pocket. 'Will this do?'

She pulled out her rear bike light and pressed the button. Its little red LED began flashing, like a warning.

'Better than nothing, I suppose.'

They found that if they held the light in front of them, its flickering glow illuminated a small circular area around them. The next room must have been tall because when Nina raised the light above their heads, she couldn't see the ceiling clearly. Instead, something else loomed above them.

'Whoa, what's that?'

But it was only a stone carving of an Egyptian Pharaoh, his arms crossed in front of him, staring past them into the distance.

'We must be in the Egyptology section,' Leo said. 'You know, where they keep all the mummies.'

Nina gasped. 'Leo! Don't you remember? The message in the first dream!'

He stared at her, his eyes growing wide. 'Of course!'

'Come on,' said Nina. 'The Girl must be here somewhere!'

There was a gap between a row of glass cabinets leading to another chamber and they headed through it.

'Any sign of the mouse?' Leo asked, looking at the floor. 'You'd have thought she would be leading us to it.'

Nina shone the light around, but the mouse had disappeared. And then a thought struck her.

'Leo?' said Nina. 'Why is the mouse hiding from us?'

'I don't know,' he said, then stopped. 'Unless it's not us she's hiding from…'

But before he could finish, a low growl came from behind them.

Nina spun around and heard her brother gasp. In the flickering red light, she could see a pale feline shape crouching in the hallway.

'Leo?' she whispered. 'Is that a cat?'

'I'm not sure,' he said. 'Would a museum have a cat?'

'I wouldn't have thought so.'

The shape stirred and began prowling towards them, menace in every step. The children started backing away, keeping as much distance as possible between themselves and the creature until their shoulders bumped up against a glass cabinet, blocking their escape.

The cat paused, its body perfectly still, surveying them from just outside the circle of red. For one fleeting moment, Nina entertained the thought that the creature might be scared of the flickering light and would keep its distance. But that hope faded as the beast continued its silent approach, and as it did so, its outline became clearer.

'That thing's much bigger than a cat,' whispered her brother.

Leo was right. It was larger than any cat she had seen. But there was something else about it too.

'Leo? Have you noticed that it doesn't have any ears?'

'You're right,' he said. 'What happened to them?'

The creature emerged into the circle of red light, and that's when Nina finally understood. 'Because it's not a cat, Leo. It's the Sphinx!'

Both of them stared, unable to move as the creature stalked towards them, long tail swishing angrily behind powerful rear haunches, hooked talons extending between large front paws. Stopping a few feet from them, its smooth marble face, framed by an ancient Egyptian head-dress, stared up at them.

Nina felt a sense of hopelessness overwhelm her. Like a dark grey cloud of despair. This was it. They were trapped. The Keeper had finally caught up with them, and this time there was no one to come to their aid. No dog, no boxer, no eagle.

But she was wrong.

From nowhere, the mouse scampered across the gap between them, its tiny body only inches from those wicked claws. Distracted by the sudden movement, the Sphinx broke eye contact, and its spell was lifted. Nina felt the blood flow back into her frozen limbs and heard the Girl's voice cry out.

'Run!'

Nina didn't need telling twice. Before the Sphinx could react, she grabbed her brother, and the next moment, they were both sprinting past sarcophagi as the sounds of a huge battle broke out behind them. Hisses, squeaks, and thumping noises echoed through the dark as they ducked through another archway, raced to the far end of the room, and came face to face with a wall of glass cabinets. It was a dead end!

'Down!' said Leo, and they ducked behind a collection of open mummy cases. Fumbling for the switch, Nina managed to switch off her flashing light. The room fell into darkness as the two of them crouched there, breathing hard and listening to the commotion in the next hall. There were grunts and snarls, followed by whacks and bangs, which grew in intensity, culminating in an enormous crash that rattled the display cabinets around them.

In the silence that followed, Nina hardly dared to breathe.

Alongside her, Leo was absolutely still. They remained like that for what seemed an age, until she couldn't stand it any longer.

'Do you think the mouse got away?' she whispered in her brother's ear.

'I don't know,' he whispered back.

'Shall we risk a look?'

He waited a few more seconds before replying. 'OK.'

Clicking her light on again, she and Leo stared out over the mummy case. In the flickering red glow, there was no sign of the Sphinx or the mouse. Rising slowly to their feet, they began tip-toeing back towards the entrance to the next chamber. Nina had almost reached the archway when she heard a scampering noise. Across the floor ran the little mouse. It stopped in front of them and rose up on its hind legs.

'You escaped!' said Nina, peering down at the little animal.

The mouse wrinkled its nose, and they heard the Girl's voice once more, though this time she sounded different, reciting a rhyme that Nina thought she might have heard before but couldn't remember where.

'Seven souls to find a key,
To pick the lock and set us free.
I am the seventh soul. Find me, and you can find the Key.'

With that, the mouse gave them a low bow before turning and running off into the darkness. Nina was about to follow and ask what she meant when a tall hooded figure loomed out of the archway, and a voice cried out in triumph:

'At last!'

Nina and Leo screamed.

The lights in the museum flickered for a moment and then came back on. Nina looked into the face of the figure standing in front of her, and the scream died on her lips.

'Mum?' she said, hardly daring to believe her eyes.

Her mother pulled back the hood of her waterproof cape and smiled down at her children. Nina noticed that she was holding a broken umbrella, its missing handle lying a few feet away. Around it lay the shattered remains of a marble statue, the tail, body, and legs scattered across the polished floor.

'You…? You attacked the Sphinx?' asked Leo in disbelief.

'Is that what it was? It was hard to tell in the dark,' said their mother, twirling the broken umbrella. 'Looks like I'll need a new one of these though.'

Nina stared at her. 'What are you doing here?'

'Following in my children's footsteps. Or was it the other way around?' She smiled at their bewildered expressions. 'When I was a girl, I had all sorts of adventures in museums. Funnily enough, that's where I met your father.'

Nina felt her mouth drop open.

'Now, wasn't there someone you came here to find?' her Mum asked. 'If so, we'd better hurry up before another Keeper comes along.'

And with that, she gave her children an enormous wink.

Epilogue

LIGHT burst from the seventh portal, its beam joining those of the six others, forming an unbroken ring that lit up the sky and the surrounding buildings. The heavy veil of clouds began to shift and dissipate under the combined glow that radiated outwards, burning away mist and fog that had for so long obscured the city.

The Hidden came stumbling from their houses into the streets and stared up at the heavens, some shielding their eyes, others blinking away tears as they struggled to adjust to this transformation of their world. First one, then another, began whispering the words that had so long been known, but never truly believed.

It began as a murmur, quiet and subdued. Those uttering it glancing around, expecting Watchers to appear and take them away. But any Watchers out on the streets were as transfixed by the beacons of light as the rest of them.

When no one tried to intervene, the murmur grew in strength. The Hidden looked to each other, understanding spreading across disbelieving faces. Their world had indeed changed. As confidence grew, so did the volume, each speaker reassured by the sight of their neighbour saying the same words, louder and louder until they were chanting, not in anger or in fear, but with hope, joy, and, finally, belief.

'Seven souls to find a key,
To pick the lock and set us free!'

The universal chorus reverberated around the narrow streets, drawing the remaining Hidden from their cellars, the canal warehouses and taverns, the dwellings on the upper levels and the rundown hovels on furthest edges of the city. All turned their faces to the light of the portals and stared at them in awe.

All save one.

The hooded figure limped away from the gathering crowds, her dark form keeping to the shadows of the buildings. Agony racked her broken body as she stumbled over the cobbles in boots that were scuffed and torn. Resting a bleeding hand against a wall, the Keeper listened to the crowds as she gathered her strength for what lay ahead. She was not safe on the streets now. Her hold on this city was crumbling, and the light of knowledge was returning, threatening to banish all of their secrets.

Well, perhaps not all, she thought. There was one secret they wouldn't find. That was hidden too well. It would take more than seven fools to shine a light upon that one. And until someone unlocked that last secret, her hold over this place would never truly be gone.

In a mocking whisper, the Keeper began to recite her own riddle under her breath.

'Seven souls to find a key,
To pick the lock and set us free?'

She glanced over her shoulder towards the distant crowds.

'But what about the lock you seek?
Its hiding place is mine to keep.'

With a bitter laugh that made her wince with pain, the Keeper limped towards the river. There a boat lay waiting to take her to the eighth and final portal, the one that not even the Watchers knew existed. For that was where she had hidden her secret, carved in stone and safe from any more interfering children.

Or so she thought…

MUSEUM PASSPORT
Stamps collected by:

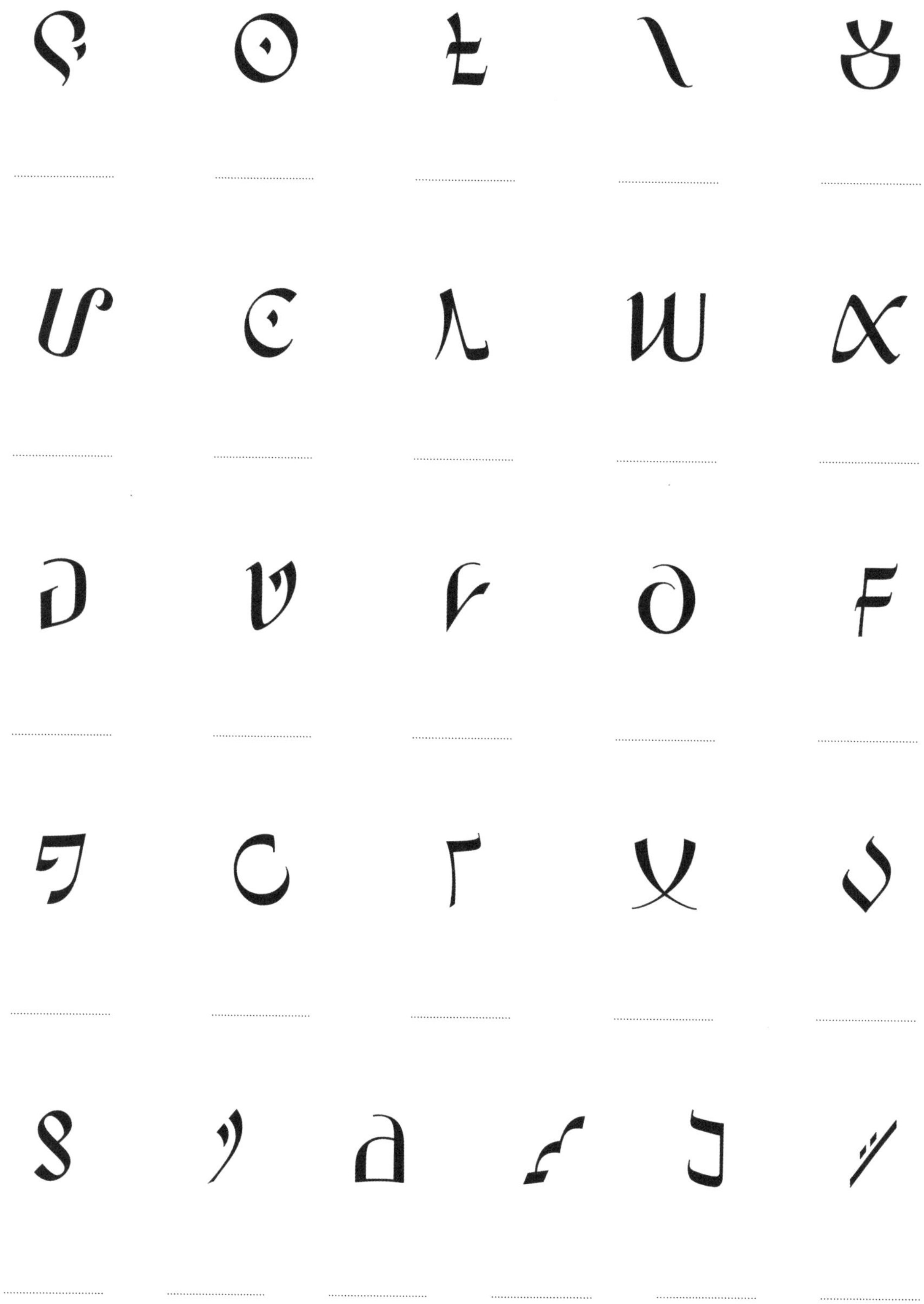

Use this page to help you decipher the Hidden Script.

E
N
S
W
MANOR STREET
KING STREET
JESUS LANE
MALCOLM STREET
HOBSON STREET
LOWER PARK STREET
PARK PARADE
PORTUGAL ST.
ST. JOHN'S RD.
RICHMOND TER.
NEW PARK STREET
PARK STREET
ROUND CHURCH ST.
SIDNEY STREET
GREEN STREET
MARKET STREET
THOMPSONS LANE
ST. JOHN'S STREET
TRINITY STREET
BRIDGE STREET
MAGDALENE STREET
CHESTERTON ROAD
TRINITY LANE
NORTHAMPTON STREET
MADINGLEY ROAD
QUEEN'S ROAD
Cambridge

THE THEORY OF RULED SURFACES

Cambridge University Press
Fetter Lane, London

New York
Bombay, Calcutta, Madras
Toronto
Macmillan

Tokyo
Maruzen Company, Ltd.

THE THEORY OF RULED SURFACES

BY

W. L. EDGE

FELLOW OF
TRINITY COLLEGE
CAMBRIDGE

CAMBRIDGE
AT THE UNIVERSITY PRESS
1931

PRINTED IN GREAT BRITAIN

CONTENTS

Section III

Section IV

CHAPTER III: QUINTIC RULED SURFACES

Section I

Section II

Section III

CHAPTER IV: SEXTIC RULED SURFACES

Section I

Section II

Section III

CHAPTER V: DEVELOPABLE SURFACES

CHAPTER VI: SEXTIC RULED SURFACES (CONTINUED)

PREFACE

In this volume all the ruled surfaces in ordinary space of orders up to and including the sixth are studied and classified. Tables shewing the different types of surfaces are given towards the end of the book, and the tables for the surfaces of the fifth and sixth orders are here obtained for the first time.

It seems that the results so obtained are of great importance; but the incidental purpose which, it is hoped, may be served by the book is perhaps of still greater importance. For there exists at present no work, easily accessible to English readers, which tests the application of the general ideas here employed in anything like the same detail. One might mention especially the use of higher space and the principle of correspondence, and these two ideas are vital and fundamental in all modern algebraic geometry. It is hoped therefore that the book may be of use to a wide circle of readers.

I wish to express here my thanks to the staff of the University Press for their unfailing accuracy in the printing and for the ready courtesy with which they have accepted my suggestions.

Notwithstanding the large number of surfaces which are herein investigated, the book would be incomplete were I not to make an acknowledgment of my obligations to Mr White, of St John's College, and Professor Baker. Even those who have only a slight knowledge of the multifariousness of Mr White's mathematical public services will be surprised to learn that he found time not only to read the proof sheets but also to read through the whole of the manuscript, and I am very grateful to him for his criticisms and suggestions.

My gratitude to Professor Baker is something more than that of a student to his teacher. He it was who first suggested that I should undertake this work, and his encouragement has been given unsparingly—and effectively—in times of difficulty. I have derived great benefit not only from my personal conversations with him but also from attending his courses of lectures. I thank him for many things; but especially for his interest, which has never flagged, and for his trust, which has never wavered.

W. L. E.

TRINITY COLLEGE
CAMBRIDGE
October 1930

CHAPTER I

INTRODUCTORY

SECTION I

PRELIMINARIES

1. The system of points on a line is determined by two of them, any third point of the line being derivable from these two; the same line is equally well determined by any two of its points. Similarly, if three points are taken which are not on the same line they determine a plane, the same plane being equally well determined by any three non-collinear points of it. Proceeding in this way we say that $n + 1$ independent points determine a linear space of n dimensions, the points being independent when they are such that no one of them belongs to the space of less than n dimensions determined by the others; the same space of n dimensions is equally well determined by any $n + 1$ independent points belonging to it.

We shall use the symbols $[n]$ and S_n to denote a space of n dimensions. In $[n]$ two spaces $[m]$ and $[n - m]$ of complementary dimensions have, in general, one point in common and no more. A space $[p]$ and a space $[q]$ have, in general, no common points if $p + q < n$, while if $p + q > n$ they have, in general, a common $[p + q - n]$. If they have in common a space $[r]$ where $r > p + q - n$, then they are contained in a space $[p + q - r]$ or $[n - s]$, where $s = r - p - q + n$. For example: two lines in ordinary space do not intersect in general; if they do so they lie in a plane. If we call the intersection of $[p]$ and $[q]$ their *meet* and the space of lowest dimension which contains them both their *join*, then the sum of the dimensions of the meet and the join is $p + q$.

2. Just as we can project, in ordinary space, on to a plane so we can project, in $[n]$, on to $[n - 1]$; if O is the centre of projection and P any point of $[n]$ the line OP meets $[n - 1]$ in a point P_1 which is the projection of P. We can then project again from a point O_1 of $[n - 1]$ on to a space $[n - 2]$ in $[n - 1]$, the line O_1P_1 meeting $[n - 2]$ in a point P_2. The passage from P to P_2 can, however, be carried out in one step, simply by joining P to the line OO_1 by a plane and taking P_2 as the intersection of the plane with $[n - 2]$. We thus speak of projecting the points of $[n]$ from a line on to $[n - 2]$. Similarly, we can project from a plane on to an $[n - 3]$, from a solid on to an $[n - 4]$, and so on; the sum of the dimensions of the space which is the centre of projection and of the space on to which we are projecting being always $n - 1$.

3. Just as the order* of a plane curve is the number of points in which it is met by a line, and the order of a twisted curve is the number of points in which it is met by a plane, so the order of a curve in [4] is the number of points in which it is met by a solid† and so on, the order of a curve in [n] being the number of points in which it is met by a space [$n - 1$] of complementary dimension. The order of a surface in [n] is the number of points in which it is met by a space [$n - 2$], just as the order of a surface in ordinary space is the number of points in which it is met by a line. It is here implied that the space [$n - 2$] has a general position in regard to the surface, otherwise it might meet it in a curve; a line in ordinary space may itself lie on a surface. Similarly the order of a locus of r dimensions is equal to the (finite) number of points in which it is met by a space [$n - r$] of complementary dimension and of general position. A locus of dimension r and order m will be denoted by a symbol M_r^m or V_r^m, and if $r = n - 1$ the locus will be spoken of as a "primal." A space [$n - 1$] lying in [n] is called a "prime" of [n].

4. If we have a curve in ordinary space its chords fill up the space; there is a finite number of them passing through a point of general position. But in [4] the chords of a curve do not fill up the space; they form a locus of three dimensions whose order is the number of points in which it meets a line. If we have a system of coordinates in [4], say five homogeneous or four non-homogeneous coordinates, the locus is given by an equation in these coordinates, and the order of the locus is the order of this equation. In [n] the chords of a curve form a three-dimensional locus whose order is equal to the number of points in which it meets an [$n - 3$]. The chords of a surface form a five-dimensional locus.

5. Suppose that we have a curve of order N in [n]; there may be a point of the curve such that any [$n - 1$] passing through it only meets the curve in $N - 2$ other points. Such a point is called a double point of the curve. In particular we have the double points of a plane curve; for example, the point $x = y = 0$ is a double point on the cubic curve

$$x^3 + y^3 = 3xyz,$$

any line through it meeting the curve in only one further point. It is known that a plane curve of order N cannot possess more than

$$\tfrac{1}{2}(N-1)(N-2)$$

double points, a k-ple point (i.e. a point such that any line through it meets the curve only in $N - k$ further points) counting as $\frac{1}{2}k(k-1)$ double

* It is always to be understood that the curves and loci spoken of are *algebraical*.

† The word *solid* will always mean a three-dimensional space. We shall sometimes find it convenient to use the word solid as well as the symbols [3] and S_3.

points*. If d is the actual number of double points possessed by the plane curve the number $\frac{1}{2}(N-1)(N-2)-d$ was called by Cayley the *deficiency* of the curve. This number is in fact the same as the *genus* of the curve. The most fundamental property of the genus is that it is invariant for birational transformation of the curve; the genus of a curve in space of any number of dimensions can therefore be defined as the deficiency of a plane curve with which it is birationally equivalent.

The explanation of what is meant by *birational transformation* must be given here. Two curves are said to be *birationally equivalent* or to be in *birational correspondence* when the coordinates of a point on either curve are rational functions of the coordinates of a point on the other. In this way to a given point of either curve there will correspond one and only one point of the other; but multiple points will prove exceptions to this rule, to a multiple point on one of the curves there will correspond several points on the other. Thus we can say that there is a (1, 1) correspondence between the two curves, with certain reservations as to the multiple points. But it appears that we can always regard a multiple point as consisting of several points on different *branches* of a curve, and if we regard the multiple point in this way we can say that the correspondence is (1, 1) without exception. Thus a birational correspondence and a (1, 1) correspondence between two curves mean the same thing; and the fundamental property of the genus is that it is the same for two curves which are in (1, 1) correspondence.

If we are considering correspondences between the points of two curves, or between the points of a single curve, then a double point must be regarded as two distinct points on different branches of the curve. At a cusp, however, there is only a single branch.

In the quadratic transformation

$$x = \frac{1}{X}, \quad y = \frac{1}{Y}, \quad z = \frac{1}{Z},$$

the rational quartic $\qquad y^2z^2 + z^2x^2 + x^2y^2 = 0,$

with nodes at the three vertices of the triangle of reference, is transformed into the conic

$$X^2 + Y^2 + Z^2 = 0,$$

and to each node of the quartic there correspond two distinct points of the conic. Corresponding to the node $y = z = 0$ we have the two points in which the conic is met by the line $X = 0$; and to either of these points on the conic corresponds the node $y = z = 0$ on the quartic, the two points on the conic giving points on two distinct branches of the quartic.

* It may be equivalent to more than this number of double points if the k tangents are not all distinct or are such that some of them meet the curve in more than $k+1$ (instead of exactly $k+1$) points at the multiple point.

On the other hand, the rational quartic

$$y^2z^2 + z^2x^2 + x^2y^2 = 2xyz\,(x + y + z)$$

has cusps at the three vertices of the triangle of reference, and is transformed by the same transformation into the conic

$$X^2 + Y^2 + Z^2 = 2\,(YZ + ZX + XY).$$

Then to each cusp of the quartic there corresponds only one point of the conic, e.g. to the cusp $y = z = 0$ corresponds the point in which the conic is touched by its tangent $X = 0$.

6. When two curves are in (1, 1) correspondence it is of course not necessary that they should belong to spaces of the same number of dimensions; either of them can belong to a space of any number of dimensions. The genus therefore of a curve in $[n]$ is simply the genus or deficiency of the projection of this curve from a space $[n - 3]$ on to a plane; the correspondence between the curve and its projection will be (1, 1) if the $[n - 3]$ is of general position. A curve has the same genus as any curve of which it is the projection.

For example, we may project the curve of intersection of two quadric surfaces in ordinary space on to a plane from a point O. If O is of general position in regard to the curve there are two and only two of its chords* which pass through O; the projection is a plane quartic with two double points and therefore of genus 1. Hence the curve of intersection of two quadrics is also of genus 1.

Of the ∞^3 possible positions of O there are four (not on the curve) for which an infinity of chords of the curve pass through O, these being the vertices of the four quadric cones which belong to the pencil of quadrics containing the curve. The projection from one of these points does not give a (1, 1) correspondence but a (2, 1) correspondence, and the genus of the curve is altered by such a projection.

A curve of genus zero is said to be a *rational curve* because the coordinates of any point on it can be expressed as rational functions of a parameter, and this parameter can be so chosen as to be a rational function of the coordinates of a point of the curve†. Thus to each point of the curve corresponds one and only one value of the parameter and to each value of the parameter corresponds one and only one point of the curve. A rational curve is birationally equivalent to a straight line and all rational curves are birationally equivalent to one another.

A curve of genus 1 is said to be an *elliptic curve*; but it is not true that all elliptic curves are birationally equivalent to one another. There is belonging to an elliptic curve an invariant called its *modulus*; and in order

* Salmon, *Geometry of Three Dimensions* (Dublin, 1914), vol. 1, pp. 355, 356.

† If we have expressed the coordinates of a point of a curve as rational functions of a parameter and this parameter is *not* a rational function of the coordinates, we can always find a second parameter which is; the second parameter is a rational function of the first and the coordinates are rational in terms of it. See Lüroth, *Math. Ann.* 9 (1875), 163.

that two elliptic curves should be birationally equivalent it is necessary and sufficient that they should have the same modulus.

A curve of genus 2 is said to be *hyperelliptic*, although not all hyperelliptic curves are of genus 2*.

7. When we project a curve C of order N in $[n]$ on to any lower space the order of the projected curve is also N provided that the centre of projection does not meet C. If the centre of projection is a space $[r]$ the space on to which we are projecting is an $[n-r-1]$; an arbitrary $[n-r-2]$ in this space meets the projected curve in a number of points equal to its order, and this number is the same as the number of points in which the $[n-1]$ joining $[n-r-2]$ to $[r]$ meets C. If C is met in M points by the centre of projection the projected curve is of order $N-M$. If we project on to a plane from an $[n-3]$ which does not meet C we know that we shall obtain a plane curve of order N with $\frac{1}{2}(N-1)(N-2)-p$ double points, where p is the genus of C. But the space $[n-2]$ which joins $[n-3]$ to any one of these double points must, unless it contains a double point of C itself, contain two different points of C; so that we have a chord of C meeting $[n-3]$. Conversely, any chord of C which meets $[n-3]$ gives rise to a double point of the projected curve. Thus, if δ is the number of actual double points of C, there must be $\frac{1}{2}(N-1)(N-2)-p-\delta$ chords of C meeting an $[n-3]$ of general position; so that *the chords of C form a three-dimensional locus of order* $\frac{1}{2}(N-1)(N-2)-p-\delta$.

8. *Normal curves.* We now introduce the important concept of a *normal curve*†. A curve is said to be *normal* when it cannot be obtained by projection from a curve of the same order in space of higher dimension. It is clear that no curve can lie in a space of higher dimension than the order n of the curve, for taking any $n+1$ points of the curve we determine thereby a space of dimension n at most, which contains the curve since it meets it in a number of points greater than its order. For example: a curve of the second order always lies in a plane.

The coordinates of a point of a rational curve of order n in $[m]$ can be expressed as rational functions of a parameter θ. If the coordinates are homogeneous, and so $m+1$ in number, the coordinates of a point of the curve can be taken as polynomials in θ. Further, θ can be so chosen that it is a rational function of the coordinates (§ 6) so that to any given value of θ there corresponds one and only one point of the curve. Then none of the $m+1$ polynomials can be of degree higher than n, for otherwise a prime S_{m-1}, which is given by a single linear equation in the

* A curve of genus 2 is the simplest example of a class of curves which are said to be *hyperelliptic*. We can have hyperelliptic curves of any genus; but *all* curves of genus 2 are necessarily hyperelliptic. See e.g. Severi, *Trattato di Geometria Algebrica*, I, 1, 159 (Bologna, 1926).

† See Severi, *ibid.* 110–111.

coordinates, would meet the curve in more than n points; while one polynomial at least must actually be of degree n. Thus a rational curve of order n cannot lie in a space of dimension greater than n, since we cannot have more than $n+1$ linearly independent polynomials of order n in θ.

On the other hand, *a rational curve of order n can always be regarded as the projection of a rational curve of order n in* $[n]$*. If the curve is in $[m]$ we can suppose the homogeneous coordinates $x_0, x_1, \dots, x_m$ of any point on it to be linearly independent polynomials of order n in a parameter θ. We can then choose $n-m$ further polynomials of order n in θ such that all the $n+1$ polynomials are linearly independent; we then take a curve in $[n]$, the homogeneous coordinates $x_0, x_1, \dots, x_n$ of a point on it being proportional to these polynomials. The former curve can be regarded as lying in the $[m]$ whose equations are $x_{m+1} = x_{m+2} = \dots = x_n = 0$ and is the projection of the normal curve from the $[n-m-1]$ whose equations are $x_0 = x_1 = \dots = x_m = 0$.

We can, merely by means of a linear transformation of the coordinates, take the coordinates of a point on a rational normal curve of order n to be

$$x_0 = \theta^n, \quad x_1 = \theta^{n-1}, \dots, x_r = \theta^{n-r}, \dots, x_{n-1} = \theta, \quad x_n = 1.$$

The expressions $(\theta^2, \theta, 1)$ for a point on a conic and $(\theta^3, \theta^2, \theta, 1)$ for a point on a twisted cubic are well known.

The curve is given uniquely by the equations

$$\frac{x_0}{x_1} = \frac{x_1}{x_2} = \dots = \frac{x_r}{x_{r+1}} = \dots = \frac{x_{n-1}}{x_n},$$

or

$$\left\| \begin{matrix} x_0 & x_1 \dots & x_r & \dots x_{n-1} \\ x_1 & x_2 \dots & x_{r+1} & \dots \; x_n \end{matrix} \right\| = 0.$$

Incidentally we have the equations of $\frac{1}{2}n(n-1)$ quadric primals containing the curve; these are linearly independent and any other quadric primal containing the curve is in fact linearly dependent from these.

The chords of the curve form the three-dimensional locus given by

$$\left\| \begin{matrix} x_0 & x_1 \dots & x_r & \dots x_{n-2} \\ x_1 & x_2 \dots & x_{r+1} & \dots x_{n-1} \\ x_2 & x_3 \dots & x_{r+2} & \dots \; x_n \end{matrix} \right\| = 0,$$

which is of order $\frac{1}{2}(n-1)(n-2)$†.

* Veronese, *Math. Ann.* 19 (1882), 208.

† The coordinates of a point on the three-dimensional locus of chords are of the form

$$(\theta^n + \lambda\phi^n, \quad \theta^{n-1} + \lambda\phi^{n-1}, \dots, \theta + \lambda\phi, \quad 1 + \lambda),$$

and depend on the three parameters θ, ϕ, λ.

For the order of the system of equations given by the vanishing of the determinants of a matrix see Salmon, *Higher Algebra* (Dublin, 1885), Lesson 19.

In particular the rational quartic curve is normal in [4] and can be given by

$$x_0 : x_1 : x_2 : x_3 : x_4 = \theta^4 : \theta^3 : \theta^2 : \theta : 1.$$

Its equations are

$$\frac{x_0}{x_1} = \frac{x_1}{x_2} = \frac{x_2}{x_3} = \frac{x_3}{x_4}$$

and it lies on six linearly independent quadric primals. It can be shewn that there is one quadric primal which contains not only the quartic curve but all its tangents; its equation is

$$x_0x_4 - 4x_1x_3 + 3x_2^2 = 0.$$

The chords of the curve form the cubic primal

$$\begin{vmatrix} x_0 & x_1 & x_2 \\ x_1 & x_2 & x_3 \\ x_2 & x_3 & x_4 \end{vmatrix} = 0.$$

We now state a fundamental result: *A curve of order n and genus p is normal in $[n-p]$ if $n > 2p-2$*; that is to say, every curve of genus p whose order n is greater than $2p - 2$ can be obtained by projection from some curve of order n and genus p in $[n-p]$*. In particular an elliptic curve of order n can always be obtained by projection from an elliptic curve of order n in $[n-1]$.

9. *Ruled surfaces.* A surface formed by a singly infinite system of straight lines is called a *ruled surface*; the lines are called the *generators* of the surface. If two different prime sections of the surface are taken it is clear that they are in (1, 1) correspondence, two points corresponding when they lie on the same generator; the sections are met each in one point by every generator. Hence all prime sections of the surface are of the same genus, so that we can speak of the genus of a ruled surface, meaning thereby the genus of its prime sections. We thus have rational ruled surfaces, elliptic ruled surfaces and so on.

Incidentally we can speak of the genus of any singly infinite set of elements, meaning thereby the genus of a curve whose points are in (1, 1) correspondence with the elements of the set.

10. Suppose now that we have a ruled surface of order n in [3]. It is clear that the tangent plane at any point contains the generator which passes through that point.

Consider the section of the surface by a plane passing through a generator g; it consists of g and a curve C_{n-1} of order $n-1$. We may

* See Clifford, "On the classification of loci," *Phil. Trans.* 169 (1879), 663; and *Collected Papers* (London, 1882), 329. Clifford's result is obtained by the use of Abelian integrals and states that $p \leqslant \frac{n}{2}$. This same result is arrived at differently by Veronese, *Math. Ann.* 19 (1882), 213.

For the complete statement with $n > 2p - 2$ see Segre, *Math. Ann.* 30 (1887), 207.

assume that, for a general position of this plane, C_{n-1} is irreducible and does not touch g. Then it will meet g in $n - 1$ distinct points. C_{n-1} is simply the locus of the points in which the plane is met by the generators, and every generator other than g meets C_{n-1} in one point. Thus C_{n-1} has the same genus as the ruled surface; to each point of C_{n-1} there corresponds a generator of the surface passing through it and conversely, the point of C_{n-1} corresponding to g being one of their $n - 1$ common points. Thus through the $n - 2$ remaining intersections of g and C_{n-1} there will pass other generators, so that we conclude that *every generator is met by* $n - 2$ *others.*

If now we take a point P on C_{n-1} the plane which contains the tangent of C_{n-1} at P and the generator which passes through P will be the tangent plane of the ruled surface at P. In particular, the tangent plane of the ruled surface at that intersection of C_{n-1} and g which is not an intersection of g with another generator is the plane of C_{n-1} itself.

If we consider any generator g, every point of g is the point of contact of a tangent plane passing through g, while every plane passing through g is a tangent plane touching the surface at some point of g. There is thus established a projectivity between the range of points on g and the pencil of planes through g; the range of points of contact is related to the pencil of corresponding tangent planes. The particular case of this property of a quadric is familiar; the generators of either system are met by those of the other in related ranges of points.

11. We have seen that every generator of a ruled surface of order n in [3] is met by $n - 2$ others. We thus have on the surface a *double curve* meeting every generator in $n - 2$ points; this curve is the locus of intersections of pairs of generators and at any point of it there are two tangent planes to the surface, one containing each of the two generators which intersect there.

Similarly we have a *bitangent developable* formed by the planes containing pairs of intersecting generators; there are $n - 2$ planes of this developable passing through each generator, and every plane of the developable touches the surface in two points—one on each of the generators lying in the plane.

The section of the ruled surface by any plane has double points at the intersections of the plane with the double curve. The tangent cone to the surface from any point has as double tangent planes those planes of the bitangent developable which pass through the point.

If the ruled surface is of order n and genus p a plane section is a curve of order n and genus p; such a curve has $\frac{1}{2}(n-1)(n-2) - p$ double points. Hence the plane must meet the double curve of the ruled surface in these $\frac{1}{2}(n-1)(n-2) - p$ points, so that the order of the double curve is $\frac{1}{2}(n-1)(n-2) - p$.

Those planes through an arbitrary point which contain the generators of the surface form a singly infinite aggregate of genus p; they meet an arbitrary plane in the tangents of a curve of class* n and genus p. Such a curve has $\frac{1}{2}(n-1)(n-2)-p$ double tangents; so that there are, passing through an arbitrary point, $\frac{1}{2}(n-1)(n-2)-p$ planes each of which contains two generators of the surface. Hence there are $\frac{1}{2}(n-1)(n-2)-p$ planes of the bitangent developable passing through an arbitrary point, so that the bitangent developable is of class $\frac{1}{2}(n-1)(n-2)-p$; the class of a developable in [3] being defined as the number of its planes which pass through an arbitrary point.

We have thus shewn that, for a ruled surface of order n and genus p, the order of the double curve and the class of the bitangent developable are both equal to

$$\frac{1}{2}(n-1)(n-2)-p.$$

12. *The classification of ruled surfaces in three dimensions.* We shall classify ruled surfaces in three dimensions according to:

(i) the order;
(ii) the genus;
(iii) the double curve;
(iv) the bitangent developable.

13. *Correspondence formulae.* The position of a point on a straight line or on any rational curve is given by a single parameter, this being chosen as in § 6. Suppose then that we have a correspondence between the points of a rational curve; this means that there is an algebraic relation connecting the parameters θ and ϕ of corresponding points P and Q, the correspondence being given by equating some polynomial in θ and ϕ to zero. If the polynomial is of degree α in θ and of degree β in ϕ we say that there is an (α, β) correspondence between P and Q; when P is given there are β corresponding positions of Q, and when Q is given there are α corresponding positions of P. It is then evident that there are $\alpha+\beta$ points which coincide with one of their corresponding points; their parameters are simply the roots of the equation of degree $\alpha+\beta$ which is obtained by equating the polynomial to zero after putting $\theta=\phi$. We shall then say that on a rational curve there are $\alpha+\beta$ coincidences in an (α, β) correspondence. This is Chasles' principle of correspondence†.

There will be certain points P for which two of the β corresponding points Q coincide; the number of these is $2\alpha(\beta-1)$ since the condition that an equation of order β should have a double root is of order $2\beta-2$

* The class of a plane curve is defined as the number of its tangents which pass through an arbitrary point.

† *Comptes Rendus*, 58 (1864), 1175.

in its coefficients*. Here it is not necessary that the correspondence should be between the points of the same curve; θ and ϕ may be the parameters of points on two different rational curves. These points P for which two corresponding points Q coincide are called branch-points of the correspondence. Similarly, there are $2\beta(\alpha - 1)$ branch-points Q for which two of the α corresponding points P coincide.

We may have two correspondences between the points P and Q of a rational curve or between the points P of one rational curve and the points Q of another rational curve; suppose that we have an (α, β) correspondence between P and Q and an (α', β') correspondence between P' and Q'; P' is on the same rational curve as P and Q' is on the same rational curve as Q. Then for any given position of P and P' the β positions of Q will, in general, be distinct from the β' positions of Q'; there are, however, $\alpha\beta' + \alpha'\beta$ positions such that if P and P' together take up one of them one of the β corresponding points Q coincides with one of the β' corresponding points Q'. The condition that two equations of orders β and β' should have a common root is of order β' in the coefficients of the first equation and of order β in the coefficients of the second equation†.

14. These results which we have obtained for rational curves can be generalised for curves of any genus p; in order to do this we must introduce the idea of the *valency*‡ of a correspondence and the idea of a *linear series of sets of points* on a curve.

If we have a curve in $[n]$ then the family of primals§

$$\lambda_0 f_0 + \lambda_1 f_1 + \ldots + \lambda_r f_r = 0$$

cuts out on the curve a *linear series of sets of points*. The primals $f = 0$ are all of the same order and the equation of any primal of the system depends linearly and homogeneously upon the $r + 1$ parameters λ; we have a *linear system* of primals. Thus on a plane curve a linear series of sets of points is cut out by a linear system of curves; on a twisted curve a linear series of sets of points is cut out by a linear system of surfaces, and so on. We will then consider for definiteness a linear series of sets of points on a plane curve.

The linear system of plane curves

$$\lambda_0 f_0 + \lambda_1 f_1 + \ldots + \lambda_r f_r = 0$$

contains ∞^r curves and cuts out on a curve $h = 0$ a linear series of sets of points. There may be an infinity of curves of the linear system passing

* Salmon, *Higher Algebra* (Dublin, 1885), 99.

† Salmon, *ibid.* 69.

‡ Called *Werthigkeit* by Brill, *Math. Ann.* 7 (1874), 611.

§ f is a homogeneous polynomial in the $n + 1$ homogeneous coordinates

$$x_0, x_1, \ldots, x_n.$$

It is assumed that these $r + 1$ polynomials f are linearly independent.

through a set of the linear series; it can be shewn that this happens when and only when there are curves of the system containing the curve $h = 0$. We can then always work with a reduced linear system of curves*, none of which contains the curve $h = 0$ as a part. Then, supposing that we are working with such a system containing the $r + 1$ parameters λ, the linear series of sets of points contains ∞^r sets, each set containing the same number n of points. Through r general points of the curve $h = 0$ there will pass just one curve of the linear system, as we have just enough conditions to determine the ratios of the parameters λ. The linear series of sets of points is then said to be of *freedom* r and is denoted by g_n^r; r general points of the curve $h = 0$ determine just one set of g_n^r. The number n is called the *grade* of the linear series.

If now we have an (α, β) correspondence between the points P and Q of a curve of genus p, and if a point P of the curve counted γ times, taken together with the β points Q which correspond to it, gives a set of points which varies in a linear series of sets of $\beta + \gamma$ points as P varies on the curve, the correspondence is said to be of *valency*† γ. It is not necessary that every set of the linear series should be given by the variation of P, but merely that all the ∞^1 sets of points so obtained should belong to some linear series of sets of $\beta + \gamma$ points. When this is so it can be shewn that a point Q of the curve counted γ times, taken together with the α points P which correspond to it, gives a set of points which vary in a linear series of sets of $\alpha + \gamma$ points as Q varies on the curve. On a general curve every correspondence has a valency; correspondences without a valency can only exist on curves which are special for their genus‡.

We can, for example, set up a correspondence between the points P and Q of a plane cubic without a double point; saying that the points P and Q correspond when the tangent at P passes through Q. To any point P corresponds one point Q, since the tangent at P only meets the cubic in one other point; to any point Q correspond four points P since four tangents can be drawn to the cubic from any point of itself; thus the correspondence is a (4, 1) correspondence. Also its valency is 2; the point P counted twice together with the point Q which corresponds to it form the complete intersection of the cubic with its tangent, and therefore vary, as P varies on the curve, in a linear series of sets of three points, viz. that cut out by the lines of the plane. The four points of contact of the tangents drawn to the curve from any point Q of itself lie on the first polar of Q, which is a conic touching the curve at Q; hence the point Q counted twice together with the four points P which correspond to it form the complete intersection of the cubic with a conic and therefore vary in a linear series of

* See Severi, *Trattato di Geometria Algebrica*, I, 1, 20 (Bologna, 1926).

† Severi, *ibid.* 198.

‡ Hurwitz, *Math. Ann.* 28 (1887), 565.

sets of six points as Q varies on the curve, viz. that cut out by the conics of the plane.

The analogues of the formulae for rational curves are as follows.

If we have on a curve of genus p *an* (α, β) *correspondence of valency* γ *there are* $\alpha + \beta + 2\gamma p$ *coincidences**. For example, there are nine coincidences in the (4, 1) correspondence just mentioned on the cubic curve of genus 1; these are simply the nine inflections of the curve. Again, *the number of branch-points* P *for which two of the* β *corresponding points* Q *coincide*† *is* $2\alpha(\beta - 1) + 2(\alpha - \gamma^2)p$ *and the number of branch-points* Q *for which two of the* α *corresponding points* P *coincide*† *is* $2\beta(\alpha - 1) + 2(\beta - \gamma^2)p$. Finally, *if we have on the same curve of genus* p *an* (α, β) *correspondence of valency* γ *and an* (α', β') *correspondence of valency* γ' *the number of pairs of points common to the two correspondences*‡ *is* $\alpha\beta' + \alpha'\beta - 2\gamma\gamma' p$.

As an example of this last result consider a plane quartic curve without double points ($p = 3$). If P and Q correspond when the tangent at Q passes through P we have a (2, 10) correspondence of valency 2; if inversely P' and Q' correspond when the tangent at P' passes through Q' we have a (10, 2) correspondence of valency 2. Then the number of pairs of points common to these two correspondences is

$$2 \,.\, 2 + 10 \,.\, 10 - 2 \,.\, 2 \,.\, 2 \,.\, 3 = 80 = 2 \times 28 + 24.$$

The interpretation of this result is clear since the curve has 28 bitangents and 24 inflections. If one of the points of contact of a bitangent is taken as a position of P and P' then the other point of contact is one of the corresponding positions of Q and also one of the corresponding positions of Q'. Since there are two points of contact of each bitangent we have in this way 56 pairs of points common to the two correspondences. Again, if the point of contact of an inflectional tangent is taken as a position of P and P' this same point is one of the corresponding positions of Q and also one of the corresponding positions of Q'.

We must also mention the fact that the valency of a correspondence can be negative; this is clear from other definitions of the valency but it also arises naturally from the idea of the equivalence of sets of points on a curve, two sets of points on a curve being *equivalent* when they belong to the same linear series.

As an example of a correspondence with negative valency let us consider the correspondence between the point P of a plane cubic without a double point and

* See Cayley, *Comptes Rendus*, 62 (1866), 586 = *Papers*, 5, 542; *Phil. Trans.* 158 (1868), 146 = *Papers*, 6, 265. Brill, *Math. Ann.* 6 (1873), 33; 7 (1874), 607. Severi, *Memorie Torino* (2), 54 (1904), 11; *Trattato di Geometria Algebrica*, I, 1, 233 (Bologna, 1926).

† This formula has been given by Professor Baker in lectures. It can be deduced from Cayley's formula (*Papers*, 6, 267). P and Q are on the same curve.

‡ Brill, *Math. Ann.* 6 (1873), 42; 7 (1874), 611. Hurwitz, *ibid.* 28 (1887), 568. This result we shall in future call *Brill's formula.*

the point R which is the second tangential of P. If the tangent at P meets the curve again in Q, Q is called the *tangential* of P; if then the tangent at Q meets the curve again in R, R is called the *second tangential* of P. Clearly to a given point P there corresponds one and only one point R.

Now it is known that if conics are drawn through four fixed points of a cubic curve the line joining their two remaining intersections with the curve meets the cubic again in a fixed point*. In particular, the conics which have four-point contact with the curve at P meet it again in two points whose join passes through R.

Take then any point O on the cubic and join OR, meeting the cubic again in R'. The conic through O which has four-point contact with the curve at P passes through R'. Moreover, if P' is any point whose second tangential is R' we can draw a conic having four-point contact with the curve at P' and passing through O and R.

Now the conics passing through O cut out on the cubic a linear series of sets of five points; one set of this series consists of R' taken with P counted four times, while another consists of R taken with P' counted four times. Thus these two sets of points are equivalent, so that we write

$$4P + R' \equiv 4P' + R.$$

Writing this in the form

$$R - 4P \equiv R' - 4P',$$

we say that the correspondence from P to R has the valency -4.

This exemplifies a general theorem which states that *the "product" of two correspondences of valencies γ_1 and γ_2 has the valency $-\gamma_1\gamma_2$*. The correspondence from P to its second tangential is the "square" of the correspondence from P to its first tangential, and this latter correspondence we have already seen to have valency 2.

15. A correspondence has, of course, two senses; in the "forward" sense the β points $Q_1, Q_2, \ldots, Q_\beta$ correspond to the point P, while in the "backward" sense the α points $P_1, P_2, \ldots, P_\alpha$ correspond to the point Q. In calculating the number of pairs of points common to two correspondences by Brill's formula we imply that we take both correspondences in the same sense: having chosen a point we proceed to the two sets which correspond to it, either both in the forward sense or both in the backward sense; the formula gives the number of positions of the chosen point for which a point of one of the two sets coincides with a point of the other.

There is a special kind of correspondence which we shall call a *symmetrical correspondence*; in such a correspondence there is only one sense, or there is only one way of passing from a given point to those points which correspond to it. The two indices of such a correspondence are equal; and if Q is one of the set of points corresponding to P then P is conversely one of the set of points corresponding to Q. As an example of such a correspondence let us consider, on a quadric S in ordinary space, the curve C which is the intersection of S with another quadric; and suppose that two points of C correspond when they lie on the same generator of S.

* Salmon, *Higher Plane Curves* (Dublin, 1879), 134.

Every generator of S meets C in two points; so that to any point P of C there correspond the two other points Q_1, Q_2 in which C is met by the generators of S through P. To Q_1 correspond P and another point P_1, while to Q_2 correspond P and another point P_2. We thus have a symmetrical (2, 2) correspondence.

The formulae giving coincidences and branch-points hold for symmetrical correspondences as for other correspondences; but it is important to remark that *the number of pairs of points common to two correspondences as given by Brill's formula must be halved when both the correspondences are symmetrical**.

Still more special correspondences are those known as *involutions*; an involution is a symmetrical correspondence in which a point P and the m points $Q_1, Q_2, \ldots, Q_m$ corresponding to it form a closed set; to any one of them correspond the remaining m. A simple example of an involution is the correspondence between the points of a plane curve of order n which are collinear with a given point O. If P is any point of the curve there are $n-1$ points corresponding to P, namely, the remaining intersections of the curve with the line OP. We thus have a set of n points such that to any one point of the set there correspond the remaining $n-1$; or we have a symmetrical $(n-1, n-1)$ correspondence which is an involution.

An involution, as consisting of ∞^1 sets of points, will have a genus just as will a curve consisting of ∞^1 points. In the example given the involution is rational, its sets being in (1, 1) correspondence with the lines of a plane pencil. We can, however, have involutions of any genus†.

16. *Zeuthen's formula*. There is a formula due to Zeuthen concerning a correspondence between the points of two curves which is of great importance. If we have an (α, α') correspondence between the points of two curves C and C' whose respective genera are p and p', so that to any given point of C there correspond α' points of C' and to any given point of C' there correspond α points of C, and if the correspondence has η branch-points on C and η' branch-points on C', then we have the relation

$$\eta - \eta' = 2\alpha\,(p' - 1) - 2\alpha'\,(p - 1).$$

We shall always refer to this as *Zeuthen's formula*‡. A geometrical interpretation of the formula has been given by Severi§.

If α and α' are both unity then η and η' are both zero; and so two curves in (1, 1) correspondence have the same genus.

* In this case Brill's formula includes each pair twice (from each end it might be said).

† Severi, *Trattato di Geometria Algebrica*, I, 1, 52 (Bologna, 1926).

‡ Zeuthen, *Math. Ann.* 3 (1871), 150.

§ *Rendiconti del Reale Istituto Lombardo* (2), 36 (1903), 495.

The formula is at once verified when the curves are both rational; it becomes then $\eta + 2a = \eta' + 2a'$. But we have already seen* that in such a correspondence $\eta = 2a\,(a' - 1)$ and $\eta' = 2a'\,(a - 1)$, so that

$$\eta + 2a = \eta' + 2a' = 2aa'.$$

17. *The genus of a simple curve on a ruled surface.* One very important application of Zeuthen's formula is the calculation of the genus of a curve on a ruled surface. We suppose that the curve is a simple and not a multiple curve on the surface; so that through a general point of the curve there passes only one generator of the surface.

Suppose that we have in a space $[r]$ a ruled surface of order n and genus p; and suppose that there is on this ruled surface a curve of order ν meeting each generator in k points. Suppose that this curve is of genus π and is touched by η generators. Then Zeuthen's formula gives

$$\eta = 2\,(\pi - 1) - 2k\,(p - 1),$$

there being a $(1, k)$ correspondence between the points of a prime section of the ruled surface and the points of the curve, two points corresponding when they lie on the same generator.

If we take an arbitrary $[r - 2]$ there is a pencil of primes passing through it; we consider the correspondence between primes of this pencil, two primes corresponding when they join $[r - 2]$ to two points of the curve lying on the same generator. Then, since any one of the primes meets the curve in ν points, there are $\nu\,(k - 1)$ primes of the pencil which correspond to it; we have a symmetrical correspondence between the primes of the pencil in which both indices are $\nu\,(k - 1)$. Since Chasles' principle of correspondence can be applied to the primes of this pencil just as it can to the points of a line there will be $2\nu\,(k - 1)$ coincidences of pairs of corresponding primes.

Now these coincidences can occur in two ways; either by the prime passing through one of the η points where the curve touches some generator or by the prime containing one of the generators which pass through the n intersections of $[r - 2]$ with the surface. On each of these generators there are k points of the curve, and we count the prime joining $[r - 2]$ to such a generator $k\,(k - 1)$ times among the coincidences. Hence

$$2\nu\,(k - 1) = \eta + nk\,(k - 1),$$

so that, eliminating η,

$$2\nu\,(k - 1) = 2\,(\pi - 1) - 2k\,(p - 1) + nk\,(k - 1),$$

whence†

$$\pi = (\nu - 1)\,(k - 1) + pk - \tfrac{1}{2}nk\,(k - 1),$$

giving the genus π of the curve in terms of the other constants.

* § 13. † Segre, *Rom. Acc. Lincei Rendiconti* (4), 3^2 (1887), 3.

We have not mentioned the fact that the curve may have double points. If it has, the formula

$$\eta = 2(\pi - 1) - 2k(p - 1)$$

is not altered; but the prime joining $[r - 2]$ to a double point P will count twice among the coincidences provided that P is not also a double point of the ruled surface. The double point must be regarded as two points P_1 and P_2 on different branches of the curve; these are on the same generator, the prime joining $[r - 2]$ to P_1 has the prime joining $[r - 2]$ to P_2 among its corresponding primes and the two coincide; and so with P_1 and P_2 interchanged. Thus

$$2\nu(k - 1) = \eta + nk(k - 1) + 2d,$$

or

$$\pi = (\nu - 1)(k - 1) + pk - \tfrac{1}{2}nk(k - 1) - d,$$

where d is strictly the number of those points of the curve which count twice among the k intersections with a generator*.

18. *The genus of a curve on a quadric.* Suppose, for example, that we have a curve on a quadric surface in [3]; it is clear that any two generators of the same system of this quadric are met by the curve in the same number of points, because planes can be drawn through them and any generator of the opposite system. Suppose then that the curve meets all generators of one system in α points and is of order $\alpha + \beta$, meeting all generators of the other system in β points. Then its genus will be

$$\begin{aligned}\pi &= (\alpha + \beta - 1)(\alpha - 1) - \alpha(\alpha - 1) - d \\ &= (\alpha - 1)(\beta - 1) - d,\end{aligned}$$

where d is the number of double points of the curve. If the curve has no double points then $\pi = (\alpha - 1)(\beta - 1)$.

This result for the genus of a curve on a quadric surface is important and will be of use subsequently. It is obtained at once by projecting the curve from a point on the quadric into a plane curve; if the point of projection is not on the curve we obtain a plane curve of order $\alpha + \beta$ with d double points, a point of multiplicity α and a point of multiplicity β, and therefore of genus

$$\tfrac{1}{2}(\alpha + \beta - 1)(\alpha + \beta - 2) - d - \tfrac{1}{2}\alpha(\alpha - 1) - \tfrac{1}{2}\beta(\beta - 1) = (\alpha - 1)(\beta - 1) - d.$$

If the point of projection is on the curve we obtain a plane curve of order $\alpha + \beta - 1$ with d double points, a point of multiplicity $\alpha - 1$ and a point of multiplicity $\beta - 1$ and therefore of genus

$$\begin{aligned}&\tfrac{1}{2}(\alpha + \beta - 2)(\alpha + \beta - 3) - d - \tfrac{1}{2}(\alpha - 1)(\alpha - 2) - \tfrac{1}{2}(\beta - 1)(\beta - 2) \\ &\qquad = (\alpha - 1)(\beta - 1) - d.\end{aligned}$$

Zeuthen's formula can also be used to find the genus of a curve on a quadric cone. More generally, if we have a cone of order n and genus p

* Segre, *Math. Ann.* 34 (1889), 3.

and on it a curve of order ν meeting every generator in k points other than the vertex, the genus of the curve is given by

$$\pi = (\nu - 1)(k - 1) + pk - \tfrac{1}{2}nk(k - 1)$$

with possibly a reduction for double points*.

19. *The ruled surface generated by a correspondence between two curves.* If in a space $[n]$ we have a correspondence between the points of two curves the lines joining pairs of corresponding points are ∞^1 in aggregate and form a ruled surface.

The order of this ruled surface can be calculated when the properties of the correspondence and of the two curves themselves are known; suppose that the correspondence is an (α, α') correspondence between two curves of orders m and m'. Let us then take a space $[n-2]$ of general position; the order of the ruled surface is the number of its intersections with $[n-2]$, i.e. the number of its generators which meet $[n-2]$, or the number of pairs of corresponding points of the two curves whose joins meet $[n-2]$.

We can set up a correspondence among the primes passing through $[n-2]$, two primes corresponding when they join $[n-2]$ to corresponding points of the two curves. It is clear that the indices of this correspondence are $m'\alpha$ and $m\alpha'$, so that there are $m'\alpha + m\alpha'$ coincidences of pairs of corresponding primes. There is clearly a coincidence when the join of two corresponding points meets $[n-2]$; and, in general, these will be the only coincidences. Hence, in general, the order of the ruled surface is $m'\alpha + m\alpha'$. Through every point of the curve of order m there pass α' generators of the surface, or we shall say that this curve is a multiple curve on the ruled surface of multiplicity α'. Similarly the curve of order m' is a multiple curve on the ruled surface of multiplicity α.

In particular, the order of the ruled surface generated by joining pairs of corresponding points in a $(1, 1)$ correspondence between two curves is, in general, the sum of the orders of the two curves.

The result which we have obtained for the order of the ruled surface is always true except when the $m'\alpha + m\alpha'$ coincidences include primes which do not contain generators of the ruled surface; this can happen only when the curves have one or more intersections which are "united points" of the correspondence. If P is an intersection of the two curves which is a united point then the α' points of the curve of order m', which correspond to P regarded as a point of the curve of order m, include P; and the α points of the curve of order m, which correspond to P regarded as a point of the curve of order m', also include P. Thus the prime joining $[n-2]$

* The result for a curve on a cone was first obtained by Sturm by application of a coincidence formula due to Schubert, *Math. Ann.* 19 (1882), 487.

to P counts among the $m'\alpha + m\alpha'$ coincidences; the generator of the surface joining the pair of points which are united is indeterminate.

It is then clear that the order of the ruled surface is always $m'\alpha + m\alpha'$ when the curves do not intersect; and it also has this value when the curves do intersect unless there are united points. But if there are i united points the order of the ruled surface* is $m'\alpha + m\alpha' - i$. Here again a still further adjustment may be necessary, as the prime joining $[n-2]$ to a united point may count more than once among the $m'\alpha + m\alpha'$ coincidences; it may be that when P is regarded as a point of the curve of order m there are more than one of the α' corresponding points coinciding with it, and inversely. This cannot happen however when we are dealing with a (1, 1) correspondence; and we can always say that *the order of the ruled surface determined by a* (1, 1) *correspondence with i united points between two curves of orders m and m' is $m + m' - i$.*

20. In order to exemplify this last result let us consider in [3] a conic and a line which intersect in a point X.

Suppose that there is a (1, 1) correspondence between them and suppose first that X is not a united point. Then to X regarded as a point of the line there will correspond a point Z of the conic and to X regarded as a point of the conic there will correspond a point T of the line. The line itself will then be a generator of the resulting ruled surface as joining the points X and T, and the line ZX will also be a generator. If the tangents to the conic at Z and X meet in Y, we can take $XYZT$ as the tetrahedron of reference; the equations to the conic are

$$xz - y^2 = t = 0,$$

and to the line

$$y = z = 0.$$

Then any point of the conic has coordinates $(\theta^2, \theta, 1, 0)$, while any point of the line has coordinates $(\phi, 0, 0, 1)$, and the (1, 1) correspondence will be determined by a bilinear relation

$$a\theta\phi + b\theta + c\phi + d = 0.$$

But we already know that to $\phi = \infty$ must correspond $\theta = 0$ and that to $\theta = \infty$ must correspond $\phi = 0$; hence $b = c = 0$ and $\theta\phi$ is constant. We can therefore take

$$\theta\phi = 1$$

* There are always united points if we consider the ruled surface generated by a correspondence between the points of the same curve. If the curve is of genus p and the correspondence of valency γ it has $\alpha + \alpha' + 2\gamma p$ united points, and the order of the ruled surface will be $m(\alpha + \alpha') - (\alpha + \alpha' + 2\gamma p)$, where m is the order of the curve. But if the correspondence is a symmetrical correspondence of index α this number will have to be halved; the order of the ruled surface is then $\alpha(m-1) - \gamma p$. Thus, in particular, the order of the ruled surface formed by the joins of pairs of an involution of pairs of points on a rational curve is $m - 1$, on an elliptic curve $m - 2$. A curve which is neither rational nor elliptic and which possesses an ordinary (rational) involution of pairs of points is always hyperelliptic; for such a curve the order of the ruled surface is $m - p - 1$.

as giving the correspondence, and a generator of the ruled surface joins the two points

$$(\theta^2, \theta, 1, 0) \text{ and } (1, 0, 0, \theta).$$

Hence the coordinates of any point of the ruled surface are of the form

$$(\theta^2 + \lambda, \theta, 1, \lambda\theta).$$

If θ is constant we have the points of a generator of the surface, and if λ is constant we have the points of a conic on the surface lying in a plane through XZ.

The coordinates satisfy the homogeneous cubic relation

$$xyz = y^3 + tz^2,$$

so that we have a ruled surface of the third order.

But suppose now that the (1, 1) correspondence between the line and conic is such that X is a united point. Then to a definite point T of the line will correspond a definite point Z of the conic, and our coordinates are as before with the bilinear relation

$$a\theta\phi + b\theta + c\phi + d = 0.$$

Now to $\theta = \infty$ corresponds $\phi = \infty$ so that $a = 0$, and to $\theta = 0$ corresponds $\phi = 0$ so that $d = 0$; hence θ is a constant multiple of ϕ and we can take without loss of generality

$$\theta = \phi.$$

Then a generator of the ruled surface joins the two points

$$(\theta^2, \theta, 1, 0) \text{ and } (\theta, 0, 0, 1),$$

and the coordinates of any point on the ruled surface are of the form

$$(\theta^2 + \lambda\theta, \theta, 1, \lambda).$$

These satisfy the homogeneous quadratic relation

$$xz = y^2 + ty,$$

so that when there is a united point the ruled surface is only of the second order.

21. Just as, given two curves of orders m and m' in (α, α') correspondence in [3], there are (subject to a deduction for united points) $m'\alpha + m\alpha'$ joins of pairs of corresponding points which meet an arbitrary line; so, dually, given two developables of classes m and m' in (α, α') correspondence in [3], there are (subject to a deduction for united planes) $m'\alpha + m\alpha'$ intersections of pairs of corresponding planes which meet an arbitrary line. Or we can say that the two developables give a ruled surface of order $m'\alpha + m\alpha'$.

In space of three dimensions we have three fundamental constructs; *curves* formed by singly infinite families of points, *ruled surfaces* formed by singly infinite families of lines, and *developables* formed by singly infinite families of planes. We have seen how a ruled surface can be generated either by joining pairs of corresponding points on two curves or by taking the intersections of pairs of corresponding planes of two developables, and how the order of such a ruled surface is given in terms of the orders of the two curves or the classes of the two developables and the constants of the correspondence.

22. It is also clear that if a correspondence is set up between the points of a curve and the generators of a ruled surface the planes so determined, as joining the points of the curve to those generators of the ruled surface which correspond to them, form a developable; and, dually, if a correspondence is set up between the planes of a developable and the generators of a ruled surface, the points of intersection of corresponding planes and lines form a curve.

Let us consider then a curve of order m and a ruled surface of order μ; suppose that to any point of the curve there correspond α generators of the ruled surface and that to any generator of the ruled surface there correspond a points of the curve. Let us calculate the class of the developable so formed; i.e. the number of its planes passing through any given point O.

We set up a correspondence between the points P and Q of the curve; the points P and Q corresponding when the line OP meets a generator of the ruled surface which corresponds to Q. Then given a point P, the line OP meets the ruled surface in μ points, and each of the generators through these points gives a points Q; so that when P is given there are μa positions of Q. Given a point Q, we have α generators of the ruled surface, each of which is joined to O by a plane meeting the curve in m points; so that when Q is given there are $m\alpha$ positions of P. The correspondence from P to Q is therefore an $(m\alpha, \mu a)$ correspondence. The correspondence is of valency zero; the points P corresponding to a given point Q form the complete intersection of the curve with a set of α planes through O. Hence there are $m\alpha + \mu a$ coincidences of points P and Q; and such a coincidence means that the plane joining a point of the curve to a corresponding generator of the ruled surface passes through O. This will be a plane of the developable unless the point of the curve happens to lie on the corresponding generator of the ruled surface; when this happens the plane of the developable is indeterminate.

Hence, subject to a deduction for united elements of the correspondence, the class of the developable is $m\alpha + \mu a$.

In particular, *if we have a* (1, 1) *correspondence between the points of a curve of order m and the generators of a ruled surface of order μ, and if there are i points of the curve which lie on the corresponding generators of the ruled surface, the planes joining corresponding elements form a developable of class $m + \mu - i$.*

If we have a (1, 1) correspondence between the points of a line and the lines of a regulus* the planes joining corresponding elements give a develop-

* The word *regulus* is used to denote either system of generators of a quadric surface. It is thus a ruled surface of the second order; the other system of generators of the quadric are not, strictly speaking, generators, but *directrices* of this surface.

able of the third class*, supposing that neither of the points in which the line meets the regulus lies on the line which corresponds to it; if however one of the two lines of the regulus which meet the line does so in the point corresponding to it the developable is only of the second class; while if both lines of the regulus which meet the line do so in the points corresponding to them we have a developable of the first class. In the first case we have the osculating planes of a twisted cubic, in the second the tangent planes of a quadric cone and in the third a pencil of planes through a line.

Analytically, let the line meet the regulus in the points X and Z; through X there passes a generator of the quadric surface on which the regulus lies meeting the line of the regulus through Z in T; similarly, Y is the point in which the line of the regulus through X is met by the generator of the complementary regulus through Z.

Then any line of the regulus is given as the intersection of two planes

$$y = \theta z, \qquad x = \theta t,$$

the line XY being given by $\theta = \infty$ and the line ZT by $\theta = 0$.

Any point of the line XZ is given by $(\phi, 0, 1, 0)$, the point X being given by $\phi = \infty$ and the point Z by $\phi = 0$.

We then set up a correspondence between θ and ϕ and join lines of the regulus to corresponding points of XZ by planes.

If $\phi = \dfrac{\theta + \beta}{\theta + \gamma}$ the planes are given by

$$(\theta + \beta)(y - \theta z) + \theta(\theta + \gamma)(x - \theta t) = 0,$$

and involve the parameter θ in the third degree.

If $\phi = \theta + \alpha$ then $\theta = \infty$ gives the point X of the line corresponding to the line XY of the regulus. The planes are given by

$$(\theta + \alpha)(y - \theta z) + \theta(x - \theta t) = 0,$$

and involve the parameter θ in the second degree.

If $\phi = \theta$ then $\theta = \infty$ gives the point X of the line corresponding to the line XY of the regulus, while $\theta = 0$ gives the point Z of the line corresponding to the line ZT of the regulus. The planes are given by

$$y - \theta z + x - \theta t = 0,$$

and involve the parameter θ in the first degree.

23. Dually, if we have a (1, 1) correspondence between the planes of a developable of class m and the generators of a ruled surface of order μ, and if there are i planes of the developable which contain the corresponding generators of the ruled surface, the points of intersection of corresponding elements form a curve of order $m + \mu - i$.

A pencil of planes and the generators of a quadric cone when projectively related give a twisted cubic, provided that no plane of the pencil contains

* von Staudt, *Beiträge zur Geometrie der Lage*, 3 (Nürnberg, 1860), 303; Reye, *Geometrie der Lage*, 2 (Stuttgart, 1907), 168.

the corresponding generator of the cone. A regulus and a pencil of planes when projectively related give a twisted cubic, provided that no line of the regulus lies in the plane which corresponds to it.

24. We may observe still further that if we have three curves in correspondence the planes joining corresponding triads of points, one point of such a triad being on each curve, will form a developable; while if we have three developables in correspondence the points of intersection of triads of corresponding planes, one plane of such a triad belonging to each developable, will form a curve. The generation of the twisted cubic by three related pencils of planes is familiar.

SECTION II

THE REPRESENTATION OF A RULED SURFACE IN THREE DIMENSIONS AS A CURVE ON A QUADRIC Ω IN FIVE DIMENSIONS

25. The lines of three-dimensional space are ∞^4 in aggregate; a line can be determined by four parameters or by the ratios of five parameters. The most convenient representation of the lines of three-dimensional space is, however, by means of the ratios of six parameters which are connected by one relation, thus being reduced effectively to five*.

Using homogeneous coordinates, let (x_1, y_1, z_1, t_1) and (x_2, y_2, z_2, t_2) be two points; and write

$$l = t_1x_2 - t_2x_1, \qquad m = t_1y_2 - t_2y_1, \qquad n = t_1z_2 - t_2z_1,$$
$$l' = y_1z_2 - y_2z_1, \qquad m' = z_1x_2 - z_2x_1, \qquad n' = x_1y_2 - x_2y_1.$$

* See Cayley, "On a new analytical representation of curves in space," *Papers*, 4 (1860), 446, where a curve is given by the complex of lines which meet it; Grassmann, *Ausdehnungslehre* (Berlin, 1862), §§ 63–65; Plücker, "On a new geometry of space," *Phil. Trans.* 155 (1865); Cayley, "On the six coordinates of a line," *Papers*, 7 (1869), 66.

From Grassmann it is clearly seen how to determine a system of coordinates for spaces of any dimension in a space of dimension n.

If we take the two points (x_1, y_1, z_1, t_1) and (x_2, y_2, z_2, t_2) of space and form the combinatory product

$$(e_1x_1 + e_2y_1 + e_3z_1 + e_4t_1)\,(e_1x_2 + e_2y_2 + e_3z_2 + e_4t_2),$$

where $e_r^2 = 0$ and $e_re_s = -e_se_r$, we have a linear function of the six coordinates of the line joining the two points.

Given a space $[k]$ in $[n]$, we take $k + 1$ independent points of the $[k]$ and write down the matrix of $k + 1$ rows and $n + 1$ columns formed by the coordinates of these points. Then the coordinates of $[k]$ are simply the $(k + 1)$-rowed determinants of the matrix, which cannot all vanish if the points are independent. These determinants also arise in combinatory products (Grassmann, *ibid.*). They are sometimes spoken of as Grassmann coordinates.

The idea of a line in [3] being linearly dependent on the six edges of a tetrahedron occurs in Grassmann's *Ausdehnungslehre* (Leipzig, 1844), 167.

Then the six quantities (l, m, n, l', m', n') are called the *coordinates of the line* joining the two points. We are justified in speaking of them in this way because their mutual ratios are the same whatever two points of the line are taken; if instead of (x_1, y_1, z_1, t_1) and (x_2, y_2, z_2, t_2) we take the points

$$(\theta x_1 + \phi x_2, \theta y_1 + \phi y_2, \theta z_1 + \phi z_2, \theta t_1 + \phi t_2)$$

and $$(\theta' x_1 + \phi' x_2, \theta' y_1 + \phi' y_2, \theta' z_1 + \phi' z_2, \theta' t_1 + \phi' t_2),$$

the six coordinates are each multiplied by $\theta\phi' - \theta'\phi$.

The lines whose coordinates satisfy a single relation are said to form a *complex* of lines; in particular, the linear relation

$$a'l + b'm + c'n + al' + bm' + cn' = 0$$

gives a *linear complex**. The lines whose coordinates satisfy simultaneously two linear relations are said to form a *linear congruence* of lines.

The six coordinates of any line satisfy the relation

$$ll' + mm' + nn' = 0.$$

Conversely, it can be shewn that any six quantities connected by this relation can be taken as the coordinates of a line.

26. If the line λ_1 joining (x_1, y_1, z_1, t_1) to (x_2, y_2, z_2, t_2) has coordinates $(l_1, m_1, n_1, l_1', m_1', n_1')$ and the line λ_2 joining $(\xi_1, \eta_1, \zeta_1, \tau_1)$ to $(\xi_2, \eta_2, \zeta_2, \tau_2)$ has coordinates $(l_2, m_2, n_2, l_2', m_2', n_2')$ the condition that the two lines should intersect is the same condition that the four points should be coplanar, or

$$\begin{vmatrix} x_1 & y_1 & z_1 & t_1 \\ x_2 & y_2 & z_2 & t_2 \\ \xi_1 & \eta_1 & \zeta_1 & \tau_1 \\ \xi_2 & \eta_2 & \zeta_2 & \tau_2 \end{vmatrix} = 0,$$

which is $$\varpi_{12} \equiv l_1 l_2' + m_1 m_2' + n_1 n_2' + l_1' l_2 + m_1' m_2 + n_1' n_2 = 0.$$

If this condition is satisfied, the six quantities

$$\kappa_1 l_1 + \kappa_2 l_2,\quad \kappa_1 m_1 + \kappa_2 m_2,\quad \kappa_1 n_1 + \kappa_2 n_2,\quad \kappa_1 l_1' + \kappa_2 l_2',$$
$$\kappa_1 m_1' + \kappa_2 m_2',\quad \kappa_1 n_1' + \kappa_2 n_2',$$

satisfy the condition

$$(\kappa_1 l_1 + \kappa_2 l_2)(\kappa_1 l_1' + \kappa_2 l_2') + (\kappa_1 m_1 + \kappa_2 m_2)(\kappa_1 m_1' + \kappa_2 m_2')$$
$$+ (\kappa_1 n_1 + \kappa_2 n_2)(\kappa_1 n_1' + \kappa_2 n_2') = 0$$

* Geometrical properties of the linear complex were studied before the coordinates of a line were introduced. See Möbius, "Über eine besondere Art dualer Verhältnisse zwischen Figuren im Raume," *Journal für Math.* 10 (1833), 317, or *Gesammelte Werke*, 1, 491.

for all values of $\kappa_1 : \kappa_2$; they are therefore the coordinates of a line which may be denoted symbolically by $\kappa_1\lambda_1 + \kappa_2\lambda_2$. Since the condition that two lines should intersect is linear in the coordinates of each line, any line which is met by both λ_1 and λ_2 must also be met by all the lines $\kappa_1\lambda_1 + \kappa_2\lambda_2$. Hence the line $\kappa_1\lambda_1 + \kappa_2\lambda_2$ is a line passing through the intersection of λ_1 and λ_2 and lying in their plane; the different lines of this plane pencil are given by the different values of the ratio $\kappa_1 : \kappa_2$.

If we have three lines λ_1, λ_2, λ_3 the relation

$$\begin{aligned}(\kappa_1 l_1 + \kappa_2 l_2 + \kappa_3 l_3)(\kappa_1 l_1' + \kappa_2 l_2' + \kappa_3 l_3') \\ + (\kappa_1 m_1 + \kappa_2 m_2 + \kappa_3 m_3)(\kappa_1 m_1' + \kappa_2 m_2' + \kappa_3 m_3') \\ + (\kappa_1 n_1 + \kappa_2 n_2 + \kappa_3 n_3)(\kappa_1 n_1' + \kappa_2 n_2' + \kappa_3 n_3') = 0\end{aligned}$$

is
$$\varpi_{23}\kappa_2\kappa_3 + \varpi_{31}\kappa_3\kappa_1 + \varpi_{12}\kappa_1\kappa_2 = 0.$$

There are ∞^1 sets of values of $\kappa_1 : \kappa_2 : \kappa_3$ satisfying this condition; and for such a set of values we have a line which may be represented symbolically by $\kappa_1\lambda_1 + \kappa_2\lambda_2 + \kappa_3\lambda_3$. This meets all the lines which meet λ_1, λ_2 and λ_3 and we thus obtain one system of generators of a quadric surface.

This supposes that the lines λ_1, λ_2, λ_3 are of general position; but if they all intersect one another we have $\varpi_{23} = \varpi_{31} = \varpi_{12} = 0$, and

$$\kappa_1\lambda_1 + \kappa_2\lambda_2 + \kappa_3\lambda_3$$

is a line for all the ∞^2 values of $\kappa_1 : \kappa_2 : \kappa_3$. Now λ_1, λ_2, λ_3 are either concurrent or coplanar; if they are concurrent $\kappa_1\lambda_1 + \kappa_2\lambda_2 + \kappa_3\lambda_3$ will be a line through their intersection, and the ∞^2 lines through their intersection are obtainable in this way; if they are coplanar $\kappa_1\lambda_1 + \kappa_2\lambda_2 + \kappa_3\lambda_3$ will be a line in their plane, and the ∞^2 lines in their plane are obtainable in this way.

If we have a linear complex

$$a'l + b'm + c'n + al' + bm' + cn' = 0,$$

for which
$$aa' + bb' + cc' = 0,$$

the linear complex is said to be special. It consists of all the lines meeting the line whose coordinates are (a, b, c, a', b', c').

27. *Line geometry in [3] considered as the point geometry of a quadric primal in* [5]. If we have six quantities (l, m, n, l', m', n') satisfying the relation $ll' + mm' + nn' = 0$ they can be regarded as the homogeneous coordinates of a point in [5] which lies on a quadric primal Ω. This quadric Ω is a general quadric; the left-hand side of its equation can be written as the sum of six squares.

Thus we have a correspondence between the lines of [3] and the points of Ω; to every line of [3] corresponds a point of Ω, while to every point of Ω corresponds a line of [3]. There are no exceptions. Hence *line geometry* *in* [3] *is exactly the same as the geometry of a quadric primal* Ω *in* [5]*, and it will be found that great simplifications arise from this point of view.

28. If we take a definite point $(\lambda, \mu, \nu, \lambda', \mu', \nu')$ of Ω and join it to an arbitrary point (l, m, n, l', m', n') of [5] the coordinates of any point on the joining line are of the form

$$(\theta\lambda + \phi l, \quad \theta\mu + \phi m, \quad \theta\nu + \phi n, \quad \theta\lambda' + \phi l', \quad \theta\mu' + \phi m', \quad \theta\nu' + \phi n'),$$

and this will lie on Ω if

$$\theta^2 (\lambda\lambda' + \mu\mu' + \nu\nu') + \theta\phi (\lambda l' + \mu m' + \nu n' + \lambda' l + \mu' m + \nu' n) + \phi^2 (ll' + mm' + nn') = 0.$$

This is satisfied by $\phi = 0$ as we should expect; it will have a double root $\phi = 0$ if

$$l\lambda' + m\mu' + n\nu' + l'\lambda + m'\mu + n'\nu = 0.$$

This equation, linear in (l, m, n, l', m', n'), is the equation of a [4]; this [4] is such that the line joining any point of it to $(\lambda, \mu, \nu, \lambda', \mu', \nu')$ touches Ω at this last point. Or the lines which touch Ω at any point lie in a prime—the *tangent prime* of Ω at the point; and the equation to the tangent prime at $(\lambda, \mu, \nu, \lambda', \mu', \nu')$ is

$$l\lambda' + m\mu' + n\nu' + l'\lambda + m'\mu + n'\nu = 0.$$

Clearly if a point P_1 of Ω lies in the tangent prime at a second point P_2 of Ω the point P_2 will lie in the tangent prime at P_1. The line P_1P_2 will then lie entirely on Ω; all tangents of Ω which meet it in points other than their points of contact must lie entirely on Ω as meeting it in at least three points. Two points of Ω which are such that either lies in the tangent prime at the other will be spoken of as *conjugate*.

It is then clear from the condition $\varpi_{12} = 0$ that two lines λ_1, λ_2 of [3] which intersect are represented on Ω by two conjugate points P_1, P_2. Then the six quantities

$$\kappa_1 l_1 + \kappa_2 l_2, \quad \kappa_1 m_1 + \kappa_2 m_2, \quad \kappa_1 n_1 + \kappa_2 n_2, \quad \kappa_1 l_1' + \kappa_2 l_2', \quad \kappa_1 m_1' + \kappa_2 m_2', \quad \kappa_1 n_1' + \kappa_2 n_2'$$

are the coordinates of a point of the line P_1P_2; since this line lies on Ω, the point must lie on Ω and therefore represents a line of [3] for all values of $\kappa_1 : \kappa_2$. Hence the points of a line on Ω represent the lines of a plane pencil in [3].

Corresponding to any line λ of [3] we have a point P of Ω; the lines of [3] which meet λ are represented on Ω by its intersection with the tangent prime at P.

* Klein, "Über Liniengeometrie und metrische Geometrie," *Math. Ann.* 5 (1872), 257, or *Gesammelte Mathematische Abhandlungen*, 1, 106; Cayley, *Papers*, 9 (1873), 79. The theory is greatly developed by Segre in his paper "Sulla geometria della retta e delle sue serie quadratiche," *Memorie Torino*, 36 (1883). See also Baker, *Principles of Geometry*, 4 (Cambridge, 1925), 40 *et seq.*

The lines of a linear complex are represented by the points of a prime section of Ω; but for a special linear complex we must take the section by a tangent prime.

29. *The planes* on* Ω. Consider now three points P_1, P_2, P_3 of Ω, each pair of which is a pair of conjugate points. Then these represent three lines $\lambda_1, \lambda_2, \lambda_3$ of [3] for which $\varpi_{23} = \varpi_{31} = \varpi_{12} = 0$. The lines P_2P_3, P_3P_1, P_1P_2 all lie on Ω; so that the plane $P_1P_2P_3$ meets Ω in a curve whose order is greater than two, and lies on Ω entirely. Then the point whose six coordinates are of the form $\kappa_1 l_1 + \kappa_2 l_2 + \kappa_3 l_3$ lies on Ω for all values of $\kappa_1 : \kappa_2 : \kappa_3$ and represents a line $\kappa_1\lambda_1 + \kappa_2\lambda_2 + \kappa_3\lambda_3$ of [3]. We thus obtain every point of the plane $P_1P_2P_3$.

We thus have two systems of planes on Ω; the points of a plane of the first system represent the lines through a point of [3], while the points of a plane of the second system represent the lines in a plane of [3]. We shall call the planes of the first system, representing lines through points of [3], ϖ-planes and the planes of the second system, representing lines in planes of [3], ρ-planes. Since there is one and only one line passing through two given points of [3] two ϖ-planes have one and only one point in common; and since there is one and only one line lying in two given planes of [3] two ρ-planes have one and only one point in common; two planes of the same system on Ω meet in a point. Given a point and a plane of [3], there will not be a line passing through the point and lying in the plane unless the point itself lies in the plane, so that two planes of Ω of opposite systems do not in general intersect. If however the point does lie in the plane we have a pencil of lines passing through the point and lying in the plane; hence if two planes of opposite systems on Ω do intersect they have a line in common.

On Ω there are ∞^3 planes of each system; through any point of Ω there pass ∞^1 of each system. There are also on Ω ∞^5 lines, ∞^2 passing through any given point on Ω†.

30. *The quadric point-cone in* [4]. We can now give a detailed description of the section of Ω by the tangent prime at a point P. The point P represents a line λ of [3]; on λ there are ∞^1 points and through λ there pass ∞^1 planes. Hence there are ∞^1 ϖ-planes on Ω and ∞^1 ρ-planes on Ω all passing through P. Two of these planes which belong to the same system will not intersect except in P, but two planes of opposite systems

* The two systems of planes on Ω are mentioned explicitly by Cayley, *Papers*, 9 (1873), 79.

† Cf. Segre, "Studio sulle quadriche in uno spazio lineare ad un numero qualunque di dimensione," *Memorie Torino*, 36 (1883), in particular p. 36.

will intersect in a line through P. The section of Ω by the tangent prime at P is nothing but these two sets of planes, since any point of Ω lying in the tangent prime represents a line of [3] meeting λ. Such a line in [3] meets λ in a point and is joined to λ by a plane, so that the representative point on Ω lies in two planes, one of each system. The line of intersection of these two planes joins the representative point to P.

If we take a section by a [3] lying in the tangent prime and not passing through P we obtain two systems each of ∞^1 lines; two lines of the same system do not intersect but every line of either system meets every line of the other; in other words, we have the two systems of generators of a quadric surface. Thus the section of Ω by a tangent prime is the same locus as is obtained by joining the generators of a quadric surface, by planes, to a point outside the [3] in which the quadric surface lies. This locus in [4] is called a *quadric point-cone**.

If we have a curve lying on a quadric point-cone in [4] and project it on to a [3] from the vertex of the point-cone we obtain a curve lying on the quadric in which [3] meets the point-cone. Thus, from a knowledge of the properties of this projected curve, we shall be able to deduce certain properties of the curve on the cone.

The section of a quadric point-cone by a [3] through its vertex is an ordinary quadric cone, unless the [3] is that determined by two planes of opposite systems of the point-cone; it then meets the point-cone simply in these two planes. Such a [3] is called a *tangent solid* of the point-cone; there are ∞^3 [3]'s through the vertex, ∞^2 of which are tangent solids.

31. *The representation of a ruled surface*. Since a line of [3] is represented by a point of Ω, a ruled surface f in [3] formed by ∞^1 lines will be represented by the curve C on Ω formed by the ∞^1 representative points†. There is thus a (1, 1) correspondence between C and the generators of f, so that the genus of C is equal to the genus of f. Moreover, the order of the ruled surface, being equal to the number of its generators which meet an arbitrary line λ of [3], is equal to the number of intersections of C with the tangent prime at an arbitrary point P of Ω, and this is simply the order of C. Thus we can say that *a ruled surface f of order n and genus p in* [3] *is represented on Ω by a curve C of order n and genus p.*

We thus see how to begin the classification of ruled surfaces mentioned in § 12. We have first to investigate how the double curve and bitangent developable can be studied by means of the curve C on Ω. Then, taking C to be of a given order and genus, different positions of C on Ω will give different kinds of double curves and bitangent developables for f.

* Cf. Baker, *Principles of Geometry*, 4 (Cambridge, 1925), 120–121.

† Cf. Voss, "Zur Theorie der windschiefen Flächen," *Math. Ann.* 8 (1874), 54. Segre, *Memorie Torino*, 36 (1883), 97.

A given generator g of f is represented on Ω by a point P of C. All generators of f which meet g are represented on Ω by points of C which lie in the tangent prime of Ω at P; but this tangent prime, meeting C twice at P, will meet it in $n - 2$ other points, where n is the order of f and C. Hence *every generator of f is met by $n - 2$ others* (cf. § 10).

32. *Torsal generators.* If we set up a correspondence between the points P and Q of C, saying that two points P and Q correspond when the chord PQ lies on Ω, we have a symmetrical $(n - 2, n - 2)$ correspondence. This correspondence is of valency 2 since the $n - 2$ points Q which correspond to any point P, when taken together with P counted twice, form the complete intersection of C with a prime. Hence the number of coincidences in the correspondence is

$$n - 2 + n - 2 + 2 . 2 . p = 2 (n + 2p - 2),$$

where p is the genus of C.

This means that, for $2 (n + 2p - 2)$ points P of C, there are only $n - 3$ chords of C passing through P and lying on Ω; the tangent of C at P lies on Ω, and the tangent prime of Ω at P meets C in three points there.

Then on the ruled surface f we can say that there are $2 (n + 2p - 2)$ generators which meet their "consecutive generators." Such generators are called *torsal generators*; the tangent plane to the ruled surface is the same for all points of such a generator. Thus a ruled surface of order n and genus p has, in general*, $2 (n + 2p - 2)$ torsal generators.

Incidentally we have proved that, if a curve of order n and genus p lies on a quadric primal in space of any number of dimensions, there are $2 (n + 2p - 2)$ tangents of the curve lying on the quadric*. This is easily verified for simple curves on an ordinary quadric surface in [3].

33. *The double curve and bitangent developable.* The degree of the double curve of the ruled surface f in [3] is the number of points in which it meets an arbitrary plane. Now the lines of such a plane are represented by the points of a ρ-plane on Ω, while the lines (including two generators of f) which pass through a point of the double curve are represented by the points of a ϖ-plane (meeting C in two points). Thus corresponding to each intersection of the double curve with a definite plane of [3] we have a ϖ-plane meeting C twice and meeting a definite ρ-plane in a line; or we have a chord of C lying on Ω and meeting the ρ-plane. Conversely, corresponding to each chord of C which meets a definite ρ-plane (and incidentally lies on Ω as meeting it in at least three points) we have two generators of f intersecting on a definite plane of [3]. Thus *the order of the double curve of f is equal to the number of chords of C which meet any given ρ-plane of*

* If C has κ cusps then the number of tangents of C which lie on Ω is only $2(n + 2p - 2) - 2\kappa$, see § 349 below.

general position. Similarly, *the class of the bitangent developable of f is equal to the number of chords of C which meet any given ϖ-plane of general position.* These two results are fundamental.

The chords of C which lie on Ω form a ruled surface R_2 on which C is a multiple curve of multiplicity $n-2$. The two points of C on a chord which lies on Ω represent two intersecting generators of f, and conversely. The generators of R_2 are thus in $(1, 1)$ correspondence both with the points of the double curve and with the planes of the bitangent developable of f. A prime section of R_2 is thus a curve whose genus is equal to that of the double curve of f and also to that of the bitangent developable of f. We can calculate this genus in the general case.

Denote a prime section of R_2 by C', and consider the $(2, n-2)$ correspondence between C and C', two points of C and C' corresponding when the line joining them is a chord of C. The number of branch-points of the correspondence on C' is simply the number of tangents of C which lie on Ω; this we have seen to be $2(n+2p-2)$. The number of branch-points of the correspondence on C is equal to the number of points P of C at which two of the $n-2$ generators of R_2 coincide. This is equal to the number of times two of the $n-2$ points Q coincide in an $(n-2, n-2)$ correspondence of valency 2 on a curve of genus p; this number* is

$$2(n-2)(n-3)+2(n-6)p.$$

Hence, applying Zeuthen's formula to the correspondence between C and C', we have, if P is the genus of C',

$$2(n-2)(n-3)+2(n-6)p-2(n+2p-2) = 4(P-1)-2(n-2)(p-1),$$

or

$$2P-2=(n-5)(n+2p-2)\dagger,$$

giving, for a ruled surface of order n and genus p, the genus P of the double curve and the bitangent developable.

34. When the ruled surface f in [3] is not completely general for its order and genus the double curve and bitangent developable may break up; when this happens the ruled surface R_2 formed by the chords of C lying on Ω will have to break up correspondingly. For each part of the double curve and bitangent developable we have a set of pairs of intersecting generators of f and thus a set of chords of C lying on Ω and forming

* See § 14.

† This result is deducible from formulae given by Salmon for the theory of reciprocal surfaces; see his *Geometry of Three Dimensions*, 2 (Dublin, 1915), 301. The application to a ruled surface is given by Cayley, *Papers*, 8 (1871), 396. If q is the rank and b the order of the double curve

$$q=2b+2P-2 \quad\text{and}\quad b=\tfrac{1}{2}(n-1)(n-2)-p.$$

The actual form of the result as here stated is given by Wiman, *Acta Mathematica*, 19 (1865), 66.

a ruled surface, say S_2, which is the corresponding part of R_2. The order of this part of the double curve of f is equal to the number of generators of S_2 which meet a definite ρ-plane, and the class of the corresponding part of the bitangent developable of f is equal to the number of generators of S_2 which meet a definite ϖ-plane. The genus of the prime sections of S_2 gives the genus of these parts of the double curve and bitangent developable.

As well as investigating the properties of the component parts of the double curve we can investigate their relations with one another, and similarly for the parts of the bitangent developable. To do this we have to study the relations between the different component ruled surfaces which constitute R_2.

35. Given a ruled surface in [3] there is, in general, a finite number of points which are *triple points* of the surface; through such points there pass three generators of the surface and they are also triple points of the double curve. Similarly we have, in general, a finite number of planes which are *tritangent planes* of the surface; in such planes there lie three generators of the surface and they are triple planes of the bitangent developable.

When the ruled surface is represented as a curve C on Ω the triple points give ϖ-planes of Ω trisecant to C, while the tritangent planes give ρ-planes of Ω trisecant to C; there is a finite number of trisecant planes of C lying on Ω. There are ∞^3 planes on Ω; and since Ω is a four-dimensional locus one condition will be necessary in order that a plane and a curve which lie on it should intersect; thus three conditions must be imposed on a plane of Ω to make it a trisecant plane of C, so that we naturally expect a finite number of such planes.

Denote for the moment the curve C of order n and genus p by C_n^p; the number of its trisecant planes lying on Ω can be calculated directly by correspondence theory.

If we take any point X on C_n^p there are $n-2$ chords of C_n^p passing through it which lie on Ω; these meet C_n^p again in points $X_1, X_2, \ldots, X_{n-2}$. We have already noticed that the correspondence between X and X_r is a symmetrical $(n-2, n-2)$ correspondence of valency 2.

In the same way each point X_r gives rise to $n-2$ points

$$X, X_r^{(1)}, \ldots, X_r^{(n-3)}.$$

Then the correspondence between X and $X_r^{(s)}$ is also symmetrical and both its indices are $(n-2)(n-3)$. The points corresponding to X are found by taking the square* of the former correspondence and leaving

* See Severi, *Memorie Torino* (2), 54 (1904), 5–9.

out the point X each of the $n-2$ times it occurs. Hence the valency is*

$$-(2)^2+n-2=n-6.$$

Since both the correspondences are symmetrical the number of common pairs of points is half that given by Brill's formula†, and is therefore

$$N=\tfrac{1}{2}\{(n-2)^2(n-3)+(n-2)^2(n-3)-2\,.\,2(n-6)p\}$$
$$=(n-2)^2(n-3)-2(n-6)p.$$

This result means that there are N points X on C_n^p such that some point X_α coincides with some point $X_\beta^{(\gamma)}$. In particular the suffixes α and β may be the same; and then the tangent of C_n^p at X_α lies on Ω. There are $2(n+2p-2)$ such points on C_n^p; and through each one of these there pass $n-3$ proper chords of C_n^p which lie on Ω; each of these chords meets C_n^p again in a point X which is included in the above N points. Thus the remaining points X are in number

$$(n-2)^2(n-3)-2(n-6)p-2(n-3)(n+2p-2)$$
$$=(n-2)(n-3)(n-4)-6(n-4)p.$$

Then for any one of these points X we have X_α and $X_\beta^{(\gamma)}$ coinciding, where α and β are not the same. This means that the chords XX_α, XX_β, $X_\alpha X_\beta$ all lie on Ω; so that $XX_\alpha X_\beta$ is a trisecant plane of C_n^p lying on Ω.

Thus these points X occur in groups of three, each group determining a trisecant plane of C_n^p which lies on Ω. Hence the number of trisecant planes of C_n^p which lie on Ω is

$$(n-4)\{\tfrac{1}{3}(n-2)(n-3)-2p\}.$$

These trisecant planes of C which lie on Ω belong half to one system of planes and half to the other. Thus, given a ruled surface of order n and genus p in [3], the number of its triple points is‡

$$\tfrac{1}{6}(n-2)(n-3)(n-4)-(n-4)p,$$

and this is also the number of its tritangent planes.

36. A conic C on Ω represents a ruled surface in [3] of the second order, or the points of C represent *one system* of generators of a quadric surface. We have in fact already noticed¶ that such a system of lines in [3] is represented by coplanar points on Ω. It is implied that the plane of C does not lie entirely on Ω. The coordinates of any point of C being of the form $\kappa_1 l_1+\kappa_2 l_2+\kappa_3 l_3$, the equation to the tangent prime there is

$$\kappa_1 T_1+\kappa_2 T_2+\kappa_3 T_3=0,$$

* Severi, *ibid.* The "product" of two correspondences whose valencies are γ_1 and γ_2 has the valency $-\gamma_1\gamma_2$.

† § 15.

‡ See the references to Cayley and Wiman in § 33. Also Castelnuovo, *Palermo Rendiconti*, 3 (1889), 33.

¶ § 26.

where $T_1 = 0$, $T_2 = 0$, $T_3 = 0$ are the tangent primes at three definite points of C, so that the tangent primes of Ω at all the points of C have in common the plane $T_1 = T_2 = T_3 = 0$. This plane meets Ω in a second conic C', and the tangent primes of Ω at all the points of C' all contain the plane of C. The lines represented by the points of C' meet all the lines represented by the points of C and conversely; thus C and C' give in [3] complementary reguli on the same quadric surface. There is no double curve or bitangent developable.

If the plane of C is a ϖ-plane we have the generators of a quadric cone, and if it is a ρ-plane we have the tangents of a plane conic. Clearly we can have point-cones and plane-envelopes represented on Ω in this way by curves of all orders and genera; in future these will be ignored.

37. *Cubic ruled surfaces.* As an application of the theory we will investigate the ruled surfaces of the third order in [3]. For this we have to consider cubic curves on Ω, and the only relevant curve is the twisted cubic C of S_3. The plane cubic is irrelevant, because if a plane cubic curve lies on a quadric the whole of its plane must do so, and we have the case mentioned at the end of § 36.

In general, S_3 meets Ω in a quadric surface Q; C will meet all the generators of one system of Q in two points and all of the other system in one point*. Through S_3 there pass two tangent primes of Ω, touching it in two points O and O'†. These two points represent two lines R and R', and every generator of the surface meets these two lines. The surface has therefore two directrices, where we define a directrix to be a line which is met by every generator of the surface.

The tangent prime at O meets Ω in a quadric point-cone containing Q; the two systems of planes on the point-cone passing through the two systems of generators on Q. We may suppose that that system of generators which are chords of C lie in the ϖ-planes through O; these same generators will then lie in the ρ-planes through O'.

Hence through any point of R there pass two generators lying in a plane through R', while any plane through R' contains two generators meeting in a point of R.

We have thus established a geometrical connection between the facts that

(*a*) a twisted cubic on a quadric meets all the generators of one system in two points and all of the other system in one point;

(*b*) a cubic ruled surface has two directrices; through each point of one there pass two generators, while through each point of the other there passes one generator.

* Salmon, *Geometry of Three Dimensions*, 1 (Dublin, 1914), 347.

† Just as there are two tangent planes of an ordinary quadric passing through a line of [3]. The poles of the primes which pass through S_3 all line on a line; this meets Ω in the two points O, O' at which the tangent primes contain S_3.

The double curve consists of the points of R, the bitangent developable of the planes through R'. An arbitrary plane of Ω meets S_3 in a point of Q, and there is only one chord of C lying on Ω and meeting this plane—that generator of Q which meets C twice and passes through the point where the plane meets S_3. Thus the double curve is of the first order and the bitangent developable of the first class.

38. It may happen however that S_3 occupies a special position in regard to Ω, meeting it in a quadric cone with vertex V. Then only one tangent prime of Ω passes through S_3, this being the tangent prime at V*. A cubic curve on the cone necessarily passes through V. Hence the second species of cubic ruled surface has a directrix line R which is also a generator. Any plane of Ω passing through V lies in the tangent prime at V and therefore meets S_3 in a line. This line will be a generator of the cone and will meet the curve C in one point other than V. Thus through any point of R there passes one generator other than R, while any plane through R contains one generator other than R.

This is in fact the cubic ruled surface of § 20.

We have thus obtained the two kinds of cubic ruled surfaces in [3] given by Cayley†.

SECTION III

THE PROJECTION OF RULED SURFACES FROM HIGHER SPACE

39. Just as a curve is said to be normal when it cannot be obtained by projection from a curve of the same order in space of higher dimension, so a ruled surface is said to be normal when it cannot be obtained by projection from a ruled surface *of the same order* in space of higher dimension.

It is well known how the descriptive theory of curves has been amplified and simplified by considering curves as the projections of normal curves, and it is natural to expect that the theory of ruled surfaces will benefit similarly by considering ruled surfaces as projections of normal ruled surfaces. There are, however, as we should again naturally expect, more complicated relations to consider in the theory of ruled surfaces than in the theory of curves; for example, the normal space for a curve of order n and genus p is unique so long as $n > 2p - 2$, but for a ruled surface of order n and genus p the normal space is only unique when $p = 0$ and

* The poles of the primes containing S_3 now lie on a line which touches Ω at V.

† *Papers*, 5, 212–213.

$p = 1$. Again, rational curves of order n are all projectively equivalent, but rational ruled surfaces of order n are not all projectively equivalent.

40. We shall, from this until § 50, be concerned solely with ruled surfaces which are rational. A rational ruled surface of order n is normal in $[n + 1]$*, all rational ruled surfaces of order n can be obtained as projections of these normal surfaces.

In the first place no surface of order n, whether ruled or not, can lie in a space of dimension greater than $n + 1$†. If it did so every prime section would be a curve lying in a space of dimension greater than its order.

In the second place, given any rational ruled surface of order n, there exists in $[n + 1]$ a normal surface of which it is the projection. For consider such a surface in $[m]$, where $2 < m < n + 1$, and take two prime sections. If the primes are of general position in regard to the surface the sections will both be rational curves of order n; the $m + 1$ homogeneous coordinates of a point on either curve can be expressed as polynomials of order n in a parameter. Since the curves are placed in $(1, 1)$ correspondence by the generators of the surface we can take the same parameter λ for both curves; so that for a point of the first curve

$$x_i = \phi_i(\lambda) \qquad (i = 0, 1, \ldots, m),$$

and for a point of the second curve

$$x_i = \psi_i(\lambda) \qquad (i = 0, 1, \ldots, m),$$

where ϕ and ψ are polynomials of order n.

Thus the coordinates of a point of the ruled surface can be expressed as rational functions of two parameters λ and ν in the form

$$x_i = \phi_i(\lambda) + \nu\psi_i(\lambda) \qquad (i = 0, 1, \ldots, m).$$

Now the two prime sections have n common points, viz. the points in which the surface is met by the $[m - 2]$ common to the two primes. Then for these points the polynomials ϕ_i must be proportional to the polynomials ψ_i, so that

$$\frac{\phi_1(\lambda_j)}{\psi_1(\lambda_j)} = \frac{\phi_2(\lambda_j)}{\psi_2(\lambda_j)} = \ldots = \frac{\phi_m(\lambda_j)}{\psi_m(\lambda_j)} = k_j \qquad (j = 1, 2, \ldots, n-1, n),$$

where $\lambda_1, \lambda_2, \ldots, \lambda_n$ are the n values of λ giving the common points of the two prime sections. We can write the coordinates of a point on the ruled surface in the homogeneous form

$$x_i = \mu\phi_i(\lambda, \mu) + \nu\psi_i(\lambda, \mu) \qquad (i = 0, 1, \ldots, m).$$

Now let us choose further pairs of polynomials ϕ and ψ of degree n in λ, the values of the ratios ϕ/ψ being also equal to the quantities k for the

* Veronese, *Math. Ann.* 19 (1882), 228. † Veronese, *ibid.* 166.

n values of λ giving the common points of the two prime sections; and then take further expressions

$$x_i = \mu\phi_i(\lambda, \mu) + \nu\psi_i(\lambda, \mu) \qquad (i = m+1, \ldots).$$

If (λ, μ, ν) are regarded as the homogeneous co-ordinates of a point in a plane the quantities x_i when equated to zero represent curves of order $n+1$; these curves all have:

(a) a multiple point of order n at $\lambda = \mu = 0$,

(b) a common point at $\mu = \nu = 0$,

(c) common points at the n points $\mu = 1, \lambda = \lambda_j, \nu = -k_j$.

Thus the number of coordinates x_i it is possible to choose which are linearly independent is the same as the number of linearly independent plane curves of order $n+1$ which have in common $n+1$ ordinary points and have also a given point of multiplicity n. But the number of such curves is

$$\tfrac{1}{2}(n+1)(n+4) + 1 - (n+1) - \tfrac{1}{2}n(n+1) = n+2.$$

We can therefore choose linearly independent coordinates

$$x_i = \mu\phi_i(\lambda, \mu) + \nu\psi_i(\lambda, \mu) \qquad (i = 0, 1, \ldots, n+1),$$

$n+2$ in number and no more.

Then these quantities x_i are the coordinates of a point on a rational ruled surface of order n in $[n+1]$, the generators being given by

$$\lambda/\mu = \text{const.}$$

This surface is normal and cannot be obtained by projection from a ruled surface of the same order in higher space. The original surface lies in the $[m]$ whose equations are $x_{m+1} = x_{m+2} = \ldots = x_{n+1} = 0$ and is the projection of the normal surface from the $[n-m]$ whose equations are

$$x_0 = x_1 = \ldots = x_m = 0.$$

To a general point of the ruled surface there corresponds one point of the plane, while to a general point of the plane there corresponds one point of the ruled surface. The correspondence between the plane and ruled surface is birational save for a certain number of exceptional points.

To a prime section of the ruled surface corresponds on the plane a curve of order $n+1$ with a fixed n-ple point and $n+1$ other fixed points. To the points in which the surface is met by a space of dimension two less than the space to which it belongs we have the variable intersections of two such plane curves; the number of these is

$$(n+1)^2 - n^2 - n - 1 = n,$$

which is, as it should be, the order of the ruled surface.

A ruled surface of order n in $[n+1]$ is necessarily a rational surface because its prime sections are rational curves.

It can be shewn* that every surface of order n in $[n+1]$ is necessarily a ruled surface except when $n = 4$.

41. The properties of the rational normal ruled surfaces were first studied by Segre in his paper on rational ruled surfaces published at Turin in 1884†. The results obtained by him are fundamental for our work, and as we shall be using them constantly we give here some account of them.

In the first place we can immediately establish the existence of rational ruled surfaces of order n in $[n+1]$ of several types which are projectively distinct. For take two spaces $[m]$ and $[n-m]$ in $[n+1]$ which do not intersect; in $[m]$ take a rational normal curve of order m and in $[n-m]$ take a rational normal curve of order $n-m$. Then if the two curves are placed in (1, 1) correspondence the ruled surface formed by joining pairs of corresponding points is of order n‡; it is rational and no two of its generators can intersect§.

Take homogeneous coordinates $(x_0, x_1, \ldots, x_{n+1})$ so that the equations of $[m]$ are $x_{m+1} = x_{m+2} = \ldots = x_{n+1} = 0$ and the equations of $[n-m]$ are $x_0 = x_1 = \ldots = x_m = 0$. Then a point of the curve in $[m]$ can be given by

$$x_0 = \lambda^m,\ x_1 = \lambda^{m-1},\ \ldots,\ x_m = 1,\ x_{m+1} = 0,\ x_{m+2} = 0,\ \ldots,\ x_{n+1} = 0,$$

while the corresponding point of the curve in $[n-m]$ is given by

$$x_0 = 0,\ x_1 = 0,\ \ldots,\ x_m = 0,\ x_{m+1} = \lambda^{n-m},\ x_{m+2} = \lambda^{n-m-1},\ \ldots,\ x_{n+1} = 1.$$

The coordinates of a point on the ruled surface are then given rationally in terms of two parameters λ and μ by the equations

$$x_0 = \lambda^m,\ x_1 = \lambda^{m-1},\ \ldots,\ x_m = 1,\ x_{m+1} = \lambda^{n-m}\mu,\ x_{m+2} = \lambda^{n-m-1}\mu,\ \ldots,\ x_{n+1} = \mu,$$

so that the coordinates of every point of the ruled surface satisfy the equations

$$\frac{x_0}{x_1} = \frac{x_1}{x_2} = \ldots = \frac{x_{m-1}}{x_m} = \frac{x_{m+1}}{x_{m+2}} = \ldots = \frac{x_n}{x_{n+1}};$$

and conversely every point whose coordinates satisfy these equations is a point of the ruled surface.

The equations to the ruled surface are therefore

$$\left\| \begin{matrix} x_0 & x_1 \ldots x_{m-1} & x_{m+1} \ldots x_n \\ x_1 & x_2 \ldots x_m & x_{m+2} \ldots x_{n+1} \end{matrix} \right\| = 0.$$

In particular, a ruled surface of order 2 in [3] is obtained by a (1, 1) correspondence between two skew lines. If the lines are $x_0 = x_1 = 0$ and $x_2 = x_3 = 0$ the equation to the ruled surface can be taken as

$$\frac{x_0}{x_1} = \frac{x_2}{x_3}.$$

* Del Pezzo, "Sulle superficie di ordine n immerse nello spazio di $n+1$ dimensioni," *Rend. dell' Accad. di Napoli*, 24 (1885), 212.

† "Sulle rigate razionali in uno spazio lineare qualunque," *Atti Torino*, 19 (1884), 355.

‡ § 19.

§ For if they did the spaces $[n]$ and $[n-m]$ would also intersect.

42. We shall always assume that the ruled surface in $[n+1]$ is not a cone and that it does not break up into separate surfaces. Further, it does not lie in any space of dimension less than $n+1$.

If there is on the surface a curve of order less than or equal to n it can only meet each generator of the surface in one point; for if it met each generator in more than one point any space containing the curve would contain the whole surface. But the surface lies in a space of dimension greater than n, whereas the curve must lie in a space of dimension less than or equal to its order. Since then the curve only meets each generator in one point it is a rational curve.

A curve on a ruled surface meeting every generator in one point will be called a *directrix*.

Thus on a ruled surface of order n in $[n+1]$ every curve C_μ of order $\mu \leqslant n$ is a rational curve. But, further, every such curve is a rational *normal* curve. For if it were contained in a $[\mu - b]$, where $b > 0$, we could take, through the curve and through any $n - \mu + b$ generators, a space $[n]$ which would meet the surface in a curve of order

$$\mu + n - \mu + b = n + b > n;$$

and this is impossible.

Moreover, we cannot have on the surface two curves the sum of whose orders is less than n. For if we have two curves C_μ and $C_{\mu'}$ of respective orders μ and μ', where $\mu + \mu' < n$, they are contained in spaces $[\mu]$ and $[\mu']$; whence the space $[\mu + \mu' + 1]$ containing these would contain the whole surface, which is not contained in a space of dimension less than $n+1$.

Similarly, if we have on the surface two curves the sum of whose orders is n they cannot intersect.

43. When we generate a normal ruled surface by means of two curves of orders m and $n - m$ we can always suppose, except when $m = n - m = \frac{1}{2}n$, that

$$m < n - m,$$

or

$$m < \frac{n}{2}.$$

Then there can be no other curve on the surface of order as small as m; or the curve of order m is the *directrix of minimum order* on the surface. We can call it for brevity the *minimum directrix*.

Now in generating the surface we can clearly take any value for m such that $1 \leqslant m \leqslant \frac{n}{2}$ (ignoring $m = 0$ which gives a cone). Two surfaces whose minimum directrices are of different orders cannot be projectively equivalent.

Thus *if n is odd we have* $\frac{n-1}{2}$ *projectively distinct types of rational normal ruled surfaces of order n in $[n+1]$; each surface has a directrix of minimum order equal to m, where m is one of the numbers* $1, 2, \dots, \frac{n-1}{2}$.

If n is even we have $\frac{n}{2}$ *projectively distinct types of rational normal ruled surfaces of order n in $[n+1]$; one surface has minimum directrices of order* $\frac{n}{2}$, *while the others have each a directrix of minimum order equal to m, where m is one of the numbers* $1, 2, \dots, \frac{n}{2}-1$.

44. We now shew that *every rational normal ruled surface of order n in $[n+1]$ is of one of these types.* To do this we must shew:

(*a*) that every ruled surface of order n in $[n+1]$ has on it a curve of order $m \leqslant \frac{n}{2}$;

(*b*) that such a surface has on it curves of order $n-m$.

Then taking curves C_m and C_{n-m} of these orders they cannot have any intersections, and the ruled surface can be given by a (1, 1) correspondence between these curves.

The proof of (*a*) is immediate; for taking a ruled surface of order n in $[n+1]$ we know that a prime $[n]$ can be taken to contain $n+1$ independent points. If then n is odd we can take a prime through $\frac{n+1}{2}$ generators arbitrarily chosen; the remaining intersection of the prime with the surface is a curve of order $\frac{n-1}{2}$ which may or may not contain other generators as parts of itself. It always includes, however, a curve which is a directrix; so that on a ruled surface of odd order n in $[n+1]$ there is always a directrix curve of order less than or equal to $\frac{n-1}{2}$. Similarly, on a ruled surface of even order n in $[n+1]$ there is always a directrix curve of order less than or equal to $\frac{n}{2}$.

Consider now a surface F_2^n with a minimum directrix γ^m of order m. If a prime $[n]$ contains more than m generators of F_2^n it will meet γ^m in more than m points and so contain it entirely, and its intersection with the ruled surface will consist of γ^m and $n-m$ generators. This further illustrates the fact that there are no curves, other than γ^m itself, on F_2^n of order less than $n-m$. If, however, a prime $[n]$ is made to contain exactly m generators of F_2^n $\left(\text{as it always can since } m < \frac{n+1}{2}\right)$ it will not contain γ^m and will meet $F_2{}^n$ further in a curve of order $n - m$; unless, however, every prime through the m generators necessarily contains a further generator. But this cannot be; for we can take a prime through m arbitrary generators and $n - 2m + 1$ arbitrary points of $F_2{}^n$; if such a prime necessarily contained a further generator it would also contain γ^m and therefore the $n - 2m + 1$ generators of $F_2{}^n$ through the chosen points; its intersection with $F_2{}^n$ would then be a curve of order at least

$$m + m + n - 2m + 1$$

or $n + 1$, which is impossible.

We have then clearly established the existence of curves of order $n - m$ on $F_2{}^n$; so that all rational normal ruled surfaces of order n in $[n + 1]$ can be obtained as in § 41.

45. Since any directrix curve of order $n - m$ and any m generators lie together in an $[n]$ all the curves of order $n - m$ can be obtained by means of primes through m generators arbitrarily chosen. We can now state the following:

On the surface $F_2{}^n$ whose minimum directrix is of order m there are ∞^{n-2m+1} curves of order $n - m$. These curves are all obtained by primes through any m fixed generators of the surface; and through any $n - 2m + 1$ points of general position on the surface there passes one such curve.

Any two curves of order $n - m$ will have $n - 2m$ intersections; a prime containing one of them meets $F_2{}^n$ further in m generators and meets the other curve in $n - m$ points of which m are on these generators, the remaining $n - 2m$ being intersections of the two curves.

In particular *the ruled surface of even order which has minimum directrices of order $\frac{n}{2}$ has ∞^1 of them; through any point of the surface there passes one such curve and no two of them can intersect. The curves can all be obtained by means of primes through any $\frac{n}{2}$ generators.*

In a similar way it can be shewn that, *if $0 \leqslant k \leqslant m$, there are, on a surface $F_2{}^n$ with a minimum directrix γ^m of order m, ∞^{n-2k+1} directrix curves of order $n - k$ such that through any $n - 2k + 1$ points of general position on the surface there passes just one. All these curves can be obtained by means of primes through any k fixed generators.* Two directrices of orders $n - k$ and $n - k'$ intersect in $n - k - k'$ points.

46. A space $[n - 1]$ of general position will meet $F_2{}^n$ in n points; we can, however, consider spaces containing generators of $F_2{}^n$. If an $[n - 1]$ contains k generators it will contain k points of γ^m; so that if $k > m$ it will contain the whole of γ^m, and its intersection with $F_2{}^n$ will consist of γ^m and a certain number of generators. If, however, $k \leqslant m$,

$[n-1]$ will not contain γ^m and its intersection with F_2^n will consist of the k generators and a certain number of isolated points. A prime through $[n-1]$ meets F_2^n in the k generators and a curve of order $n-k$; this curve will meet $[n-1]$ in $n-k$ points of which k lie on the generators, the remaining $n-2k$ giving the isolated intersections of F_2^n with $[n-1]$. Hence *an* $[n-1]$ *through* k *generators of* F_2^n, *where* $k \leqslant m$, *meets* F_2^n, *in general, in these generators and in* $n-2k$ *points.*

47. Having then such a knowledge of the properties of a normal surface in $[n+1]$ we can deduce the properties of a rational ruled surface of order n in $[3]$ by projecting from a space $[n-3]$. The spaces $[n-2]$ joining $[n-3]$ to the points of the normal surface F meet the $[3]$ in the points of the projected surface f, while the spaces $[n-1]$ joining $[n-3]$ to the generators of F meet the $[3]$ in the generators of f. Surfaces f derived by projection from the same type of normal surface are projectively equivalent; but surfaces f derived from different types of normal surfaces are not. Knowing a method of generating F by a $(1, 1)$ correspondence between two directrix curves we can deduce a method of generating f, and so if we wish obtain the equation to f.

In order to give a first illustration of this work we shall obtain the two cubic ruled surfaces of $[3]$, already met with in §§ 37, 38, by projection of the normal cubic ruled surface in $[4]$*.

48. In $[4]$ there is only one type of cubic ruled surface F; it has a directrix line λ and ∞^2 directrix conics. Through any two points of F (not on the same generator and neither of them on λ) there passes one directrix conic; while any two directrix conics have a single intersection. Project F from a point O of S_4 on to a solid Σ; we get a cubic ruled surface f in Σ. The lines joining O to the points of F meet Σ in the points of f, while the planes joining O to the generators of F meet Σ in the generators of f.

Through a general point of S_4 there passes one plane containing a directrix conic of F. There cannot be more than one, because the intersection of two such planes is the intersection of the two directrix conics which they contain, and this lies on F. But there certainly exists one such plane; for any solid through the point meets F in a twisted cubic, one of whose chords passes through the point, and the two points in which the chord meets F determine a directrix conic whose plane contains the chord.

If then O is a general point of S_4 there is a plane π passing through it which contains a directrix conic Γ; and π meets Σ in a line R which is a double directrix of f, two generators of f passing through every point of R. The plane joining O to λ, the line directrix of F, meets Σ in a line R' which

* Cf. Veronese, *loc. cit.* 229–232.

is a second directrix of f; through any point of R' there passes one generator of f (see Fig. 1).

Any plane of Σ passing through R' is joined to O by a solid containing λ and therefore meeting F in λ and two generators g_1 and g_2*. This solid meets π in a line through O, and this line must meet Γ in the two points $g_1\Gamma$ and $g_2\Gamma$. Then g_1 and g_2 project into two generators of f which intersect in a point of R and lie in the plane through R' from which we started. Hence any plane through R' contains two generators of f which meet in a point of R.

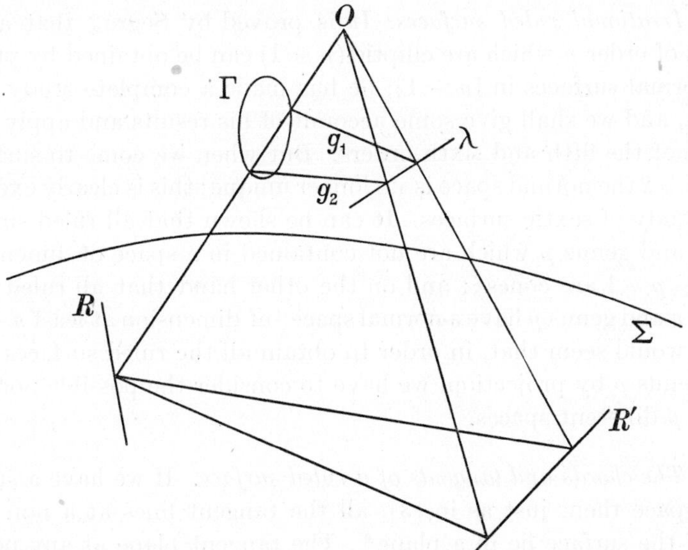

Fig. 1.

This shews that f is a cubic ruled surface in Σ belonging to the first of our two species. Since F can be generated by placing its directrix line in (1, 1) correspondence with any of its directrix conics* we deduce at once that f can be generated by placing two lines R, R' in (1, 2) correspondence.

49. This general type of surface has naturally been obtained by selecting a general point of projection. Let us then take a point O in a plane through λ which contains a generator g of F, and project from O on to a solid Σ. Then the plane $O\lambda g$ meets Σ in a line R which is a directrix and also a generator of f.

It is clear from the projection that any plane through R contains one other generator of f, while through any point of R there passes one other

* § 44.

generator of f. Thus we have our second type of cubic ruled surface in three-dimensional space.

From the known generation of F we deduce that f can be generated by a line and conic with a point of intersection placed in (1, 1) correspondence without a united point*. If we regard F as generated by a (1, 1) correspondence between its directrix line λ and one of its directrix conics Γ this point of intersection is the projection of the point $g\Gamma$. The point of intersection is not a united point because the two points in which g is met by λ and Γ project into different points of R†.

50. *Irrational ruled surfaces.* It is proved by Segre‡ that all ruled surfaces of order n which are elliptic ($p = 1$) can be obtained by projection from normal surfaces in $[n - 1]$; he has made a complete study of these surfaces, and we shall give some account of his results and apply them to surfaces of the fifth and sixth orders. But when we come to surfaces for which $p = 2$ the normal space is no longer unique; this is clearly exemplified in our study of sextic surfaces. It can be shewn that all ruled surfaces of order n and genus p which are not contained in a space of dimension less than $n - p + 1$ are cones§; and on the other hand that all ruled surfaces of order n and genus p have a normal space‖ of dimension at least $n - 2p + 1$. Thus it would seem that, in order to obtain all the ruled surfaces of order n and genus p by projection, we have to consider the possible normal surfaces in p different spaces.

51. *The chords and tangents of a ruled surface.* If we have a surface in higher space then, just as in [3], all the tangent lines at a non-singular point of the surface lie in a plane¶. The tangent plane at any point of a ruled surface must clearly contain the generator of the ruled surface which passes through the point; and it is the fact that the tangent planes at the different points of the generator form a pencil of planes related to the range of points on the generator and all lie in a [3]¶. We shall speak of this [3] as the *tangent solid* of the ruled surface along the generator.

We thus have a four-dimensional locus M_4 formed by these ∞^1 tangent solids of the ruled surface; we can also regard M_4 as consisting of the ∞^2 tangent planes or of the ∞^3 tangent lines of the ruled surface. If the ruled surface lies in [4] there will be a finite number of its tangent solids (or planes or lines) passing through any point of [4]. If the ruled surface lies

* Cf. § 20.

† Concerning this surface we may also refer to Reye, *Die Geometrie der Lage*, 3 (Leipzig, 1923), 156.

‡ "Ricerche sulle rigate ellittiche di qualunque ordine," *Atti Torino*, 21 (1886), 868.

§ Segre, *ibid.* § 2.

‖ Segre, *Math. Ann.* 34 (1889), 4.

¶ Del Pezzo, *Palermo Rendiconti*, 1 (1887), 243–245.

in $[r]$, where $r > 4$, there will be a finite number of its tangents meeting an $[r-4]$ of general position, and this number is the order of M_4.

The chords of the ruled surface form a five-dimensional locus M_5 on which the locus M_4 formed by the tangents lies. If the surface is in [4] there will be ∞^1 chords of it through a general point of [4]. If the surface is in [5] there will be a finite number of its chords passing through a general point of [5]; this number is the number of "apparent double points" of the surface. If the surface is in $[r]$, where $r > 5$, there will be a finite number of its chords meeting an $[r-5]$ of general position, and this number is the order of M_5.

For example, on the rational ruled surface $F_2{}^n$ in $[n+1]$

$$\left\| \begin{matrix} x_0 & x_1 \dots x_{m-1} & x_{m+1} \dots x_n \\ x_1 & x_2 \dots x_m & x_{m+2} \dots x_{n+1} \end{matrix} \right\| = 0,$$

the coordinates of any two points can be taken as

$$(a^m, \quad a^{m-1}, \dots, 1, \quad a^{n-m}b, \dots, ab, \quad b),$$

and

$$(\alpha^m, \quad \alpha^{m-1}, \dots, 1, \quad \alpha^{n-m}\beta, \dots, \alpha\beta, \quad \beta).$$

Then the coordinates of any point on the line joining these are seen to satisfy

$$\left\| \begin{matrix} x_0 & x_1 \dots x_{m-2} & x_{m+1} \dots x_{n-1} \\ x_1 & x_2 \dots x_{m-1} & x_{m+2} \dots x_n \\ x_2 & x_3 \dots x_m & x_{m+3} \dots x_{n+1} \end{matrix} \right\| = 0,$$

which represents a locus of five dimensions and of order $\frac{1}{2}(n-2)(n-3)$.

52. In the actual projection of a ruled surface from higher space these two loci M_4 and M_5 are useful for studying any double curve which there may be on the projected surface. When the surface is in $[r]$ we project on to [3] from an $[r-4]$; the locus M_5 meets $[r-4]$ in a curve ϑ; through each point of this curve there passes a chord of F and the $[r-3]$ joining $[r-4]$ to such a chord meets the [3] Σ on to which we are projecting in a double point of the projected surface f. We thus have the double curve of f in (1, 1) correspondence with the curve in which M_5 meets $[r-4]$. The chords of F meeting $[r-4]$ give on F a curve C in (2, 1) correspondence with the double curve of f; the number of branch-points of this correspondence on C is the number of tangents of C which meet $[r-4]$, and this is simply the order of M_4. Thus the genus of the double curve of f is the same as that of the curve ϑ in which M_5 meets $[r-4]$; it can also be calculated by Zeuthen's formula when we know the genus of C.

There will, of course, not be a curve in $[r-4]$ unless $r > 5$; if $r = 5$ we have a finite number of chords of F passing through each point of a line, while if $r = 4$ we have an infinity of chords of F passing through a single point: in both these cases, however, we still have the curve C on F.

The projection of the cubic ruled surface in [4] exemplifies this; the chords of F passing through an arbitrary point O lie in a plane and meet F in the points of a directrix conic Γ. There are two tangents of Γ passing through O.

53. We already know, by means of the representation of f as a curve on Ω, that f will have, in general, a finite number of triple points: this is confirmed by the projection. The triple points of f must arise from spaces $[r-3]$ passing through the centre of projection $[r-4]$ and meeting F each in three points. Now the spaces $[r-3]$ in $[r]$ which contain $[r-4]$ are in aggregate ∞^3, and one condition is necessary for an $[r-3]$ to meet a surface in $[r]$. Hence there are, containing $[r-4]$, ∞^2 spaces $[r-3]$ each meeting F in one point, ∞^1 spaces $[r-3]$ each meeting F in two points and a finite number of spaces $[r-3]$ each meeting F in three points. The first set simply joins $[r-4]$ to the ∞^2 points of F; the second set contains the ∞^1 chords of F which meet $[r-4]$; the third gives the triple points of f. The singularities of a general ruled surface in [3] are a double curve and a finite number of triple points, these points being also triple points of the double curve.

For a ruled surface in [4] the only singularities, in general, are a finite number of double points. If the surface is a projection of a non-singular ruled surface in [5] this is clear at once, for we have already seen that there is a finite number of chords of this surface passing through a general point of [5]. If the surface is the projection of a surface in $[r]$, when $r > 5$, the centre of projection is an $[r-5]$, and this, if it is of general position, meets the M_5 formed by the chords of the surface in a finite number of points.

54. *Conclusion.* We have now two powerful methods of obtaining the different kinds of ruled surfaces in [3]; the first by considering the surfaces as curves on Ω, the second by projection of normal surfaces from higher space. For surfaces which are the most general of their order and genus we must choose the curve to have a general position on Ω, and the centre of projection to have a general position in regard to the normal surface. To obtain the other surfaces we specialise the position of the curve on Ω, and the position of the centre of projection in regard to the normal surfaces.

The first method is only applicable to the ruled surfaces in [3], whereas the second is equally applicable to ruled surfaces in any space; but the duality of the surface is lost in the second method, whereas it is retained in the first; it is only in [3] that the line is the self-dual element. The two methods will have to lead to the same results; and we may confidently expect a greater efficiency than usual when we have two such different methods confirming the workings of one another.

We proceed then to the main task of classifying ruled surfaces in [3], beginning with those of the fourth order.

CHAPTER II

QUARTIC RULED SURFACES

INTRODUCTORY

55. The object of this chapter is to give a detailed and exhaustive classification of the quartic ruled surfaces of three-dimensional space. The most general type of surface is mentioned by Chasles*; the surfaces were studied and classified, though not quite exhaustively, by Cayley†, who obtained his different types by means of directing curves and gave algebraic equations for them. The complete classification was first given by Cremona‡, who generated his surfaces by means of correspondences between two curves.

We shall illustrate the general methods of this volume by obtaining the quartic ruled surfaces of [3] in two ways:

(*a*) by regarding their generators as represented by the points of a quartic curve on a quadric Ω in [5] (§ 31);

(*b*) by regarding them as projections of normal quartic ruled surfaces in higher space.

56. Lines in [3] are ∞^4 in aggregate; there are thus ∞^1 lines satisfying three conditions. It is one condition for a line to meet a curve; so that the lines which meet each of three given curves C_1, C_2, C_3 are ∞^1 in aggregate and form a ruled surface. Salmon remarked§ that if the curves C_1, C_2, C_3 are of respective orders m_1, m_2, m_3 then the order of the ruled surface is $2m_1m_2m_3$; further, the three curves are multiple curves on the surface; through every point of C_1 there pass m_2m_3 generators, through every point of C_2 m_3m_1 generators and through every point of C_3 m_1m_2 generators. Cayley added the further statement that if C_2 and C_3 have α intersections, C_3 and C_1 have β intersections and C_1 and C_2 have γ intersections, then the order of the ruled surface is reduced to $2m_1m_2m_3 - m_1\alpha - m_2\beta - m_3\gamma$, while through every point of C_1 there pass $m_2m_3 - \alpha$ generators, through

* *Comptes Rendus*, 52 (1861), 1094.

† *Papers*, 5 (1864), 214–219, and 6 (1868), 312–328.

‡ *Memorie dell' Accademia di Bologna* (2), 8 (1868), 235; *Opere*, 2, 420. Concerning quartic ruled surfaces we may refer also to Reye, *Die Geometrie der Lage*, 2 (Stuttgart, 1907), 301, and Sturm, *Liniengeometrie*, 1 (Leipzig, 1892), 48.

§ *Cambridge and Dublin Mathematical Journal*, 8 (1853), 45; cf. *Geometry of Three Dimensions*, 2 (Dublin, 1915), 90.

every point of C_2 $m_3 m_1 - \beta$ generators and through every point of C_3 $m_1 m_2 - \gamma$ generators*.

Cayley then chose sets of directing curves which would give ruled surfaces of the fourth order. For example, one such set can be taken to consist of two conics C_1 and C_2 with two common points and a line C_3 meeting one of the conics, say C_1. Then

$$m_1 = 2, \qquad m_2 = 2, \qquad m_3 = 1,$$
$$\alpha = 1, \qquad \beta = 0, \qquad \gamma = 2,$$

and we have a ruled surface of order 4 on which C_2 is a double conic and C_3 a double line. He did not succeed however in discovering all the quartic ruled surfaces in this way†.

Incidentally we also have a ruled surface formed by the chords of one curve which meet another given curve; or by the lines trisecant to a given curve. Formulae can be given for the orders of such ruled surfaces; we shall see below that a quartic ruled surface is formed by the chords of a twisted cubic which meet a given line.

57. Cremona on the other hand generated the quartic ruled surfaces by means of a (1, 1) correspondence between two conics. In general the conics will not degenerate and will not intersect; but further types of surfaces are obtained if one or both of the conics degenerates into a line counted doubly, and still further types can arise if the two curves intersect.

It can at once be shewn by elementary methods that the ruled surface is of the fourth order. For let the two conics be C and C' and suppose that an arbitrary line meets their planes in p and q. Then an arbitrary plane through the line gives a pair of points x, y on C and a pair of points z', u' on C'. Then as the plane varies in the pencil the pairs of points x, y will describe an involution on C, the join of every pair of points passing through p; while the pairs of points z', u' describe an involution on C', the join of every pair of points passing through q; the pencils of lines through p and q in the planes of the two conics are thus homographically related. But to the points x, y of C there will correspond, in the (1, 1) correspondence between the conics, points x', y' of C'; and as the points x, y describe the involution on C the points x', y' will describe an involution on C'. The join of x' and y' thus passes through a fixed point p', and the pencil of lines through p' in the plane of C' is thus homographic with the pencil

* *Papers*, 5 (1864), 203.

† There are, as we shall see, ten species of quartic ruled surfaces with rational plane sections and two with elliptic plane sections; in Cayley's first paper we find the two elliptic ones and six of the rational ones. This paper was seen by Cremona before he published his own, and meanwhile Cayley discovered two other rational quartic ruled surfaces. He did not know of the existence of the remaining two species until he was informed of them by Cremona.

of lines through p in the plane of C. We have then in the plane of C' two homographic pencils of lines with vertices p' and q; the locus of intersections of corresponding lines is a conic. This conic meets C' in four points, and the plane joining any one of these four points to pq contains a pair of corresponding points of C and C' and therefore a generator of the ruled surface. We have thus four generators of the surface meeting pq, so that the ruled surface is of the fourth order.

It is clear that the planes of C and C' are bitangent planes of the ruled surface, each meeting it in a conic and two generators. The plane of C, for example, meets C' in two points and therefore contains the two generators which join those points to the corresponding points of C.

Further, there are three double points of the ruled surface in an arbitrary plane. In the plane of C we have the intersection of the two generators lying therein and two other points, namely, those intersections of the generators with C which do not correspond to the two intersections of the plane with C'. The double curve of the ruled surface is thus a twisted cubic*.

The (1, 1) correspondence between C and C' determines a projectivity between their planes†; there are certain lines in either plane which intersect their corresponding lines in the other plane, and the planes of such pairs of intersecting lines are known to form a developable of the third class‡. Such a plane necessarily contains two generators of the ruled surface; and conversely every bitangent plane of the ruled surface will meet the planes of C and C' in lines which correspond to one another in the projectivity. Thus we see that the quartic ruled surface has a bitangent developable of the third class.

Just as the points of the surface which lie in a plane containing two generators, but not themselves on either of the generators, lie on a conic, so the tangent planes of the surface which pass through a point of intersection of two generators, but do not themselves contain either of these generators, touch a quadric cone.

After these preliminary remarks we proceed to the classification of the quartic ruled surfaces by the two methods; the reader is referred for further investigations to Cremona's paper.

* The double curve, being algebraic, meets every plane of the space containing the ruled surface in the same number of points. It is then sufficient, in order to be able to say that the double curve is a twisted cubic, to prove that it meets the plane of C in three points.

† von Staudt, *Geometrie der Lage*, 2 (Nürnberg, 1857), 149; Reye, *Geometrie der Lage*, 2 (Stuttgart, 1907), 10.

‡ von Staudt, *Geometrie der Lage*, 3 (Nürnberg, 1860), 326; Reye, *Geometrie der Lage*, 2 (Stuttgart, 1907), 163.

SECTION I

RATIONAL QUARTIC RULED SURFACES CONSIDERED AS CURVES ON Ω

58. The generators of a rational quartic ruled surface are represented on Ω by the points of a rational quartic curve C. Such a curve necessarily lies in a space S_4 and may be contained in a space S_3, so that we consider five possibilities as follows:

I. C is a rational normal quartic lying in an S_4 which has no special relation in regard to Ω.

II. C lies in a tangent prime T of Ω.

III. C lies in a tangent prime T of Ω and passes through O, the point of contact of Ω and T.

IV. C lies in an S_3, the intersection of tangent primes to Ω at two points O and O'.

V. C lies in an S_3 through which there passes only one tangent prime of Ω, S_3 meeting Ω in a quadric cone with vertex V.

59. Let us now examine the general case I.

To find the degree of the double curve of the ruled surface we take a plane ρ on Ω and find how many planes ϖ there are which meet this plane ρ in a line and also meet C in two points*. The chord joining the points of C in such a plane ϖ would have to meet ρ (on its line of intersection with ϖ). But ρ meets S_4 in a line; and we know that any line in S_4 is met by three chords of C†, because when we project C from the line on to a plane we obtain a rational quartic, i.e. a plane quartic with three double points. A chord of C which meets the line lies entirely on Ω as meeting it in three points, and therefore a plane ϖ passes through it. We therefore obtain three planes ϖ such as we require.

Hence the double curve is of the third order.

Similarly the bitangent developable is of the third class.

The tangent prime of Ω at any point P of C meets S_4 in a solid which contains the tangent of C at P and meets C in two points other than P. Hence every generator of the surface is met by two others. On any generator there lie two points of the double curve, while through any generator there pass two planes of the bitangent developable.

Since the points of C lie in an S_4 which does not touch Ω the generators of the surface belong to a linear complex which is not special. The surface was thus given by Cayley, as that formed by the chords of a twisted cubic belonging to a linear complex‡.

* § 33. † Cf. § 8. ‡ *Papers*, 6, 316.

The chords of a twisted cubic are ∞^2 in aggregate; they are therefore represented on Ω by the points of a surface V. Since one chord of the cubic can be drawn through any point of the space [3] in which it lies, the surface V meets every plane ϖ on Ω in one point; and since there are three chords of the cubic in any plane of the [3], the surface V meets every plane ρ on Ω in three points. Hence V is of order 4, meeting an arbitrary solid in four points. This surface V is in fact the surface known as Veronese's surface*.

The statement that the chords of a twisted cubic belonging to a linear complex form a rational quartic ruled surface is the same as the statement that the section of Veronese's surface by a prime is a rational quartic curve.

60. *Quartic ruled surfaces of type II.* A tangent prime T of Ω meets Ω in a quadric point-cone†; this contains the two systems of planes on Ω through the point of contact O. Any solid of T meets Ω in a quadric surface; and the lines joining O to every point of this quadric surface lie on Ω. The rational quartic C is projected from O into a rational quartic on this quadric. Remembering that the generators of the quadric lie on the planes of the two systems through O we can at once subdivide type II into three parts:

II (A). C meets every plane ϖ through O in three points and every plane ρ through O in one point.

II (B). C meets every plane ϖ through O in one point and every plane ρ through O in three points.

II (C). A chord of C passes through O; C meets every plane of Ω through O in two points.

The point O of Ω represents a line R; this is a directrix of the quartic surface, being met by every generator.

When the surface is of the type II (A) there are three generators passing through every point of R, while there is one generator lying in each plane through R.

To find the double curve we take, as before, an arbitrary plane ρ, and we consider those chords of C which meet this plane. These are the three chords of C which meet the line of intersection of the plane ρ with the tangent prime T, and are therefore those chords of C which lie in the plane ϖ joining this line to O.

If we now interpret this result in the space S_3 containing the ruled surface the plane ρ represents an arbitrary plane of S_3; and the three planes ϖ which represent the three intersections of this plane of S_3 with the double

* For this surface, regarded as representing the chords of a twisted cubic, see Baker, *Principles of Geometry*, 4, 52–55, where references to the literature concerning it will also be found.

† Cf. § 30.

curve all coincide in a single plane through O. Hence the three points of intersection of the plane of S_3 and the double curve all coincide in the intersection of this plane with the line R.

Hence the double curve is the line R counted three times.

To find the bitangent developable we take an arbitrary plane ϖ; this meets T in a line which is met by three chords of C, and the bitangent developable of the surface is a general developable of the third class.

When the surface is of the type II (B) there is one generator passing through each point of R and three generators lying in any plane through R. The double curve is a non-degenerate twisted cubic, while the bitangent developable consists of the pencil of planes through R counted three times.

When the surface is of the type II (C) there are two generators which pass through any point of R and two which lie in any plane through R.

An arbitrary plane ρ meets T in a line; one of the three chords of C which meet the line is contained in the plane ϖ joining it to O. Hence the double curve consists of R and a conic. R and the conic intersect; their point of intersection is represented by the ϖ-plane which contains the chord of C passing through O. Similarly, the bitangent developable consists of the pencil of planes through R together with the tangent planes of a quadric cone, one tangent plane of the cone passing through R. This tangent plane of the cone is represented on Ω by the ρ-plane which contains the chord of C passing through O.

61. *Quartic ruled surfaces of type III.* We can subdivide III into two parts; since the projection of C from O on to a solid in T is now a twisted cubic we have:

III (A). C meets every plane ϖ through O in two points and every plane ρ through O in one point other than O.

III (B). C meets every plane ϖ through O in one point and every plane ρ through O in two points other than O.

The point O represents a line R which is a directrix and also a generator of the ruled surface.

In the type III (A) there are two generators other than R passing through each point of R and one generator other than R lying in each plane through R. An arbitrary plane ρ meets T in a line; but the three chords of C meeting this line all lie in the plane ϖ joining it to O. Hence the double curve is the line R counted three times. An arbitrary plane ϖ meets T in a line, and the plane ρ joining this line to O contains one chord of C. There will be two other chords of C meeting the line, so that the bitangent developable consists of the pencil of planes through R together with the tangent planes of a quadric cone.

In the type III (B) there are two generators other than R lying in any plane through R and one generator other than R passing through any point of R. The double curve consists of R and a conic, the bitangent developable of the pencil of planes through R counted three times.

62. *Quartic ruled surfaces of type IV.* In IV we have a rational quartic C lying on the quadric surface in which Ω is met by S_3. We have then two possibilities:

IV (A). C meets all generators of one system in three points and all of the other system in one point.

IV (B). C has a double point and meets every generator in two points.

Through a general point of S_3 we can draw three chords to either of these rational quartics; in the second case we include the line to the double point.

The points O and O' of Ω represent lines R and R', which are both met by every generator; the surface has two directrices.

The planes of the two systems on Ω which pass through O and O' meet S_3 in the two systems of generators of the quadric surface. Each generator is the intersection of a plane of one system through O with a plane of the opposite system through O'.

In IV (A) we may suppose that the generators trisecant to C lie in the ϖ-planes through O and in the ρ-planes through O'. Then through any point of R there pass three generators lying in a plane through R'; any plane through R' contains three generators meeting in a point of R. The double curve consists of the points of the line R counted three times; the bitangent developable consists of the planes through the line R' counted three times.

In IV (B) the double point of C represents a double generator G of the surface. Through any point of R there pass two generators lying in a plane through R' and through any point of R' there pass two generators lying in a plane with R. The double curve therefore consists of the points of R, R', G, while the bitangent developable consists of the three pencils of planes through R, R', G.

63. *Quartic ruled surfaces of type V.* In V C lies on a quadric cone Q with vertex V and must therefore have a double point. If two quadrics in S_3 touch there are three cones through their curve of intersection, one of which has its vertex at the double point; so that V can be subdivided according as

V (A), the double point of C is not at V,

or V (B), the double point of C is V.

Through every generator of Q there passes a plane of Ω of either system.

In V (A) the surface has a directrix line R; through any point of R there pass two generators which lie in a plane with R, while any plane through

R contains two generators meeting in a point of R. R is represented on Ω by the point V.

An arbitrary plane of Ω meets S_3 in a point P on Q, and it is clear that the projection of C from P on to a plane of S_3 is a quartic curve with a double point and a tacnode, the tangent at the tacnode being the intersection of the plane with the tangent plane of the cone along the generator through P. Hence the three chords of C which pass through P consist of the generator PV counted twice and the line to the double point.

Hence the double curve consists of the directrix R counted twice and a double generator, while the bitangent developable consists of the planes through R counted twice and the planes through the double generator.

In V (B) the surface has a directrix line R which is also a double generator. C meets every generator of Q in one point other than V; so that through any point of R there passes one generator other than R, while every plane through R contains one generator other than R.

An arbitrary plane of Ω meets S_3 in a point P on Q, and the projection of C from P on to a plane of S_3 has a triple point. Hence the three chords of C passing through P all coincide with PV. The double curve is therefore the line R counted three times, while the bitangent developable consists of the planes through R counted three times.

64. This completes the determination of the rational quartic ruled surfaces of ordinary space. We have obtained in all ten species, and these are the same as the ten species obtained by Cremona. A table of the surfaces is given on p. 303.

65. *The representation of the double curve and bitangent developable.* Two generators of the surface which intersect are represented on Ω by two points of C such that the chord joining them lies entirely upon Ω. This chord will meet an arbitrary prime in a point which can be taken as representative either of the point of the double curve in which the two generators intersect or of the plane of the bitangent developable in which the two generators lie*. Hence the chords of C which lie on Ω trace out in the prime a curve D which is in (1, 1) correspondence with both the double curve and the bitangent developable.

We assume that C is general unless the contrary is stated.

The chords of C form a locus U_3 of three dimensions; any point of this locus which is on Ω and not on C must be on a chord of C that lies entirely on Ω. Hence these chords form a ruled surface in the S_4 containing C, this ruled surface being the intersection of Ω and U_3. The section of this ruled surface by a prime or, what is the same thing, by an S_3 lying

* Cf. § 33.

in S_4, gives us the curve D. The S_3 will meet Ω in a quadric surface and U_3 in another surface; and D is the intersection of these two surfaces.

If C is projected from a line in S_4 on to a plane we have a quartic curve with three double points, so that the line must be met by three chords of C. Hence U_3 is of the third order and may be denoted by $U_3{}^3$. Moreover, if C is projected from a line which meets it on to a plane we have a plane cubic with one double point, so that the line is only met by one chord of C besides those passing through its intersection with C. Hence C is a double curve on $U_3{}^3$. Since no plane can meet C in four points no two chords of C can intersect except on C itself, so that there is no double surface on $U_3{}^3$. The section of $U_3{}^3$ by an S_3 is a four-nodal cubic surface.

The curve D in S_3 is therefore the intersection of a four-nodal cubic surface with a quadric passing through the nodes; this is a sextic curve with four double points. It lies on the quadric and meets every generator in three points; so that if it is projected from a point of the quadric on to a plane we obtain a sextic with two triple points and four double points. This is a rational curve.

66. If the curve D should happen to break up into one or more parts we expect the double curve and the bitangent developable to break up into the same number of parts.

Let us consider in particular the case II (C). C lies in a prime T touching Ω in a point O; a chord of C passes through O, while every plane of Ω through O meets C in two points.

Every chord of C which lies entirely upon Ω is such that the plane joining it to O also lies entirely upon Ω. Hence we can clearly separate these chords into two distinct classes, those joined to O by planes ϖ and those joined to O by planes ρ. We therefore expect D to break up, and moreover to break up into two similar parts.

Consider those points of an arbitrary S_3 of T lying on chords which are joined to O by ϖ-planes; they form a curve D_1 lying on the quadric Q in which S_3 meets Ω. One system of generators of Q is joined to O by ϖ-planes, and clearly there is one point of D_1 on each of these generators. A generator of Q of the opposite system is joined to O by a ρ plane: this plane contains one chord of C, so that the generator of Q is met by two other chords; these must be joined to O by ϖ-planes. Hence on this generator we have two points of D_1.

Hence D_1 is a twisted cubic meeting the generators of Q in ϖ-planes in one point and the generators of Q in ρ-planes in two points.

Similarly, those points of S_3 lying on chords that are joined to O by ρ-planes form a twisted cubic D_2 which meets the generators of Q in ϖ-planes in two points and the generators of Q in ρ-planes in one point.

Through any point of C there pass two chords which lie entirely on Ω, and these will be joined to O by planes of opposite systems. This holds in particular for the four points of intersection with S_3.

Thus we have again the intersection of a quadric with a four-nodal cubic surface; but here the intersection D breaks up into two twisted cubics, D_1 and D_2, each passing through the four nodes. D_1 and D_2 have one other common point lying on the chord of C which passes through O.

The pairs of generators of the surface which meet in the points of R and whose planes touch a quadric cone are represented on Ω by the pairs of points of C which lie in the ϖ-planes through O. The chords of C joining these points form a cubic ruled surface ϕ_1*, so that the points of R and the tangent planes of the cone are in (1, 1) correspondence with the generators of ϕ_1. The section of ϕ_1 by S_3 is the twisted cubic D_1. ϕ_1 has a directrix line l_1 and the plane ϖ_0 passing through l_1 represents the vertex of the quadric cone.

Similarly, the pairs of generators of the surface which lie in the planes through R and whose points of intersection lie on a conic are represented on Ω by the pairs of points of C which lie in the ρ-planes through O. The chords of C joining these points form a cubic ruled surface ϕ_2, so that the planes through R and the points of the conic are in (1, 1) correspondence with the generators of ϕ_2. The section of ϕ_2 by S_3 is the twisted cubic D_2. ϕ_2 has a directrix line l_2 and the plane ρ_0 passing through l_2 represents the plane of the conic.

The planes ϖ_0 and ρ_0 do not lie in T.

67. We can also consider in this way the curves C of type III. Suppose for definiteness that C is of the type III (B). The ruled surface formed by the chords of C which lie on Ω breaks up into two parts; the cubic cone projecting C from O and the cubic ruled surface formed by those chords of C which lie in the ρ-planes through O but do not themselves pass through O. The tangent of C at O belongs both to the cone and to the ruled surface, and the plane ϖ through this tangent represents a point of intersection of R and the double conic. The plane of the double conic is represented on Ω by the ρ-plane which contains the directrix of the cubic ruled surface.

* These chords join the pairs of an involution on C. The joins of the pairs of points of an involution on a rational curve of order n form a ruled surface of order $n-1$ (see footnote to § 19).

SECTION II

RATIONAL QUARTIC RULED SURFACES CONSIDERED AS PROJECTIONS OF NORMAL SURFACES IN HIGHER SPACE

68. The rational quartic ruled surfaces f of ordinary space can all be obtained as projections of the rational normal quartic ruled surfaces F of S_5; the projection will be from a line l not meeting F. There are two kinds of surfaces F; the general surface with ∞^1 directrix conics and the surface with a directrix line.

We first confine our attention to the general surface F, and find that by suitably choosing l we can obtain six types of surfaces f. From the known methods of generating F we deduce methods of generating these six types of surfaces; all these methods are given in Cremona's paper.

The other four types are obtained by projection from the surface with a directrix line.

69. *The normal surface in* [5] *with directrix conics.* The general surface F has ∞^1 directrix conics; any such conic is determined by one point of F and no two conics intersect.

We first assume that l has a general position, and project from l on to a solid Σ.

A prime through l meets F in a rational normal quartic curve, three of whose chords will meet l. Hence in any prime through l there are three planes that pass through l and meet two generators of F. Projecting: on any plane section of f there are three points through which two generators pass. Thus the double curve of f is a twisted cubic.

The planes of the ∞^1 conics on F meet any prime in lines forming a ruled surface A. The prime meets F in a rational normal quartic, and the generators of A must be chords of this curve since each one meets F in the two points where it cuts the corresponding directrix conic. Further, these chords join pairs of an involution on the curve because each conic is determined by one point of F. Thus they form a cubic ruled surface. This shews that the planes of the directrix conics form a locus V_3^3.

The line l, having a general position, does not meet the V_3^3; but a plane ϖ drawn through l meets the planes of three directrix conics Γ_1, Γ_2, Γ_3. ϖ meets Σ in a point P. Then through ϖ and Γ_1 there passes a prime which meets F in Γ_1 and two generators; the projections of these two generators will lie in a plane through P. There are two other bitangent planes through P arising from the primes $\varpi\Gamma_2$ and $\varpi\Gamma_3$. Hence there are three bitangent planes of f passing through a general point P of Σ, so that the bitangent developable of f is of the third class.

f is therefore of the type I.

F can be generated by a (1, 1) correspondence between any two of its directrix conics. Hence the most general quartic ruled surface of ordinary space can be generated by a (1, 1) correspondence between two conics.

70. F contains ∞^3 directrix cubics, any such curve being determined by three points of F. All these can be obtained as prime sections of F residual to any given generator. Any one of these curves lies in a solid; it is easily seen that for general positions of l none of these solids contains l.

Suppose, however, that l is taken in one of these solids σ. Then the projected surface f has a directrix line R, the intersection of Σ and σ. A plane through l lying in σ meets F in the three points where it meets the directrix cubic of σ; hence through any point of R there pass three generators of f. A prime containing σ meets F again in one generator; hence every plane through R contains one generator of f.

Thus f is of the type II (A).

F can be generated by placing a directrix cubic and a directrix conic in (1, 1) correspondence with a united point. Hence the surface f can be generated by taking a line and a conic with a common point P and placing them in (1, 3) correspondence with P as a united point. To P regarded as a point of the conic corresponds P regarded as a point of the line; while to P regarded as a point of the line correspond three points of the conic of which P is one.

71. Now let l be taken so as to meet a plane γ of V_3^3, γ containing a directrix conic Γ. The solid $l\gamma$ meets Σ in a line R which is a directrix of f. A plane through l lying in the solid $l\gamma$ meets γ in a line having two points of intersection with Γ, and therefore meets two generators of F. Hence through any point of R there pass two generators of f. Moreover, a prime through $l\gamma$ meets F in Γ and two generators, so that any plane through R contains two generators of f.

Thus f is of the type II (C).

f can be generated by placing a line and a conic in (1, 2) correspondence.

With this last choice of l the solid $l\gamma$ will not in general contain a generator of F, but we may clearly choose l so that it does. Then f has a directrix line R which is also a generator. Any plane through R contains one other generator, while through any point of R there pass two generators other than R itself.

Here f is of the type III (A).

To determine a generation for f suppose that F is generated by means of Γ and some other directrix conic Γ'; the solid $l\gamma$ containing a generator g which meets Γ in X and Γ' in X' (Fig. 2).

The solid $l\Gamma$ meets Σ in the directrix R, while the planes joining l to the points of Γ' meet Σ in the points of a conic C.

Now consider the plane lX'. Since it lies in the solid lg or $l\gamma$ it meets the plane γ in a line, and therefore meets Σ in a point on R. Hence R and C have a common point P. The point X' on Γ' gives the corresponding point X on Γ, which is clearly projected into a point Q of R different from P.

Hence the (1, 1) correspondence between Γ and Γ' gives a (1, 2) correspondence between R and C, P not being a self-corresponding point.

Thus f may be generated by taking a line and a conic with a common point and placing them in (1, 2) correspondence without a united point.

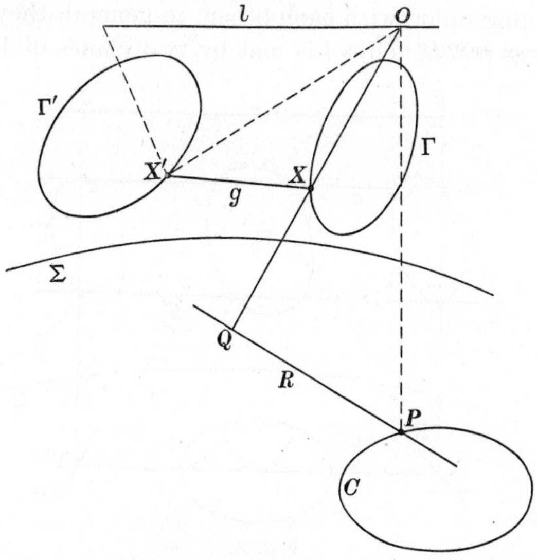

Fig. 2.

72. Further, we may choose l to meet two planes γ and γ' of V_3^3, these planes containing directrix conics Γ and Γ'. Then f has two directrices R and R', the intersections of the solids $l\gamma$ and $l\gamma'$ with Σ. Let l meet γ and γ' in P and P' respectively.

The lines of γ through P give an involution on Γ. This gives an involution of pairs of generators of F, and thus an involution on Γ' also. But the lines of γ' through P' give a second involution on Γ' which will have a pair of points in common with the former. This pair of points gives a pair of generators g and g' on F; and clearly g, g', l lie in a solid as having two common transversals. Thus the projected surface f has a double generator.

A prime through l and γ meets F in Γ and two generators which meet Γ' in a pair of points collinear with P'. Thus a plane through R contains two generators of f which intersect in a point of R'. Similarly a plane through R' meets f in a pair of generators which intersect in a point of R.

Hence f is of the type IV (B).

We may clearly generate f by a (2, 2) correspondence between two lines R and R'; but this will not be the most general (2, 2) correspondence, it must be specialised so as to give the double generator.

Conversely, take two generators g and g' of F; the solid gg' does not meet F again*. Take l in the solid gg'.

Any point p of g determines a conic of F meeting g' in a point p'; the plane of this conic meets the solid gg' in the line pp'. Also, through p there passes a transversal of g, g', l meeting g' in a point q'.

The ranges (p') and (q') on g', both being homographic with the range (p) on g, are homographic with each other; in general, they will have two self-corresponding points. Thus l is met by two planes of V_3^3 as before.

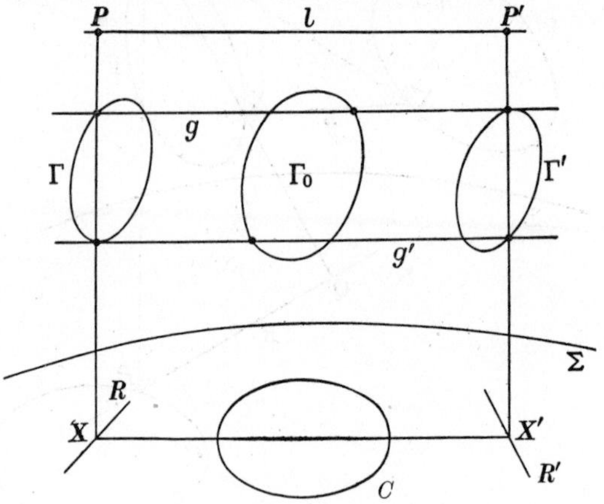

Fig. 3.

But it may happen that the two self-corresponding points coincide, so that l meets only one plane of V_3^3. The surface f has now a double generator and a directrix R, but R must be regarded as a coincidence of two directrices. Any plane through R contains two generators, while through any point of R there pass two generators, f being of the type V (A).

The V_3^3 formed by the planes of the directrix conics meets an arbitrary solid in a cubic curve passing through the four points of intersection of the solid with F. But a solid containing a pair of generators g and g' of F is met by the planes of the directrix conics in lines which give homographic ranges on g and g' and therefore form a regulus.

A line l in the solid meets the regulus in two points, and on projecting we have a surface f of the type IV (B); but if l is taken to touch the quadric surface on which the regulus lies we have a surface f of the type V (A).

73. We can give another generation for a surface of type IV (B) which can immediately be specialised to give the type V (A).

* § 46.

We have generated f by placing its two directrices R, R' in (2, 2) correspondence with united elements X, X' corresponding to one another; whence the double generator XX'.

Let C be the projection of Γ_0, a third directrix conic of F (Fig. 3).

The plane of C is the intersection of Σ with the prime containing l and Γ_0. This prime meets γ in a line through P and γ' in a line through P'; hence the two generators which it contains must be the pair g and g' that determine a solid containing l. Thus the plane of C contains the line XX'.

We may therefore generate f by a (1, 2) correspondence between R and C; to the point X in which R meets the plane of C there must correspond two points of C collinear with X, these giving the double generator XX'.

To the points of R correspond pairs of points of C which form an involution; thus the chords of C which join these pairs of points all pass through a fixed point. This point will lie on XX' and is in fact X'. For the two generators of f which issue from any point of R both meet R', so that their plane contains R' and meets the plane of C in a line through X'.

Similarly the points of R' give rise to pairs of points on C whose joins all pass through X.

This at once suggests the following generation for a surface of the type V (A): take a line R and a conic C in (1, 2) correspondence, every point of R giving a corresponding pair of points of C whose join passes through the point in which R meets the plane of C.

74. *The normal surface in* [5] *with a directrix line.* We now consider the projections of the surface F which has a directrix line λ.

Taking first a general position of l, the projected surface f has a directrix line R, the intersection of Σ with the solid $l\lambda$. A prime through $l\lambda$ meets F in λ and three generators, so that any plane through R contains three generators of f. A plane through l lying in the solid $l\lambda$ meets λ in one point, so that through any point of R there passes one generator of f.

Hence f is of the type II (B).

F can be generated by a (1, 1) correspondence between λ and a directrix cubic. Hence f can be generated by a (1, 1) correspondence between a line R and a twisted cubic.

The planes through λ which contain the generators of F form a locus U of three dimensions, which does not meet a line of general position.

But if l is chosen to meet a plane π of U the solid $l\pi$ meets Σ in a line R which is a directrix and also a generator of f. The primes through the solid $l\lambda$ now meet F in sets of three generators of which one is always the generator in π. Thus any plane through R contains two generators of f other than R, while through any point of R there passes one generator of f other than R.

Hence f is of the type III (B).

By reasoning similar to that employed in obtaining the generation for the type III (A) we see that f can be generated by a line and twisted cubic with a point of intersection, placed in (1, 1) correspondence without a united point.

Further, l may meet two planes of U. Then f has a directrix R which is also a double generator. Any plane through R contains one other generator, while through any point of R there passes one other generator. Here f is of the type V (B).

f can be generated by taking a twisted cubic and one of its chords, and placing them in (1, 1) correspondence without any united point.

It is easily seen that the locus U is of the third order, meeting an arbitrary solid in the points of a cubic curve. If l met three planes of U it would lie entirely on U and so meet F, so that we do not consider this possibility.

75. F contains ∞^3 directrix cubics, they can all be obtained as prime sections residual to any given generator. In general l does not lie in a solid with any of these curves; if, however, it happens that l and one of the cubics do lie in the same solid σ the projected surface f will have two directrices, R, the intersection of Σ with the solid $l\lambda$, and R', the intersection of Σ with the solid σ.

A prime through $l\lambda$ meets F in λ and three generators and meets σ in a plane through l. Hence any plane through R contains three generators meeting in a point of R'. Through any point of R there passes one generator. Thus f is of the type IV (A).

f is generated by placing two lines R and R' in (3, 1) correspondence. This last generation is mentioned by Cremona.

We have now completed the determination of the rational quartic ruled surfaces of ordinary space; the results obtained by the two methods are in complete agreement with one another and also with Cremona's results.

SECTION III

ELLIPTIC QUARTIC RULED SURFACES

76. We must now give a short account of those surfaces which are elliptic; i.e. those whose plane sections are elliptic quartic curves. The generators of such a surface will be represented on Ω by the points of an elliptic quartic curve C, which necessarily lies in a solid S_3.

77. In general, S_3 will be the intersection of the tangent primes to Ω at two points O and O'; these two points represent lines R and R' which are directrices of the surface. S_3 meets Ω in a quadric Q; every generator of Q is met by C in two points and is the intersection of a plane of Ω through O with a plane of the opposite system through O'.

Hence through any point of R there pass two generators which lie in a plane through R', while through any point of R' there pass two generators which lie in a plane through R.

The double curve consists of the lines R and R', while the bitangent developable consists of the pencils of planes through R and R'. A plane section of the surface is a quartic with double points on R and R'.

This is the surface which is generated by means of the most general (2, 2) correspondence between two lines R and R'. It is Cayley's first species and Cremona's eleventh.

This general type of elliptic quartic ruled surface is the most general type of Segre's "rigate biquadratiche*."

An elliptic quartic curve is determined by eight points on a quadric†; hence a ruled quartic surface can be made to contain eight lines of a linear congruence.

78. Suppose now that only one tangent prime of Ω passes through S_3, S_3 meeting Ω in a quadric cone with vertex V. C lies on this cone and does not pass through V. Each generator of the cone meets C in two points and is the intersection of two planes of Ω, one of each system.

The point V represents a line R which is a directrix of the surface.

Any plane of Ω meets S_3 in a point P of the cone. The projection of C from P on to a plane of S_3 is clearly a quartic with a tacnode; so that the two chords of C which can be drawn through P consist of the generator PV counted twice.

The double curve is thus the line R counted twice, while the bitangent developable consists of the planes through R counted twice. Through any point of R there pass two generators which lie in a plane with R. A plane section of the surface is a quartic with a tacnode on R.

This surface is Cayley's fourth species and Cremona's twelfth.

79. An elliptic quartic ruled surface cannot contain a simple directrix or a conic; but if we take a plane through a generator we obtain a cubic curve on the surface. We have in this way ∞^2 cubic curves on the surface. Through any two general points on the surface there pass two of these curves, because the line joining the two points meets the surface in two other points, and through either of the two generators passing through the latter points there is a plane containing the former points. In general two of the cubic curves will intersect in two points on the line of intersection of their planes; the other two points of intersection of this line

* *Memorie Torino*, 36 (1885), 142.

† Salmon, *Geometry of Three Dimensions*, 1 (Dublin, 1914), 360.

with the surface being on the generators which lie in the planes of the cubic curves.

To generate the surface with two directrices we take a line R and a plane cubic curve without a double point, the curve passing through the point P in which R meets its plane. We then place the line and cubic in (1, 2) correspondence with P for a united point. The pairs of points of the cubic which correspond to the points of R must be collinear with a fixed point P' of the curve*; the range of points on R is related projectively to the pencil of lines through P', the point P of the range corresponding to the ray $P'P$ of the pencil. The planes joining the points of the range to the corresponding rays of the pencil all pass through a line R' which passes through P'†.

From this we can deduce at once the generation for an elliptic quartic ruled surface with one directrix. We take a line R and an elliptic cubic curve with a point of intersection P and place them in (1, 2) correspondence with P as a united point. But here the pairs of points of the curve which correspond to the points of the line are collinear with P itself; and the two generators which pass through any point of R are co-planar with R. The correspondence is at once determined by a projectivity between the points of the range on R and the lines of the pencil through P, the point P of the range corresponding to the tangent of the cubic curve at P. This latter is the generator of the surface which lies in the plane of the cubic curve.

SECTION IV

ALGEBRAICAL RESULTS CONNECTED WITH QUARTIC RULED SURFACES

80. We first obtain the equations of the different kinds of quartic ruled surfaces by the methods which we have given for generating them. The results may be compared with those in Salmon's *Geometry of Three Dimensions*‡.

The surface of the type I is generated by the chords of a twisted cubic which belong to a linear complex.

We can take the coordinates of any point on the cubic to be $(\theta^3, \theta^2, \theta, 1)$; the six coordinates of the line joining the two points for which the parameter has the values λ and μ are then

$$\lambda^2 + \lambda\mu + \mu^2, \qquad \lambda + \mu, \qquad 1, \qquad -\lambda\mu, \qquad \lambda\mu(\lambda + \mu), \qquad -\lambda^2\mu^2.$$

* The joins of the pairs of points of a g_2^1 on a plane cubic without a double point all meet the curve again in the same point.

† If there were not a united element the planes would touch a quadric cone.

‡ 2 (Dublin, 1915), §§ 546–554.

Suppose now that the chord belongs to the linear complex

$$bl + 2fm + cn - (b + 2g)\, l' + 2hm' - an' = 0.$$

Then

$$a\lambda^2\mu^2 + b\,(\lambda + \mu)^2 + c + 2f\,(\lambda + \mu) + 2g\lambda\mu + 2h\lambda\mu\,(\lambda + \mu) = 0.$$

Now the coordinates of any point on the chord are

$$\lambda^3 + k\mu^3, \qquad \lambda^2 + k\mu^2, \qquad \lambda + k\mu, \qquad 1 + k,$$

for which

$$xz - y^2 = k\lambda\mu\,(\lambda - \mu)^2, \quad xt - yz = k\,(\lambda + \mu)\,(\lambda - \mu)^2, \quad yt - z^2 = k\,(\lambda - \mu)^2,$$

so that the locus of the chords is the quartic ruled surface

$$a\,(xz - y^2)^2 + b\,(xt - yz)^2 + c\,(yt - z^2)^2 + 2f\,(xt - yz)\,(yt - z^2)$$
$$+ 2g\,(yt - z^2)\,(xz - y^2) + 2h\,(xz - y^2)\,(xt - yz) = 0,$$

on which the existence of the twisted cubic as a double curve is clear. This then may be taken to represent the general surface* of type I.

If, however, we have

$$b\,(b + 2g) - 4fh + ac = 0$$

the surface degenerates into one formed by the chords of the cubic which meet the line whose coordinates are

$$\{-(b + 2g), \quad 2h, \quad -a, \quad b, \quad 2f, \quad c\}$$

and is of the type II (B).

Let us now take the surface of the type II (A).

We take a line and a conic in (1, 3) correspondence with a united point†. The sets of three points of the conic which correspond to the points of the line form a singly infinite set of triangles whose sides all touch another conic. The two conics have four common tangents; these touching the first conic in double points of four of the sets of three points. Take two of these four points as X and Y; the plane of the conic being $z = t$ and the line being $x = y = 0$. Let Z be the point of the line which gives rise to the set of three points with the double point X and T the point of the line which gives rise to the set of three points with the double point Y. Let the equation of the conic be

$$yz + zx + xy = z - t = 0.$$

Then any point of the conic can be written $(\theta, 1 - \theta, \theta^2 - \theta, \theta^2 - \theta)$, while any point of the line is $(0, 0, \phi, 1)$; and the general (1, 3) relation

$$\phi\,(a\theta^3 + b\theta^2 + c\theta + d) = A\theta^3 + B\theta^2 + C\theta + D$$

must become

$$\phi\,(\theta - 1)^2\,(a\theta + \beta) = \theta^2\,(a\theta + \gamma).$$

Any point of the surface is

$$(\theta, \quad 1 - \theta, \quad \theta^2 - \theta + \lambda\phi, \quad \theta^2 - \theta + \lambda),$$

so that

$$z - \phi t = x\,(\theta - 1)\,(1 - \phi),$$

and

$$\phi = \frac{x^2\,\{ax + \gamma\,(x + y)\}}{y^2\,\{ax + \beta\,(x + y)\}}.$$

Thus

$$(x + y)\,(z - \phi t) + xy\,(1 - \phi) = 0,$$

$$(yz + zx + xy)\,y^2\,\{ax + \beta\,(x + y)\} = \{xy + t\,(x + y)\}\,x^2\,\{ax + \gamma\,(x + y)\},$$

which divides by $x + y$, giving

$$zy^2\,\{ax + \beta\,(x + y)\} - tx^2\,\{ax + \gamma\,(x + y)\} = xy\,\{ax\,(x - y) + \gamma x^2 - \beta y^2\},$$

$$z\,\{\beta y^3 + (a + \beta)\,xy^2\} - t\,\{\gamma x^2 y + (\gamma + a)\,x^3\} = xy\,\{(\gamma + a)\,x^2 - axy - \beta y^2\}.$$

* Salmon, § 549. † § 70.

Writing then $z = \zeta - x$ and $t = \tau - y$ we find*

$$\zeta\,(ay^3 + bxy^2) + \tau\,(cx^2y + dx^3) = ex^2y^2.$$

For a surface of the type II (C) we must take a line and a conic in (1, 2) correspondence†. Let the line meet the plane of the conic in Y, and let X and Z be the points of contact of the tangents from Y. Then the conic is

$$xz - y^2 = t = 0.$$

Take T on the line.

Then any point of the conic is $(\theta^2, \theta, 1, 0)$, while any point of the line is $(0, \phi, 0, 1)$. The points of the line give rise to pairs of an involution on the conic; one of these pairs will be on a line through Y, and we can take T to correspond to this pair. Since this pair divides X and Z harmonically (the join passing through the pole of XZ) we can take their parameters to be $+1$ and -1, so that the (1, 2) relation will be of the form

$$\phi\,(a\theta^2 + b\theta + c) = \theta^2 - 1.$$

Any point of the surface is $(\lambda\theta^2, \lambda\theta + \mu\phi, \lambda, \mu)$, giving

$$x = \theta^2 z, \qquad y = \theta z + \phi t = \theta z + \frac{\theta^2 - 1}{a\theta^2 + b\theta + c}\,t,$$

$$(y - \theta z)\,(a\theta^2 + b\theta + c) = (\theta^2 - 1)\,t,$$

$$ax\,(y - \theta z) + byz\theta - bzx + cz\,(y - \theta z) = t\,(x - z);$$

or

$$axy - bzx + cyz + t\,(z - x) = \theta\,(azx - byz + cz^2).$$

Squaring this we have the equation to the surface in the form

$$[cyz - bzx + axy + zt - tx]^2 = xz\,(ax - by + cz)^2.$$

This clearly has the double line $z = x = 0$ and also a double conic, the intersection of the plane

$$ax - by + cz = 0$$

with the quadric

$$cyz - bzx + axy + zt - tx = 0,$$

or with the quadric

$$b\,(y^2 - zx) + t\,(z - x) = 0.$$

The planes $x = 0$ and $cy + t = 0$ give a torsal generator, as also do the planes $z = 0$ and $ay - t = 0$, the respective tangent planes being $x = 0$ and $z = 0$.

The intersection of the surface with the plane $t = 0$ is given by

$$\begin{aligned} 0 &= (cyz - bzx + axy)^2 - xz\,(ax - by + cz)^2 \\ &= \{y\,(ax - by + cz)^2 - b\,(zx - y^2)\}^2 - xz\,(ax - by + cz)^2 \\ &= (zx - y^2)\,[b^2\,(2x - y^2) - 2by\,(ax - by + cz) - (ax - by + cz)^2] \\ &= (zx - y^2)\,[(b^2 - 2ac)\,zx - a^2x^2 - c^2z^2], \end{aligned}$$

which consists of the original conic together with two lines through Y.

The equation of this pair of lines can be written

$$(ax + by + cz)\,(ax - by + cz) + b^2\,(y^2 - zx) = 0,$$

so that they pass through the two points of intersection of the double conic and the conic $xz - y^2 = t = 0$; the two conics lying on a quadric.

For a surface of the type III (A) we take a line and conic with a point of intersection and place them in (1, 2) correspondence without a united point†.

* Cf. Salmon, § 546. † § 71.

The pairs of corresponding points on the conic form an involution; take the two double points of this as X and Y, and let the corresponding points be Z and T. Then we can take the line to be $x = y = 0$ and the conic to be

$$yz + zx + xy = z - t = 0.$$

Any point of the line can be written $(0, 0, \phi, 1)$ and any point of the conic $(\theta, 1 - \theta, \theta^2 - \theta, \theta^2 - \theta)$. The (1, 2) relation must be of the form

$$\phi\,(\theta - 1)^2 = \theta^2 a.$$

Then the coordinates of any point of the surface are

$$(\theta,\ 1 - \theta,\ \theta^2 - \theta + \lambda\phi,\ \theta^2 - \theta + \lambda)$$

for which $$z - \phi t = x\,(\theta - 1)\,(1 - \phi),$$

so that $$z\,(\theta - 1)^2 - a\theta^2 t = x\,(\theta - 1)\,[(\theta - 1)^2 - a\theta^2],$$

or $$(x + y)\,(zy^2 - atx^2) = xy\,(ax^2 - y^2).$$

Writing $-t = y + \tau$ and $z = \zeta - x$, we obtain

$$(y^2\zeta + a\tau x^2)\,(x + y) = mx^2y^2,$$

and we take for the equation of the surface*

$$mx^2y^2 = (x + y)\,(x^2t + y^2z).$$

For a surface of the type III (B) we may take a line and a twisted cubic with a point of intersection and place them in (1, 1) correspondence without a united point†. We will, however, obtain this surface as the reciprocal of III (A).

The equation of the surface III (A) is

$$\mu x^2y^2 = (x + y)\,(x^2t + y^2z).$$

A tangent plane is $$lx + my + nz + pt = 0,$$

where $$n = (x + y)\,y^2, \qquad p = (x + y)\,x^2,$$

and $$lx + my = -\,(nz + pt) = -\,\mu x^2y^2.$$

Also $$nx^2 + py^2 = 2x^2y^2\,(x + y),$$

so that $$2\,(lx + my)\,(x + y) + \mu\,(nx^2 + py^2) = 0,$$

or, since this is homogeneous in x and y and $x^2 : y^2 = p : n$,

$$lp + mn + (l + m)\sqrt{np} + \mu np = 0,$$

or $$(lp + mn + \mu np)^2 = (l + m)^2\,np.$$

This being the tangential equation of the surface III (A), the point-equation of the surface III (B) can be written‡

$$(xt + yz + \mu zt)^2 = zt\,(x + y)^2.$$

It has a double conic $x + y = xt + yz + \mu zt = 0$ and a double line $z = t = 0$ which meets the conic in $(1, -1, 0, 0)$.

To generate a surface of the type IV (A) we take two lines R and R' in (3, 1) correspondence‖. There will be four points of R' for which two of the three corresponding points on R coincide. Take two of these four points as X and Y, the corresponding coincident elements being Z and T. Any point of R' is $(\theta, 1, 0, 0)$, while any point of R is $(0, 0, \phi, 1)$; the (1, 3) relation between θ and ϕ is necessarily of the form

$$\theta = \frac{\alpha\phi^3 + \beta\phi^2}{\gamma\phi + \delta}.$$

* Cf. Salmon, § 548.

† § 74.

‡ Cf. Salmon, § 548.

‖ § 75.

Then any point of the surface has coordinates $(\theta, 1, \lambda\phi, \lambda)$, or

$$[\alpha\phi^3 + \beta\phi^2, \quad \gamma\phi + \delta, \quad \lambda\phi(\gamma\phi + \delta), \quad \lambda(\gamma\phi + \delta)].$$

Hence
$$\frac{x}{y} = \frac{\alpha z^3/t^3 + \beta z^2/t^2}{\gamma z/t + \delta} = \frac{(\alpha z + \beta t)\, z^2}{(\gamma z + \delta t)\, t^2}$$

and the equation of the surface is *

$$x(\gamma z + \delta t)\, t^2 = y(\alpha z + \beta t)\, z^2.$$

To generate the surface of the type IV (B) we take two lines R, R' in (2, 2) correspondence, the correspondence being specialised so as to give a double generator †. In a general (2, 2) correspondence there will be four points of either line giving rise to pairs of coincident points on the other; but here two of the four points will themselves coincide. Take then X and Y as the corresponding double elements; and let Z be another point on R which gives rise to a pair of coincident points T on R'. Any point of R is $(\phi, 0, 1, 0)$ and any point of R' is $(0, \theta, 0, 1)$, the (2, 2) relation will be of the form

$$\phi = \alpha\phi^2 + \beta\theta\phi + \gamma\theta^2.$$

Any point of the surface is $(\lambda\phi, \mu\theta, \lambda, \mu)$, whence

$$\frac{x}{z} = \phi, \qquad \frac{y}{t} = \theta,$$

and
$$\frac{x}{z} = \alpha\frac{x^2}{z^2} + \beta\frac{xy}{zt} + \gamma\frac{y^2}{t^2},$$

or
$$xzt^2 = \alpha x^2t^2 + \beta xyzt + \gamma y^2z^2;$$

and we have for the equation of the surface ‡

$$y^2z^2 + mxyzt + t^2(axz + bx^2) = 0.$$

There is a second generation which can be used for a surface of the type IV (B) ‖; we take a line and conic in (1, 2) correspondence, making the two points of the conic which correspond to the point in which the line meets the plane collinear with this point. Take the point of intersection of the line with the plane of the conic as Y; the points X and Z being the points of contact of the tangents from Y. Then the conic is $t = xz - y^2 = 0$, with points $(\theta^2, \theta, 1, 0)$, and we can take the parameters of the two points which correspond to Y as ± 1. Any point of the line is $(0, \phi, 0, 1)$, if we take T on the line. The pairs of points of the conic which correspond to the points of the line form an involution; we shall take T as the point which gives rise to the pair of the involution including Z. Then the (1, 2) relation between ϕ and θ must be of the form

$$\phi(\theta^2 - 1) = A\theta^2 + B\theta.$$

Any point of the surface is $(\lambda\theta^2, \lambda\theta + \mu\phi, \lambda, \mu)$, giving

$$x = \theta^2 z, \qquad y = \theta z + \phi t = \theta z + t\frac{A\theta^2 + B\theta}{\theta^2 - 1},$$

* Cf. Salmon, § 547.

† § 72.

‡ Cf. Salmon, § 553.

‖ § 73

i.e. $$(y - \theta z)(\theta^2 - 1) = (A\theta^2 + B\theta)\,t,$$

$$x(y - \theta z) - z(y - \theta z) = t(Ax + Bz\theta),$$

$$xy - yz - Atx = \theta(Bzt + zx - z^2);$$

and on squaring we have the equation of the surface in the form

$$(yz - xy + Atx)^2 = zx(x - z + Bt)^2.$$

This surface has clearly the double lines $x = z = 0$ and $x - z = t = 0$. Writing it in the form

$$\{y(z - x + Bt) + t(Ax - By)\}^2 = zx(x - z + Bt)^2,$$

we see that it has also a double line

$$x - z + Bt = Ax - By = 0.$$

The line $x - z = t = 0$ is a double generator; it meets the other two lines which are double directrices.

Now if $B = 0$ the two directrices coincide, and we have a surface of the type V (A) whose equation is

$$(yz - xy + Atx)^2 = xz(x - z)^2.$$

The pair of points of the conic which corresponds to any point of the line is now such that its join passes through Y.

The section by any plane $\alpha x + \beta y + \gamma z + At = 0$ is a quartic curve with a tacnode at $x = z = 0$ and another ordinary node.

To generate a surface of the type V (B) we take a twisted cubic and one of its chords and place them in (1, 1) correspondence without any united points*. Take X and Y to be the points where the line meets the cubic; any point of the line is then $(\theta, 1, 0, 0)$. Also, θ may be taken as the parameter of the cubic, and if Z and T correspond to X and Y respectively any point of the curve can be taken to have coordinates

$$\theta(\theta - \beta), \quad \theta(\theta - \alpha), \quad \theta(\theta - \alpha)(\theta - \beta), \quad (\theta - \alpha)(\theta - \beta).$$

Any point of the ruled surface will have coordinates

$$\theta(\theta - \beta) + \lambda\theta, \quad \theta(\theta - \alpha) + \lambda, \quad \theta(\theta - \alpha)(\theta - \beta), \quad (\theta - \alpha)(\theta - \beta).$$

Then $$z - \alpha t = (\theta - \alpha)\,t, \qquad z - \beta t = (\theta - \beta)\,t,$$

$$yz - xt = \theta t\{\theta^2 - (\alpha + 1)\theta + \beta\};$$

so that $$(yz - xt)(z - \alpha t)(z - \beta t) = zt\{z^2 - (\alpha + 1)zt + \beta t^2\}$$

is the equation of the surface.

By taking two other planes of the pencil $z + kt = 0$ instead of $z = 0$ and $t = 0$ we can reduce this equation to the form†

$$z^2t^2 = (az^2 + bzt + ct^2)(yz - xt).$$

To generate the general elliptic quartic surface, which we may call a surface of the type VI (A), we take two lines and place them in (2, 2) correspondence‡.

* § 74. † Cf. Salmon, § 548. ‡ § 77.

On either line there will be four points for which the two corresponding points coincide. Take, on one of the lines, two of these points as X and Y, the corresponding double elements on the other line being Z and T. Any point of the first line is $(\theta, 1, 0, 0)$ and any point of the second is $(0, 0, \phi, 1)$ with a $(2, 2)$ relation

$$a\theta^2 + \theta\,(c\phi^2 + d\phi + e) + b\phi^2 = 0.$$

Any point of the ruled surface is $(\lambda\theta,\ \lambda,\ \mu\phi,\ \mu)$ so that $\theta = \frac{x}{y}$ and $\phi = \frac{z}{t}$. The $(2, 2)$ relation gives

$$a\frac{x^2}{y^2} + \frac{x}{y}\left(c\frac{z^2}{t^2} + d\frac{z}{t} + e\right) + b\frac{z^2}{t^2} = 0,$$

and the equation of the surface is

$$ax^2t^2 + xy\,(cz^2 + dzt + et^2) + by^2z^2 = 0.$$

To generate the type of elliptic quartic ruled surface with one directrix, which we may call the type VI (B), we take a line R and a plane elliptic cubic curve; this cubic passes through the point P in which R meets its plane. We then place the line and the cubic in $(1, 2)$ correspondence with P as a united point, the pairs of points of the cubic which correspond to the points of R all having their joins passing through P*. Let the cubic curve lie in the plane $z = 0$, the point P being $x = y = z = 0$ and the tangent to the curve there $x = z = 0$. Then the equation to the curve may be written

$$xt^2 + (ax^2 + 2bxy + cy^2)\,t + Ax^3 + 3Bx^2y + 3Cxy^2 + Dy^3 = 0.$$

We take R, passing through P, to be the intersection of the planes $x = 0$ and $y = 0$. We refer the points of R projectively to the pencil of lines $x = ky$, $z = 0$ in such a way that the point P of R corresponds to the line $x = 0$ of the pencil, i.e. we take the point $(0, 0, k, 1)$ of R to correspond to the line $x = ky$, $z = 0$ of the pencil. Then the coordinates of a point of the ruled surface are

$$(k\eta,\quad \eta,\quad k\lambda,\quad 1 + \lambda),$$

where η is a root of

$$k + (ak^2 + 2bk + c)\,\eta + (Ak^3 + 3Bk^2 + 3Ck + D)\,\eta^2 = 0.$$

If then (x, y, z, t) denotes the point on the ruled surface we have

$$\frac{x}{y} + \frac{ax^2 + 2bxy + cy^2}{y^2}\,\frac{xy}{xt - yz} + \frac{Ax^3 + 3Bx^2y + 3Cxy^2 + Dy^3}{y^3}\,\frac{x^2y^2}{(xt - yz)^2} = 0,$$

and the equation to the surface is†

$$(xt - yz)^2 + (ax^2 + 2bxy + cy^2)\,(xt - yz) + (Ax^3 + 3Bx^2y + 3Cxy^2 + Dy^3)\,x = 0.$$

The section of this surface by a plane is a quartic curve having a tacnode at the point where R meets the plane.

* § 79.

† Cf. Salmon, § 554.

Thus the equations of the different types of quartic ruled surfaces are as follows:

I $a(xz-y^2)^2+b(xt-yz)^2+c(yt-z^2)^2$
$+2f(xt-yz)(yt-z^2)+2g(yt-z^2)(xz-y^2)+2h(xz-y^2)(xt-yz)=0.$

II (A) $zy^2(ay+bx)+tx^2(cy+dx)=ex^2y^2.$

II (B) As in I, but with the relation $b^2+2bg-4hf+ac=0.$

II (C) $(cyz-bzx+axy+zt-tx)^2=xz(ax-by+cz)^2.$

III (A) $mx^2y^2=(x+y)(x^2t+y^2z).$

III (B) $(xt+yz+\mu zt)^2=zt(x+y)^2.$

IV (A) $x(\gamma z+\delta t)t^2=y(\alpha z+\beta t)z^2.$

IV (B) $\left.\begin{array}{l} y^2z^2+mxyzt+t^2(az+bx)x=0 \\ (yz-xy+Atx)^2=zx(x-z+Bt)^2 \end{array}\right\}.$

V (A) $(yz-xy+Atx)^2=zx(x-z)^2.$

V (B) $z^2t^2=(az^2+bzt+ct^2)(yz-xt).$

VI (A) $ax^2t^2+xy(cz^2+dzt+et^2)+by^2z^2=0.$

VI (B) $(xt-yz)^2+(ax^2+2bxy+cy^2)(xt-yz)+(Ax^3+3Bx^2y$
$+3Cxy^2+Dy^3)x=0.$

81. If in [5] we take two conics and place them in (1, 1) correspondence we obtain the most general rational normal quartic ruled surface.

Let the planes of the conics be $x_0=x_1=x_2=0$ and $x_3=x_4=x_5=0$. We may then take a point of the first conic as $(0, 0, 0, \theta^2, \theta, 1)$ and the corresponding point of the second as $(\theta^2, \theta, 1, 0, 0, 0)$. Then any point on the ruled surface has coordinates of the form

$$(\theta^2,\ \theta,\ 1,\ \lambda\theta^2,\ \lambda\theta,\ \lambda),$$

so that the equations of the ruled surface are*

$$\frac{x_0}{x_1}=\frac{x_1}{x_2}=\frac{x_3}{x_4}=\frac{x_4}{x_5}.$$

If θ is constant we have a generator of the surface; if λ is constant we have a conic on the surface. We thus obtain ∞^1 directrix conics. The equations to the plane of any one of these are

$$x_3=\lambda x_0, \qquad x_4=\lambda x_1, \qquad x_5=\lambda x_2,$$

so that the equations of the V_3^3 formed by the planes are

$$\frac{x_0}{x_3}=\frac{x_1}{x_4}=\frac{x_2}{x_5}.$$

This clearly contains the quartic surface.

All directrix conics can be obtained as residuals of prime sections through any two fixed generators. The equation of the prime, which contains the conic whose points are $(\theta^2, \theta, 1, k\theta^2, k\theta, 1)$ and the two generators given by $(\alpha^2, \alpha, 1, \lambda\alpha^2, \lambda\alpha, 1)$ and $(\beta^2, \beta, 1, \mu\beta^2, \mu\beta, 1)$, is

$$k[x_0-(\alpha+\beta)x_1+\alpha\beta x_2]=x_3-(\alpha+\beta)x_4+\alpha\beta x_5.$$

Take a point $(\xi_0, \xi_1, \xi_2, \xi_3, \xi_4, \xi_5)$ on V_3^3 and any other point whatever $(x_0, x_1, x_2, x_3, x_4, x_5)$.

* § 41.

Then the coordinates of any point on the line joining them are

$$(\xi_0 + \mu x_0, \quad \xi_1 + \mu x_1, \quad \xi_2 + \mu x_2, \quad \xi_3 + \mu x_3, \quad \xi_4 + \mu x_4, \quad \xi_5 + \mu x_5),$$

and if this point lies on V_3^3 we have

$$\frac{\xi_0 + \mu x_0}{\xi_3 + \mu x_3} = \frac{\xi_1 + \mu x_1}{\xi_4 + \mu x_4} = \frac{\xi_2 + \mu x_2}{\xi_5 + \mu x_5}.$$

These equations are satisfied by $\mu = 0$ as they should be. There will be two roots $\mu = 0$, or the line will touch the locus, if we have

$$\xi_0 x_4 + x_0 \xi_4 = \xi_1 x_3 + x_1 \xi_3,$$
$$\xi_1 x_5 + x_1 \xi_5 = \xi_2 x_4 + x_2 \xi_4,$$
$$\xi_2 x_3 + x_2 \xi_3 = \xi_0 x_5 + x_0 \xi_5;$$

and in virtue of the equations satisfied by ξ these may be written

$$\frac{x_4}{\xi_4} + \frac{x_0}{\xi_0} = \frac{x_3}{\xi_3} + \frac{x_1}{\xi_1},$$
$$\frac{x_5}{\xi_5} + \frac{x_1}{\xi_1} = \frac{x_4}{\xi_4} + \frac{x_2}{\xi_2},$$
$$\frac{x_3}{\xi_3} + \frac{x_2}{\xi_2} = \frac{x_5}{\xi_5} + \frac{x_0}{\xi_0};$$

so that the tangents of V_3^3 at ξ lie in a solid—the tangent solid of V_3^3, whose equations are

$$\frac{x_0}{\xi_0} - \frac{x_3}{\xi_3} = \frac{x_1}{\xi_1} - \frac{x_4}{\xi_4} = \frac{x_2}{\xi_2} - \frac{x_5}{\xi_5}.$$

This tangent solid will, of course, contain the plane of V_3^3 which passes through ξ; to find the points common to the solid and V_3^3 we write

$$\frac{x_0}{x_3} = \frac{x_1}{x_4} = \frac{x_2}{x_5} = \lambda$$

in the equations of the solid, which become

$$x_3\left(\frac{\lambda}{\xi_0} - \frac{1}{\xi_3}\right) = x_4\left(\frac{\lambda}{\xi_1} - \frac{1}{\xi_4}\right) = x_5\left(\frac{\lambda}{\xi_2} - \frac{1}{\xi_5}\right);$$

and since $\xi_0/\xi_3 = \xi_1/\xi_4 = \xi_2/\xi_5 = \kappa$, say, we have

$$\frac{x_3}{\xi_3}\left(\frac{\lambda}{\kappa} - 1\right) = \frac{x_4}{\xi_4}\left(\frac{\lambda}{\kappa} - 1\right) = \frac{x_5}{\xi_5}\left(\frac{\lambda}{\kappa} - 1\right).$$

Now these equations are satisfied by $\lambda = \kappa$; we have thus the plane of V_3^3 passing through ξ. But they are also satisfied by

$$\frac{x_3}{\xi_3} = \frac{x_4}{\xi_4} = \frac{x_5}{\xi_5},$$

which make also, from the equations of the solid,

$$\frac{x_0}{\xi_0} = \frac{x_1}{\xi_1} = \frac{x_2}{\xi_2},$$

so that we obtain the points of a straight line.

Incidentally through every point ξ of V_3^3 there passes a line whose equations are

$$\frac{x_0}{\xi_0} = \frac{x_1}{\xi_1} = \frac{x_2}{\xi_2}, \qquad \frac{x_3}{\xi_3} = \frac{x_4}{\xi_4} = \frac{x_5}{\xi_5}.$$

We have thus ∞^2 lines on $V_3{}^3$. Each of them is a directrix, meeting every generating plane. The ∞^1 generators of the quartic surface are a particular set of these lines.

The coordinates of any point on the chord of the surface which joins the points $(\theta^2, \theta, 1, \lambda\theta^2, \lambda\theta, \lambda)$ and $(\phi^2, \phi, 1, \mu\phi^2, \mu\phi, \mu)$ may be taken as

$$(\theta^2 + \nu\phi^2, \quad \theta + \nu\phi, \quad 1 + \nu, \quad \lambda\theta^2 + \mu\nu\phi^2, \quad \lambda\theta + \mu\nu\phi, \quad \lambda + \mu\nu),$$

and the equations of the chord can be taken as

$$\begin{aligned} x_0 - x_1(\theta + \phi) + x_2\theta\phi &= 0, \\ x_3 - x_4(\theta + \phi) + x_5\theta\phi &= 0, \\ \lambda(x_1 - \phi x_2) &= x_4 - \phi x_5, \\ \mu(x_1 - \theta x_2) &= x_4 - \theta x_5, \end{aligned}$$

the equation of any other prime through the chord being a linear combination of these four.

These equations shew that through a general point of [5] there passes one and only one chord of the surface; if the coordinates of the point are substituted in the four equations the first two will give θ and ϕ and the last two λ and μ.

The only exception is when

$$\frac{x_0}{x_3} = \frac{x_1}{x_4} = \frac{x_2}{x_5},$$

or the point lies on $V_3{}^3$, as is obvious geometrically.

Thus a general rational quartic ruled surface in [4] has one double point, but there is also a rational quartic ruled surface in [4] with a double line. This latter is obtained by projecting the normal surface from a point of $V_3{}^3$ and is generated by a line and a conic in (2, 1) correspondence.

CHAPTER III

QUINTIC RULED SURFACES

SECTION I

RATIONAL QUINTIC RULED SURFACES CONSIDERED AS CURVES ON Ω

82. There is a classification of quintic ruled surfaces given by Schwarz*, the surfaces being classified by means of their double curves. When this has been obtained we can at once deduce, by the principle of duality, a second classification of quintic ruled surfaces by means of their bitangent developables. These two classifications are quite different; two surfaces which belong to different classes according to one classification can very well belong to the same class according to the other—this is sufficiently clear from Cremona's table of quartic ruled surfaces and is quite evident from the classification of the quintic surfaces themselves that we shall obtain. Thus, although Schwarz's classification is exhaustive, it is such that another, which is not included in it, can be deduced immediately from it. It is then surely desirable to obtain the more precise classification which includes both of these; and when this has been obtained the application of the principle of duality can only reproduce it.

The work is more complicated than that for the quartic ruled surfaces; one cause of this is the higher degree of the double curve and class of the bitangent developable. For the rational quartic ruled surface the double curve is a twisted cubic, and if it breaks up it must contain a line as a part of itself; this is always easy to detect when we represent the generators of the ruled surface as the points of a curve C on Ω. But for the rational quintic ruled surface the double curve is a sextic, and if this breaks up it does not necessarily contain a line.

It will, of course, be necessary to make use of the properties of quintic curves; for some of these we can refer to a paper by Marletta†, while others that are required will be obtained in the course of the work; certain loci connected with the curve are investigated in so far as their properties are required. At the end of his paper Marletta mentions this representation of the generators of a rational quintic ruled surface, dividing the surfaces into three main classes and referring to Schwarz's paper.

* "Über die geradlinigen Flächen fünften Grades," *Journal für Math.* 67 (1867), 23–57.

† "Sulle curve razionali del quinto ordine," *Palermo Rendiconti*, 19 (1905), 94–119.

The rational quintic curves on a quadric Ω in [5]

83. Any rational quintic curve may be regarded as the projection of a rational normal quintic in [5]*. We may project on to a [4] from a point on a chord of the normal curve; this shews that it is possible to have a rational quintic in [4] with a double point. Similarly, by projecting from a line meeting two chords of the normal curve, we may have a rational quintic in [3] with two double points and, by projecting from a line in a trisecant plane of the normal curve, we may have a rational quintic in [3] with a triple point.

We shall then divide the rational quintic curves on Ω into seven classes:

I. The rational normal curve in [5].

II. The curve lies in a prime which does not touch Ω.

III. The curve lies in a tangent prime of Ω but does not pass through the point of contact.

IV. The curve lies in a tangent prime of Ω and passes through the point of contact.

V. The curve lies in a tangent prime of Ω and has a double point at the point of contact.

VI. The curve lies on the section of Ω by an S_3 through which pass two tangent primes of Ω.

VII. The curve lies on the quadric cone in which Ω is met by an S_3 which touches it.

84. We can at once subdivide these classes. If a rational quintic C lies in a tangent prime T touching Ω in a point O then, when projected from O on to any solid of T, it becomes a rational quintic lying on a quadric surface. If the curve passes through O it becomes a rational quartic, while if it has a double point at O it becomes a twisted cubic. The rational curves of the third and fourth orders which lie on a quadric surface are well known; we give here those of the fifth order. There are two kinds:

(*a*) The residual intersection of the quadric with a quartic surface passing through three of its generators of the same system. This curve meets all the generators of one system in four points and all of the other system in one point.

(*b*) The residual intersection of the quadric with a cubic surface which passes through a generator and touches the quadric in two points. This curve has two double points; it meets all generators of one system in three points and all of the other system in two points.

There are also two kinds of rational quintic curves which lie on a quadric cone:

(*a*) The residual intersection of the cone with a cubic surface passing through a generator and touching the cone in two points. This curve has

* § 8.

two double points; it passes through the vertex and meets every generator in two points other than the vertex.

(*b*) The residual intersection of the cone with a nodal cubic surface passing through a generator, the node being at the vertex of the cone. This curve has a triple point at the vertex and meets every generator of the cone in one point other than the vertex.

We are now in a position to give a more minute classification of the rational quintic curves C on Ω.

It may be remarked here that if we have a rational quintic curve in [5] there is one trisecant plane passing through a general point of [5]*. Hence the rational quintic in [4], if it has not a double point, has a trisecant chord.

85. We now classify the rational quintic curves which lie on Ω as follows:

I. The rational normal curve in [5].

II. (A) C lies in a prime which does not touch Ω.

(B) C lies in a prime which does not touch Ω, and has a double point.

III. C lies in a tangent prime T of Ω but does not pass through the point of contact O.

(A) C meets every plane ϖ through O in four points and every plane ρ through O in one point.

(B) C meets every plane ϖ through O in one point and every plane ρ through O in four points.

(C) C meets every plane ϖ through O in three points, every plane ρ through O in two points, and has a double point; O lying on a chord of C.

(D) C meets every plane ϖ through O in two points, every plane ρ through O in three points, and has a double point; O lying on a chord of C.

(E) C meets every plane ϖ through O in three points and every plane ρ through O in two points; two chords of C passing through O.

(F) C meets every plane ϖ through O in two points and every plane ρ through O in three points; two chords of C passing through O.

IV. C lies in a tangent prime T of Ω and passes through the point of contact O.

(A) C meets every plane ϖ through O in three points and every plane ρ through O in one point other than O.

(B) C meets every plane ϖ through O in one point and every plane ρ through O in three points other than O.

(C) C meets every plane of Ω through O in two points other than O and has a double point.

* Marletta, *loc. cit.* § 12.

(D) C meets every plane of Ω through O in two points other than O and has its trisecant passing through O.

V. C lies in a tangent prime T of Ω and has a double point at the point of contact O.

(A) C meets every plane ϖ through O in two points and every plane ρ through O in one point other than O.

(B) C meets every plane ϖ through O in one point and every plane ρ through O in two points other than O.

VI. C lies on the quadric Q in which Ω is met by an S_3 through which pass two tangent primes of Ω.

(A) C meets all generators of Q of one system in four points and all of the other system in one point.

(B) C meets all generators of Q of one system in three points and all of the other system in two points, and has two double points.

VII. C lies on the quadric cone in which Ω is met by an S_3 touching it in a point V.

(A) C passes through V, meets every generator of the cone in two points other than V, and has two double points.

(B) C has a triple point at V and meets every generator of the cone in one point other than V.

The general surface in [3]

86. The generators of a ruled surface of the fifth order in [3] will be represented on Ω, if the surface is general, by the points of a rational normal quintic curve C. If C is projected from any plane on to another plane we obtain a plane quintic curve which is rational, and has therefore six double points. Hence, in the [5] containing C, a plane is met by six chords of the curve. This is true in particular for a plane of Ω.

Hence the double curve of the ruled surface is of order six, while the bitangent developable is of the sixth class*.

87. *The genus of the double curve.* We have just seen that there are six chords of C meeting an arbitrary plane. Hence the chords of C form a locus U_3^6, of three dimensions and of the sixth order. If we project C from a plane which meets it in one point on to another plane we obtain a rational quartic with three double points; so that the plane is only met by three chords of C other than those which pass through its point of intersection with C. Hence C is a triple curve on U_3^6. There is no double surface on U_3^6 because no two chords of C can intersect in a point not lying on C†.

* See § 33.

† For if they did there would be a [4] meeting C in more than five points. If the curve is given by $x_0 : x_1 : x_2 : x_3 : x_4 : x_5 = \theta^5 : \theta^4 : \theta^3 : \theta^2 : \theta : 1$, the equations of U_3^6 are

$$\left\| \begin{matrix} x_0 & x_1 & x_2 & x_3 \\ x_1 & x_2 & x_3 & x_4 \\ x_2 & x_3 & x_4 & x_5 \end{matrix} \right\| = 0.$$

The tangent prime to Ω at any point of C meets C in three other points; hence through any point of C there pass three chords lying on Ω. The chords of C lying on Ω form a ruled surface with C as a triple curve; this is merely the intersection of Ω and U_3^6. The curve of intersection of this ruled surface with a prime is in (1, 1) correspondence with the points of the double curve and the planes of the bitangent developable*.

Now a prime S_4 meets C in five points a, b, c, d, e, and meets U_3^6 in a sextic surface with these five points as triple points and no other singularities. Also S_4 meets Ω in a quadric primal through a, b, c, d, e. Hence the chords of C which lie on Ω meet S_4 in a curve of order 12 with these five points for triple points.

Project this curve from the line ab on to a plane in S_4. We obtain a sextic with three triple points. Any solid through ab will meet U_3^6 in a sextic curve of which ab is a part; but if the solid contains the plane abc it will meet U_3^6 in the lines bc, ca, ab and a twisted cubic passing through a, b, c. This cubic can only meet a plane through ab in one other point. Thus it is clear that no plane through ab can meet the curve of order 12 in more than one point in addition to a and b. Thus the plane sextic which we obtain has no singular points other than three triple points, and is therefore an elliptic curve. Hence the curve of order 12 is also an elliptic curve.

Thus we have proved that the double curve of the ruled surface is an elliptic curve, while the planes of the bitangent developable form an elliptic family.

88. *The triple point and the tritangent plane.* By a result already found† for curves of any order and genus we see that if a rational quintic curve C lies on Ω there are two of its trisecant planes also lying on Ω.

It is at once seen that these two planes cannot belong to the same system of planes on Ω. For suppose, if possible, that we have two planes ϖ_1 and ϖ_2 of the same system, both trisecant to C. ϖ_1 and ϖ_2 intersect in a point A and lie in a [4], and since no [4] can meet C in more than five points A must lie on C. But ϖ_1 and ϖ_2 both lie in the tangent prime of Ω at A, which only meets C in three points other than A. Hence our supposition is false.

There is then one plane of each system of Ω which is trisecant to C; so that the rational quintic ruled surface has one triple point and one tritangent plane.

89. We now know that the double curve of the ruled surface is an elliptic sextic curve with a triple point. If we project this from a point of itself on to a plane we obtain an elliptic quintic curve; this has a triple point which is the projection of the triple point on the sextic and it must have

* Cf. §§ 33 and 65. † § 35.

two further double points. Hence through any point of the double curve there pass two of its trisecants. These are precisely the two generators of the ruled surface which intersect in this point of the double curve; and we can therefore generate the surface by the trisecants of an elliptic sextic curve with a triple point*.

It is not difficult to see which are the three generators of the surface passing through the triple point. The plane containing two of the tangents at the triple point will meet the curve in a single further point P, and if the curve is projected from P on to a plane the triple point becomes, on the resulting quintic curve, a triple point at which two tangents coincide. Thus this quintic curve will only have one other double point, so that only one proper trisecant of the sextic curve passes through P. The line joining P to the triple point is a generator of the ruled surface. The other two generators passing through the triple point are at once determined similarly.

Further consideration of the surfaces whose generators do not belong to a linear complex

90. Considering again the rational normal quintic C, let us take a plane meeting C in a single point P. In general there are three points of this plane, other than P, through which pass chords of C. But suppose that there is an infinite number of chords of C which meet the plane; the plane then meets U_3^6 in a curve Γ.

If we project C from P on to a space [4] we obtain a rational normal quartic, and there is no point of [4], which is not on the curve, through which two chords of the curve can pass. Hence no line through P can meet U_3^6 in more than one point other than P. This shews that Γ, if of order n, has a point at P of multiplicity $n-1$, and $n \geqq 2$.

If we project C from a line in the plane of Γ on to a space [3] we obtain a rational quintic with n double points. Hence we must have $n \leqq 2$.

* For the degree of a ruled surface formed by trisecants of a curve see Zeuthen, *Annali di Matematica* (2), 3 (1869), 183–185.

The result given by Zeuthen is only true for curves having the singularities which he prescribes; it does not hold, for example, for a curve with a triple point. In the first correspondence proof given by Zeuthen a triple point gives rise to 6 $(m-3)$ coincidences of the points x and n; and, taking an elliptic sextic curve with a triple point, we find a quintic ruled surface as we should do.

If we have an elliptic sextic with three double points, then Zeuthen's formula gives four for the degree of the ruled surface formed by the trisecants. There are two trisecants passing through any point of the curve, and this would seem at first to be at variance with our work on quartic ruled surfaces, where we shewed that the double curve was of the third order. But this quartic ruled surface is none other than the unique quadric containing the curve, counted twice. The trisecants are the generators of this quadric. Since a quadric which is made to contain $2n$ arbitrary points of an elliptic curve of order n will contain the curve entirely, this quadric is determined by the three double points and six other points of the curve.

There is no quadric containing the curve with a triple point.

Thus $n = 2$, and Γ is a conic passing through P.

The chords of C through the points of Γ form a ruled surface.

There is no doubt that such planes actually exist. For consider an involution g_2^1 of pairs of points on C. It is known that the chords joining the pairs of g_2^1 form a quartic ruled surface*. This ruled surface cannot have a directrix line; for, if it had, any three of its generators, having a common transversal, would belong to a [4]; and no [4] can meet C in six points. Hence it has ∞^1 directrix conics, one conic passing through each point of the surface†. All these conics can be obtained as residuals of prime sections through any two fixed generators, so that each conic meets C in one point.

The planes of these conics are planes such as we require; such a plane will be called a secant plane (of U_3^6). There are ∞^2 involutions g_2^1 on C; each gives a quartic ruled surface lying on U_3^6 and ∞^1 secant planes of U_3^6. There are thus ∞^3 secant planes of U_3^6. Through a general point of [5] there will pass a finite number of these secant planes; but through a point of U_3^6 there pass ∞^1, and through a point of C there pass ∞^2.

If any point X is taken in a secant plane which meets C in P, the line XP meets the conic Γ in a second point P' through which there passes a chord k of C. The plane PkX is thus the trisecant plane of C which passes through X. Hence if a secant plane passes through X it must contain one of the three lines which join X to the three points of C lying in the trisecant plane through X.

91. *The geometry of the secant planes*. There are ∞^3 secant planes, each meeting C in one point; if we have a quadric Ω containing C it will not, in general, be possible to choose the parameters on which a secant plane depends so that it lies entirely on Ω. But the general quadric Ω containing C is linearly dependent from ten quadrics, so that we should be able to choose Ω to contain a secant plane.

The condition that a quadric in [5] should represent the lines of a space [3] is simply that it should be a general quadric and not a cone; if we take a general quadric passing through C, and containing a secant plane, to represent the lines of a space [3], the curve C will represent the generators of a quintic ruled surface in [3] whose double curve and bitangent developable

* See footnote to § 19. If the g_2^1 is given by $A - B(\theta_1 + \theta_2) + C\theta_1\theta_2 = 0$ on the curve $x_0:x_1:x_2:x_3:x_4:x_5 = \theta^5:\theta^4:\theta^3:\theta^2:\theta:1$, the quartic ruled surface is

$$\left\| \begin{matrix} x_0 & x_1 & x_2 \\ x_1 & x_2 & x_3 \\ x_2 & x_3 & x_4 \\ x_3 & x_4 & x_5 \\ A & B & C \end{matrix} \right\| = 0.$$

† § 43.

break up, because the chords of C which lie on the quadric form a ruled surface which breaks up.

Suppose now that Ω contains a secant plane meeting C in a point P, this being a ρ-plane. The involution determined on C by the conic Γ in which the secant plane meets $U_3{}^6$ gives a chord PA through P; this, in common with all the other generators of the quartic surface, lies on Ω. Through P there pass two other chords PQ, PR which lie on Ω (Fig. 4).

Through Q there passes a chord of C meeting Γ in Q' and through R there passes a chord of C meeting Γ in R'. Then the three lines PQ, QQ', PQ' lie on Ω, so that PQQ' is a plane ϖ_1 which is trisecant to C. Similarly

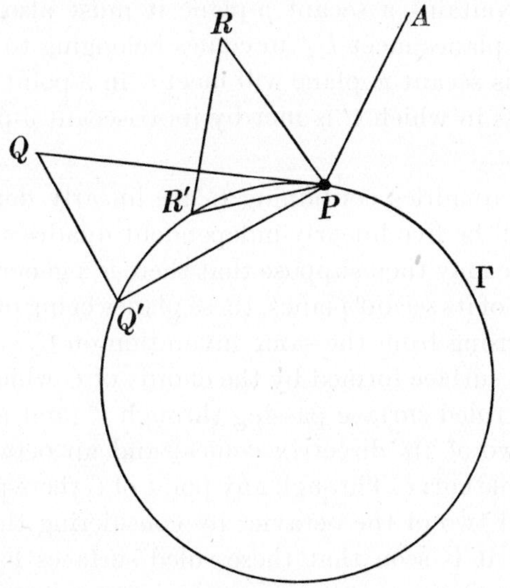

Fig. 4.

PRR' is a plane ϖ_2 which is trisecant to C. But there is only one plane ϖ trisecant to C, so we must conclude that this plane is PQR, the chord QR meeting Γ.

Hence, if we have a quadric Ω containing C and also a secant plane ρ which meets C in P, the plane ϖ of Ω which is trisecant to C passes through P.

Let this trisecant ϖ-plane meet C in P, Q, R and suppose that Ω contains two secant planes ρ_1 and ρ_2 through P. Each of these determines an involution on C, the common pair of the two involutions being Q, R. Hence we have two other chords PP_1 and PP_2 through P and lying on Ω, one arising from each involution. But it is impossible for four chords PP_1, PP_2, PQ, PR all passing through P to lie on Ω.

Hence it is impossible for Ω to contain two secant ρ-planes passing through P.

The planes of the directrix conics of a quartic ruled surface in [5] form a locus V_3^3 of three dimensions and the third order*, and therefore meet an arbitrary solid S_3 in the points of a twisted cubic.

Suppose then that Ω contains C and also the quartic ruled surface arising from an involution g_2^1 on C. Then a solid S_3 meets Ω in a quadric Q and meets the V_3^3 formed by the planes of the directrix conics in a twisted cubic which meets Q in six points. Four of these six points will be the points of intersection of S_3 with the quartic surface; the other two give planes which lie on Ω entirely, since each meets it in a conic and a point. Since these two planes cannot intersect they are of opposite systems.

Hence, if Ω contains a secant ρ-plane it must also contain a secant ϖ-plane; the two planes meet U_3^6 in conics belonging to the same quartic ruled surface. This secant ϖ-plane will meet C in a point P', this being one of the three points in which C is met by its trisecant ρ-plane.

92. Since the quadrics containing C are linearly dependent from ten quadrics there will be five linearly independent quadrics containing C and a secant plane. We may then suppose that there is a general quadric Ω containing C and two of its secant planes, these planes being of opposite systems on Ω and both arising from the same involution on C.

Then the ruled surface formed by the chords of C which lie on Ω breaks up into a quartic ruled surface passing through C (and met by the secant planes on Ω in two of its directrix conics) and an octavic ruled surface having C as a double curve. Through any point of C there pass one generator of the quartic and two of the octavic; by considering the correspondence thus set up on C it is seen that these ruled surfaces have two common generators, say g and g'.

The section of the composite ruled surface by a [4] gives an octavic curve with five double points and a quartic curve passing through these points; both these curves are rational.

It is easily shewn† that any general plane of Ω will meet the quartic ruled surface in two points and the octavic in four points. Thus the points of C represent the generators of a quintic ruled surface in [3]; the double curve breaks up into a conic and a rational quartic, while the bitangent developable breaks up into a quadric cone and a developable of the fourth class whose planes form a rational family.

Suppose that PQR is the ϖ-plane which is trisecant to C and let the secant ρ-plane pass through P. Then PQ and PR are generators of the

* § 69.

† A plane ϖ of Ω meets the secant ϖ-plane in a point O. These two planes lie in the tangent [4] of Ω at O, which meets Ω in a quadric point-cone and the quartic ruled surface in a directrix conic and two generators. These two generators each meet the first ϖ-plane.

octavic surface while QR is on the quartic. Thus PQR represents the triple point of the ruled quintic; the double conic passes through this point while the double quartic has a double point there. Further, the two parts of the double curve intersect in two other points, these being represented on Ω by the ϖ-planes through g and g'*.

Similarly the quartic developable has a double plane which touches the quadric cone (this being the tritangent plane of the ruled quintic), while they have also two other common tangent planes.

The plane of the double conic is represented on Ω by the secant ρ-plane; it therefore contains a generator of the ruled quintic passing through the triple point. The vertex of the quadric cone lies on a generator which is in the tritangent plane.

93. *The surface with three double conics.* The quadrics containing C and a secant plane are linearly dependent from five quadrics. Such a quadric meets any other secant plane in two definite points; one of these is on C and the other on that chord of C which belongs to both the involutions determined on C by the two secant planes. If the quadric is made to pass through four further points of the second secant plane (not lying on the same conic with the two fixed points) it will contain the secant plane entirely. Thus there will be a quadric containing C and two secant planes.

Suppose then that Ω contains C, a secant plane ρ_1 meeting C in P and a secant plane ρ_2 meeting C in Q. There is a plane ϖ of Ω meeting C in three points P, Q, R. The ruled surface formed by the chords of C lying on Ω is in general of order 12 with C for a triple curve; here it consists of a quartic ruled surface containing C and the chord QR, a quartic ruled surface containing C and the chord RP, and therefore also of a third quartic ruled surface containing C and the chord PQ. There is a directrix conic of this last surface passing through R; the plane of this conic meets Ω in the conic itself and also in a line of the plane PQR; it therefore lies on Ω entirely and is a secant plane ρ_3.

Ω will also contain three secant planes ϖ_1, ϖ_2, ϖ_3 belonging to the same three quartic surfaces; these meet C in three points P', Q', R' and the trisecant plane $P'Q'R'$ is a ρ-plane of Ω.

A general plane of Ω of either system meets each quartic ruled surface in two points. Thus the curve C represents the generators of a quintic ruled surface in a space [3]; the double curve of this surface consists of three conics and the bitangent developable of three quadric cones. The planes of the conics intersect in the point represented on Ω by the plane PQR, these planes themselves being represented by the planes ρ_1, ρ_2, ρ_3.

* Cf. Schwarz, *loc. cit.* p. 37.

The intersection of the planes of the three conics lies on all the conics, and is the triple point. Similarly the tritangent plane touches all the cones and is the plane joining the three vertices.

Any two involutions on C have a common pair of points, so that any two of the three quartic surfaces have a common generator. Thus any two of the three double conics have a second common point on the line of intersection of their planes, this point being represented on Ω by the plane ϖ passing through the common generator of the two quartic surfaces concerned*. Similarly any two of the three quadric cones have a second common tangent plane passing through the line joining their two vertices.

Surfaces whose generators belong to a linear complex which is not special

94. We turn now to the quintic ruled surface in [3] whose generators are represented by the points of a curve C on Ω, this curve lying in a space [4] which does not touch Ω. We assume, unless the contrary is stated, that C has not a double point; we are dealing then with a surface of the type II (A).

If we project C from a line on to a plane in [4] we obtain a quintic curve which, as a rational curve, must have six double points. Hence six chords of C meet the line, so that the chords of C form a locus V_3^6 of three dimensions and the sixth order.

Any plane of Ω meets the space [4] in a line lying on Ω; this line is met by six chords of C, and no other chords of C can meet the plane. Hence we have a quintic ruled surface whose double curve is of the sixth order and whose bitangent developable is of the sixth class.

95. *The locus* V_3^6. The curve C has a trisecant chord t† meeting it in three points P, Q, R.

If we project C from a line which meets it on to a plane of [4] we obtain a rational quartic with three double points; hence the line is met by three chords of C other than those which pass through its point of intersection with C. Hence C is a triple curve on V_3^6.

If we project from a line meeting t we obtain a rational quintic with a triple point and three double points, so that the line is met by three chords of C other than t. Hence t is a triple line on V_3^6.

If we project from a line through P we obtain a rational quartic with three double points, one of these arising from t. Hence the line is only met by two chords of C which do not pass through P, so that P, Q, R are quadruple points on V_3^6.

If we project C from one of its chords on to a plane we obtain a cubic with a double point; hence every chord of C is met by one other chord in

* Cf. Schwarz, *loc. cit.* p. 44. † Marletta, *loc. cit.* p. 101.

a point not on C, these two chords lying in a quadrisecant plane of C. This at once suggests a double surface F_2 on V_3^6. The order of F_2 is the number of points in which it is met by a plane of [4]; the plane meets V_3^6 in a sextic curve having this same number of double points.

This number of double points is known when we know the genus of a plane section of V_3^6. Now, since C is the projection of a rational normal curve in [5], V_3^6 is the projection of the locus U_3^6 of § 87. Hence the genus of the plane sections of V_3^6 is the same as that of the sections of U_3^6 by solids.

We then consider in [5] the curve in which a solid Σ is met by the chords of a rational normal quintic curve C_0. If we take any four trisecant planes of C_0 then it is clear that the chords of C_0 are obtained as the intersections of corresponding primes of four doubly infinite projectively related systems of primes, each of the four trisecant planes being the base of one of the doubly infinite systems. The section by Σ then gives four projectively related "stars" of planes, each with a base point. If Σ is met by a chord of C_0 the point of meeting is an intersection of corresponding planes of the four stars. But the locus of such points is known to be a sextic curve of genus *three**, and this is then the section† of U_3^6 by Σ.

The plane sections of V_3^6 are therefore also of genus three, and thus have *seven* double points. Hence we have on V_3^6 a double surface F_2^7 of order seven.

The section of V_3^6 by a quadrisecant plane of C consists of the six chords of C lying in the plane; the section of F_2^7 consists of the four points of C together with the three diagonal points of the quadrangle formed by them.

A trisecant plane PXY of C meets V_3^6 in the three chords PX, PY, XY and a cubic curve having a double point at P. This curve meets XY again in a point W; the section of F_2^7 by the plane PXY consists of the points X, Y, W together with P counted four times. P, Q, R are quadruple points on F_2^7.

A trisecant plane XYZ of C meets V_3^6 in the three chords YZ, ZX, XY and in a cubic curve passing through X, Y, Z and having a double point O. This curve meets the lines YZ, ZX, XY again in points U, V, W. The plane XYZ meets F_2^7 in the seven points X, Y, Z, U, V, W, O.

* Schur, *Math. Ann.* 18 (1881), 15.

† The surface which is the prime section of U_3^6 is a sextic surface in [4] generated by four doubly infinite systems of solids projectively related to each other. It is a particular case of that considered by Veronese, *Math. Ann.* 19 (1882), 232–233. The projection of this sextic surface in [4] on to a solid is the same as the surface which is the section of V_3^6 by a solid. This surface in [3] has a double curve of order 7 (the section of F_2^7) and, on this double curve, a triplanar point, this being the intersection of [3] with the trisecant t of C. Further, since the solid meets C in five points, and the ten chords joining these points are lines of V_3^6, the sextic surface has ten lines on it.

The section of V_3^6 by a plane through t and a point X of C consists of t counted three times together with the three chords XP, XQ, XR. The point X is the only point of F_2^7, other than the points of t, which can lie in this plane. A solid containing t will meet F_2^7 in t counted three times and in a quartic curve passing through P, Q, R.

t is a triple line on F_2^7, but C is only a simple curve.

96. *The genus of the double curve.* A quadric containing C will also contain t; its intersection with F_2^7 therefore consists of C, t counted three times, and a sextic curve; the total intersection being a curve of order 14. Hence those chords of C which lie on Ω form a ruled surface of order 12 in [4], the intersection of Ω and V_3^6. This ruled surface has C for a triple curve and t for a triple generator; it has also a double sextic curve meeting every generator in one point and passing through P, Q, R.

If we take the section of this ruled surface by a [3] we obtain a curve in (1, 1) correspondence with the double curve of the ruled quintic. The curve is of order 12, having six triple points and six double points; it is the intersection of a quadric and a sextic surface, so that it meets each generator of the quadric in six points. If we project the curve from a point of the quadric on to a plane of the [3] we obtain a curve of order 12 with six triple points, six double points, and two sextuple points; its genus is therefore

$$55 - 18 - 6 - 30 = 1,$$

so that it is elliptic.

Thus the ruled quintic has an elliptic double curve of order 6, while the planes of its bitangent developable form an elliptic family of class 6. Moreover, the double curve has a triple point; the three generators passing through it lie in a plane and are represented on Ω by the points P, Q, R*. Also the bitangent developable has a tritangent plane; the three generators therein pass through a point. For this surface the tritangent plane passes through the triple point; the plane ρ of Ω passing through t represents the tritangent plane, while the plane ϖ of Ω passing through t represents the triple point.

It is clear, either by the geometry of the planes on Ω or by the geometry of the linear complex, that at a triple point on any ruled surface whatever whose generators all belong to a linear complex the three generators which intersect there lie in a plane. Similarly, the three generators in any tritangent plane pass through a point.

97. *An associated ruled surface.* We have just seen that the prime sections of the ruled surface formed by the chords of C which lie on Ω are elliptic curves; this enables us to shew that the sextic curve which forms part of the intersection

* Cf. Marletta, *loc. cit.* p. 117.

of Ω and F_2^7 is also an elliptic curve*. Its points thus represent the generators of an elliptic sextic ruled surface f^6 in the original space [3]; this passes through the double curve of the quintic ruled surface and is touched by the planes of the bitangent developable of the quintic surface, and it contains the three generators which meet in the triple point and lie in the tritangent plane.

Suppose then that we have in [3] a rational quintic ruled surface whose generators belong to a linear complex. Take any point x on the double curve, and the plane of the two generators which meet in x. Then this plane meets the surface again in a cubic curve. This cubic meets each generator in three points; one point on each generator is a point where the plane (which is a bitangent plane) touches the surface, the other two are points of the double curve. The remaining point y in which the plane meets the double curve is a double point on the cubic curve. If we had started with the point y instead of the point x then the bitangent plane through y would have met the surface in two generators and a cubic curve having a double point at x. The lines such as xy, chords of the double curve and axes of the bitangent developable, generate an elliptic sextic ruled surface f^6 whose generators belong to the same linear complex as do those of the quintic surface.

The curve of intersection of the two ruled surfaces, in all of order 30, will consist of the double curve of the quintic surface counted twice, a certain number of common generators, and another curve. Since every generator of f^6 can only meet the quintic surface in one point other than the two points in which it meets the double curve, this other curve meets the generators of f^6 each in one point and is therefore elliptic. Moreover, it meets each generator of the quintic ruled surface in three points, and an elliptic curve on a rational quintic ruled surface which meets each generator in three points is of order 9†. Hence the two ruled surfaces have in common this curve of order 9, the double curve of the quintic ruled surface counted twice, and nine common generators. These last consist of the three generators through the triple point of the quintic surface and six others‡.

* There is a (1, 2) correspondence between the points of this curve and the chords of C on Ω, to which we can apply Zeuthen's formula with $\alpha = 1$, $\alpha' = 2$, $p' = 1$, $\eta = \eta' = 0$.

The assumption that $\eta = 0$ is the assumption that the two chords of C which intersect at a point of the sextic curve never coincide. We shall see later that there are four special chords of C lying on F_2^7; if Ω were to contain any of these chords we could not assume η to be zero. But, in general, the assumption is true. The points P, Q, R do not count as branch-points of the correspondence.

If Ω contained one or more of the special chords of C we should not have a sextic curve of intersection on F_2^7.

† § 17.

‡ This result shews that the sextic curve of intersection of Ω and F_2^7 has six intersections with C other than P, Q, R.

In the first paper of Segre's, referred to in § 17, we find a formula for the number of intersections of two simple (non-multiple) curves on a ruled surface. There is a corresponding formula for the number of intersections of two multiple curves on a ruled surface, but it is subject to modification as certain intersections may be included more than once. For two curves of orders m and m' of multiplicities s and s' on a ruled surface of order n, the curves meeting each generator of the surface in k and k' points respectively, the formula gives the number of intersections as

$$i = msk' + m's'k - nkk'.$$

If we apply this formula to the triple quintic curve and the double sextic curve

98. Suppose that we take any point X on C; is there a line through X which is not a chord of C and yet lies on V_3^6? If we project C from X on to a space [3] we obtain a rational quartic without a double point. If such a line through X existed it would meet [3] in a point through which an infinite number of chords of the quartic pass; this would then be the vertex of a quadric cone containing the quartic, and there are no such cones*. But this reasoning does not hold for the three points P, Q, R. If we project from P we obtain a rational quartic with a double point; there are two quadric cones containing this quartic whose vertices are not at the double point†, so that we expect two lines through P lying on V_3^6. We shall call these lines axes.

We can also obtain some information as to these axes by projecting a rational normal quintic from a point on to a space [4]. If we project from X (see the end of § 90) any axes of the projected curve must arise from secant planes through X; so that we get a finite number of axes, any one of which must pass through one of P, Q, R. Further, since any line in the secant plane through X meets the conic in that plane in two points there are two chords of the projected curve passing through any point of an axis.

The chords of C meeting any axis form a quartic ruled surface in [4] on which the axis is a double line—the projection of a normal quartic ruled surface in [5] from a point in the plane of one of its directrix conics.

99. *The geometry of the axes.* We have two axes through each of the points P, Q, R, giving six in all; call them p, p', q, q', r, r', where p and p' pass through P. They lie not only on V_3^6 but also on F_2^7.

On any axis there are two points such that there is only one chord of C passing through each of them; if the axis is the projection of a conic Γ from a point X in a secant plane in [5], these two points arise from the two tangents of Γ which pass through X. We may call these "pinch-points."

There is a cubic ruled surface ϕ containing C; the directrix of ϕ is the trisecant of C, while every generator of ϕ meets C in one point. The ∞^2 conics of ϕ give the ∞^2 quadrisecant planes of C‡. No two quadrisecant

which lie on the ruled surface of order 12 formed by those chords of C which lie on Ω, it appears that the two curves have fifteen intersections. But these really consist of the three intersections P, Q, R and the six others each counted twice. See the Note at the end of the volume.

* Salmon, *Geometry of Three Dimensions* (Dublin, 1914), p. 359, and above § 63.

† We can regard the quartic curve as the intersection of the two quadrics

$$2xy + z^2 - t^2 = 0 \quad \text{and} \quad y^2 - m^2z^2 + n^2t^2 = 0.$$

‡ Marletta, *loc. cit.* pp. 101, 102. For the cubic ruled surface see § 48 above.

planes of C can intersect except on ϕ. The ∞^1 quadrisecant planes of C which pass through any point of ϕ lie on a quadric point-cone, and all belong to one system of its planes.

Consider the $V_3{}^3$ formed by the planes of the directrix conics of a normal quartic ruled surface in [5]; project it on to a space [4] from a point O of itself, O lying in the plane of a directrix conic Γ. We obtain a quadric point-cone; one system of planes of this cone is the projection of the planes of the directrix conics; the other system of planes is the projection of those solids which contain pairs of generators of the quartic surface and pass through O, meeting the plane of Γ in lines through O*.

This result shews that the quadrisecant planes passing through the points of an axis all intersect in the same point, forming one system of planes of a quadric point-cone.

Any axis determines an involution on C; denote, for example, by (p) the involution determined by p. Since any two involutions on C have a common pair of points the involutions (p) and (r) give a chord joining their common pair; this chord meeting both p and r. But any chord of C is met by only *one* chord beside those passing through the two points in which it meets C. Hence the chord must meet at least one of p and r in a pinch-point.

The quadrics in [4] containing C are linearly dependent from four quadrics. Thus we can make such a quadric contain p by assigning two points of p; there is a pencil of quadrics passing through C and p. Moreover, such a quadric, besides passing through Q and R, meets each of q, q', r, r' in fixed points†. Hence we can find a quadric of the pencil containing q. This quadric will contain the point of r which lies on the chord common to (q) and (r), so that if this point is different from the intersection of r with the chord common to (p) and (r) the quadric will contain r entirely. There is a similar statement concerning r'. But it is impossible for the quadric to contain p, q and both the axes r and r'; for then we should have chords of C lying on it and forming a ruled surface of order at least $4 \times 4 = 16$, which is impossible. We must therefore conclude that the quadric containing C, p, q contains one of r and r', say r, while the chord common to (p) and (r') and the chord common to (q) and (r') meet r' in the same point. We may denote the quadric by pqr.

Denote by $(pq)\,r'$ the fact that the chord common to (p) and (r') and the chord common to (q) and (r') meet r' in the same point.

* Through each point of $V_3{}^3$ there passes a line meeting all its generating planes. See the footnote to § 9 of Segre's paper, "Sulle varietà normali a tre dimensioni," *Atti Torino*, 21 (1885), 95. Also § 81 above.

† It meets q for instance in the point where it is met by the chord common to (p) and (q). It does not, however, meet p' in a fixed point, because the chord common to (p) and (p') is QR.

There are four quadrics

$$pqr, \quad pq'r', \quad p'qr', \quad p'q'r,$$

which contain C and three axes, and we have

$$\begin{matrix} (pq)\,r', & (pq')\,r, & (p'q)\,r, & (p'q')\,r', \\ (qr)\,p', & (qr')\,p, & (q'r)\,p, & (q'r')\,p', \\ (rp)\,q', & (rp')\,q, & (r'p)\,q, & (r'p')\,q', \end{matrix}$$

the twelve elements of this array being determined by the first one.

Now from the three statements

$$(pq)\,r', \quad (qr')\,p, \quad (r'p)\,q,$$

we see that the involutions (p), (q), (r') have a common chord (we cannot have three co-planar chords common to these pairs of involutions); this meets the three axes p, q, r' which must therefore lie in a solid since they have two transversals. We have four such solids which we may denote by

$$[pqr'], \quad [pq'r], \quad [p'qr], \quad [p'q'r'].$$

Let us denote the four common chords of the sets of three involutions by

$$\overline{pqr'}, \quad \overline{pq'r}, \quad \overline{p'qr}, \quad \overline{p'q'r'}.$$

The first of these, for example, is a transversal of the axes p, q, r'.

The points in which $\overline{pqr'}$ meets the axes p, q, r' are pinch-points on at least two of them; since the six axes are on the same footing it is probable that all the three points of intersection will be pinch-points.

We are thus led to the supposition that the unique quadrisecant plane through $\overline{pqr'}$ does not contain any other chord, but touches C at both ends of the chord $\overline{pqr'}$. Thus we find four pairs of intersecting tangents of C.

The existence of these pairs of intersecting tangents can be seen in another way, for the tangents form a ruled surface which is the projection, from a point, of the ruled surface formed by the tangents of a normal curve in [5]. Now any surface whatever in [5] has a finite number of "apparent double points"*; the number will be reduced by the existence of a cuspidal curve on the surface, but we can still expect a certain number, and on projection these give pairs of intersecting tangents of C.

The number of pairs of intersecting tangents of C can be found directly.

Take any point Q of C. The quadrisecant planes of C which pass through Q are the planes of the ∞^1 directrix conics of the cubic ruled surface ϕ which pass through Q. Since any one of these conics is determined by one point of any generator of ϕ they cut out on C an ordinary involution of sets of three points, and such an involution has four double points. Hence there are four quadrisecant planes which pass through Q and contain tangents of C.

* The only surface in [5] without any apparent double points is the surface of Veronese. See Severi, *Palermo Rendiconti*, 15 (1901), 41, 42.

Now let us establish a correspondence between the points P and Q of C; two points corresponding when the tangent at P meets a chord through Q other than QP. We have just seen that to any position of Q there correspond four positions of P. Also a tangent of C is met by one chord other than those passing through its point of contact*, so that to any position of P there correspond two positions of Q. We have then, on the rational curve C, a (4, 2) correspondence between P and Q; there are eight points P for which the two corresponding points Q coincide†. Hence there are eight tangents of C which are met by other tangents, and these divide into four pairs of intersecting tangents.

The tangents of C therefore form a (developable) ruled surface whose cuspidal curve C is of order 5 and which has four double points.

The chords which join the points of contact of the pairs of intersecting tangents are none other than the four chords

$$\overline{pqr'}, \quad \overline{pq'r}, \quad \overline{p'qr}, \quad \overline{p'q'r'}.$$

The four planes which touch C twice can be taken in pairs in six ways; the six solids formed by the six pairs of chords of contact each contain one of the six axes.

The four chords of contact lie on F_2^7.

A bitangent plane of C meets V_3^6 in the two tangents together with the chord of contact counted four times; it meets F_2^7 in the chord of contact and the point of intersection of the two tangents.

There is one more remark which may be made concerning the configuration of the six axes.

It is easily shewn, in ordinary space, that in general there are four quadric cones passing through the curve of intersection of two quadrics. But if the two quadrics touch their intersection is a rational quartic curve with a double point; the four cones become the cone projecting the curve from its double point (this cone counting doubly) with two other cones. Now the plane of the two tangents to the quartic at its double point contains the vertices of these last two cones.

Hence the solid containing the tangents of C at Q and R contains the axes p and p', with two other similar results. We thus have three solids which we may denote by

$$[pp't_Qt_R], \quad [qq't_Rt_P], \quad [rr't_Pt_Q].$$

100. Consider now the quintic ruled surface whose generators are represented by the points of a rational quintic C in [4], C lying on a quadric which contains also the axis p‡.

* For on projecting C from the tangent on to a plane we obtain a cubic with a double point.

† If we have an (r, s) correspondence between points P and Q on a rational curve then there are $2r(s-1)$ positions of P for which two of the s points Q coincide (§ 13).

‡ This quadric is regarded as a prime section of Ω.

The ruled surface formed by the chords of C which lie on the quadric here breaks up into a quartic ruled surface passing through C, and having p for a double line, and an octavic ruled surface having C for a double curve. The trisecant t lies on the first of these ruled surfaces and is double on the second.

Every line of Ω lying in [4] meets the quartic* in two points and therefore the octavic in four points. Hence we have a quintic ruled surface whose double curve consists of a conic and a quartic and whose bitangent developable consists of a quadric cone and a developable of the fourth class.

The quartic has a double point which lies on the conic, this being represented by the plane ϖ of Ω through t; also the developable of the fourth class has a double tangent plane which touches the quadric cone, this being represented by the plane ρ of Ω through t.

Through any point of C there pass one generator of the quartic ruled surface and two of the octavic; by considering the correspondence thus set up on C it is easily seen that the surfaces have two common generators. Hence the quartic curve and the conic have two further common points, while the developable of the fourth class and the quadric cone have two further common tangent planes. The common generators of the quartic and octavic ruled surfaces are $\overline{pqr'}$ and $\overline{pq'r}$.

The prime section of Ω on which C lies now contains the two chords $\overline{pqr'}$ and $\overline{pq'r}$. Hence the curve of order 14 in which it meets $F_2{}^7$ is made up as follows

$$C + p + \overline{pqr'} + \overline{pq'r} + 3t + c_3,$$

where c_3 denotes a twisted cubic, which must be a double curve on the octavic ruled surface.

The section of this ruled surface by a solid is thus a curve of the eighth order lying on a quadric and meeting each generator in four points, the curve having nine double points†. This curve is rational; it represents the double quartic curve of the ruled surface and also the bitangent developable of the fourth class.

The section of the quartic ruled surface by a solid is a rational quartic curve with a double point on p.

101. *The surface with three double conics.* Suppose that we have a rational quintic ruled surface in a space [3] whose generators are represented by the points of a quintic C lying on the section of Ω by a [4]; the axes p, q, r also lying on the quadric.

* A solid through the line meets Ω in a quadric with the line as generator and the quartic in a quartic curve, with a double point, lying on this quadric.

† Five arising from C, one from t, and three from c_3.

Then the ruled surface formed by the chords of C which lie on Ω breaks up into three quartic ruled surfaces; each of these passes through C and has a double line, while any two of them have a common generator. A line on Ω lying in [4] meets each of these surfaces in two points, and t lies on each surface.

Hence the quintic ruled surface in [3] has three double conics which all pass through one point, this being represented on Ω by the plane ϖ through t, while any two of the conics have a second intersection. The bitangent developable consists of three quadric cones all having a common tangent plane, this being represented on Ω by the plane ρ through t, while any two of the cones have a second common tangent plane. The tritangent plane passes through the triple point.

The quadric Ω now contains the three lines $\overline{pqr'}$, $\overline{pq'r}$, $\overline{p'qr}$; these are, in fact, the common generators of the three pairs of quartic ruled surfaces.

The tangent planes at the different points of one of these lines, say $\overline{pqr'}$, to either of the quartic surfaces on which it is a generator, are the same; the two tangents of C at the ends of its chord $\overline{pqr'}$ intersect and their plane touches both the quartic surfaces at all points of $\overline{pqr'}$. We can say that $\overline{pqr'}$ is a torsal generator of both surfaces. The two quartic curves in which the surfaces are met by an arbitrary solid will touch at the intersection of the solid with $\overline{pqr'}$.

The curve of order 14 in which Ω and F_2^7 intersect is now

$$C + p + q + r + \overline{pqr'} + \overline{pq'r} + \overline{p'qr} + 3t.$$

The section by a solid of the composite ruled surface formed by the chords of C which lie on Ω consists of three rational quartic curves lying on the same quadric; each curve has a double point and there are six points common to the three curves. Any two of the curves, besides having these six points in common, touch each other at another point.

102. *The surface with a double generator.* If C lies in a non-tangent prime S_4 of Ω and has a double point P its points represent the generators of a rational quintic ruled surface in [3]; the generators belong to a linear complex and there is a double generator G represented by P. Any line of S_4 is met by five proper chords of C.

Any plane of Ω meets S_4 in a line l lying on Ω; this line is met by five proper chords of C, and the plane lP meets Ω in l and another line passing through P. Hence we have a ruled surface whose double curve consists of the points of a double generator G together with a quintic, while the bitangent developable consists of the planes through a double generator G together with a developable of the fifth class.

The tangent prime of Ω at P meets S_4 in a [3] which meets C in four points at P and therefore in one other point Q. Thus G is met by one other generator g.

Through any point of C there pass three chords lying on Ω; except that through P we have the single chord PQ and through Q the chord QP and one other chord.

Take the plane ϖ_1 through PQ. A plane ρ which meets ϖ_1 in a line must meet S_4 in a line intersecting PQ. This line is only met by three chords of C other than PQ, for if we project C from the line on to a plane of S_4 we obtain a rational quintic with a triple point and three double points. The plane ϖ_1 represents the point Gg, so that any plane through this point meets the quintic double curve in only three other points.

Thus the quintic ruled surface has a double curve consisting of a double generator G and a quintic. These meet in a point which is a double point of the quintic, while through this point there passes one other generator.

The bitangent developable consists of a developable of the fifth class together with the planes through G. One of these planes is a double tangent plane of the developable; this is the plane Gg and is represented on Ω by the plane ρ_1 through PQ.

Consider again a rational quintic C in S_4 with a double point P. Projecting from a general line of S_4 on to a plane we obtain a quintic with six double points; hence the line is met by five chords. Projecting from a line meeting C we obtain a quartic with three double points, so that this line is met by two chords other than those which pass through its point of intersection with C. Projecting from a line through P we obtain a cubic with one double point, so that this line is met by one chord not passing through P. Hence the chords of C form a locus V_3^5 of three dimensions and of the fifth order, on which C is a triple curve and P a quadruple point.

Further, if we take a chord of C passing through P, and project C on to a plane from a line meeting this chord, we see that the chord must be double on V_3^5. The chords of C through P form a cubic cone which is a double surface on V_3^5.

Consider now a quadric Q_3 containing C. It meets the cubic cone just mentioned in C and also in one of its generators PQ. The chords of C which lie on Q_3 form a ruled surface of order ten, the intersection of Q_3 and V_3^5, on which C is a triple curve and PQ is a double generator. The section of this ruled surface by a solid is a curve of order ten with five triple points and one double point; it is the intersection of a quadric and a quintic surface, so that it meets every generator of the quadric in five points. If it is projected from a point of the quadric on to a plane we obtain a curve of order ten with five triple points, one double point and two quintuple points, which is therefore a rational curve.

The quintic double curve of the ruled surface is therefore also a rational curve. If we project it from a point of itself on to a plane we obtain a rational quartic with three double points. Hence there are two trisecants of the quintic curve passing through any point of it, and the ruled surface is formed by these trisecants.

Any line on Ω meets the ruled surface formed by the chords of C lying on Ω in five points, but if the line passes through P it only has one other intersection with the surface because P is a quadruple point thereon. Now any plane ρ on Ω which passes through P meets S_4 in such a line, so that any plane passing through the double generator G of the quintic ruled surface meets the double quintic curve in only one point not on G. Hence the quintic curve meets G in two points besides the double point; this shews at once that the quintic curve is rational.

Similarly, there are two planes of the developable, other than its double tangent plane, which pass through G.

103. If we project C from a point of itself on to an S_3 we obtain a rational quartic with a double point; there are two quadric cones containing this quartic whose vertices are not on the curve, so that we expect to find two lines through any point of C which lie on V_3^5 and are not chords of C. These lines will form a ruled surface with C for a double curve.

The existence of these lines is also seen by projecting a normal quintic in [5] from a point O on one of its chords. There are ∞^1 secant planes* through such a point, one for each involution on the curve which contains the extremities of the chord as a pair. Thus we have a finite number of secant planes joining O to any point of the curve, and in S_4 a finite number of lines through any point of C. The chords of C meeting such a line form a cubic ruled surface, the projection of a quartic ruled surface in [5] from a point O on it.

The quadrics of S_4 containing C are linearly dependent from five quadrics. It would thus seem that there is a quadric containing C and one of the lines, and so the ruled surface formed by the chords of C lying on the quadric breaks up into a cubic ruled surface passing through C and a septimic ruled surface having C for a double curve. It would, however, be wrong to conclude from this that we have found a new species of quintic ruled surface belonging to the type II (B); for it can easily be shewn that a quadric in S_4 which contains a cubic ruled surface is necessarily a point-cone.

Surfaces with a directrix line which is not a generator

104. Consider a ruled surface whose generators are represented by the points of a curve C lying in a tangent prime T of Ω. T touches Ω in a point O; O represents a line R which is a directrix of the ruled surface.

* Cf. § 90.

If C is of the type III (A) it meets every plane ϖ through O in four points and every plane ρ through O in one point. An arbitrary plane ρ meets T in a line and the plane ϖ through this line is the plane joining it to O. This contains four points and therefore six chords of C, so that the double curve of the ruled surface is the line R counted six times. There are four generators passing through every point of R and there is one generator lying in every plane through R.

An arbitrary plane ϖ meets T in a line and the plane ρ through this line joins it to O. This contains only one point of C; there will be six chords of C meeting the line so that in general the bitangent developable is non-degenerate and of the sixth class.

Similarly in III (B) we have a surface whose double curve is non-degenerate and of the sixth order, while the bitangent developable consists of the planes through R counted six times. Any plane through R contains four generators, while through any point of R there passes one generator.

Remembering that C has a trisecant we see that in III (A) there is a tritangent plane and in III (B) there is a triple point. Also the bitangent developable in III (A) and the double curve in III (B) are seen to be elliptic precisely as in § 96.

105. We have seen in § 99 that we can have a quadric point-cone containing C and an axis; we may then regard this cone as a section of Ω by T.

Thus in III (A) the bitangent developable may break up into a quadric cone and a developable of the fourth class, this latter having a double tangent plane which touches the former, and there being also two other common tangent planes. The quadrisecant planes of C meeting the axis are the ϖ-planes of the cone.

Also in III (B) the double curve may break up into a conic and a quartic; the quartic has a double point lying on the conic and the curves have also two other intersections. The quadrisecant planes of C meeting the axis are the ρ-planes of the cone.

106. We shall now shew how a rational quintic curve C can be found, in [4], so that it lies, together with three axes, on a quadric point-cone.

Take two planes π, π' in a space S_4 intersecting in a point O. Then taking three arbitrary points A, B, C in π and three arbitrary points A', B', C' in π' there is thus defined a collineation between the planes; the points A, B, C, O of π corresponding to the points A', B', C', O of π'. If a conic in π is drawn through O to have ABC as a self-conjugate triangle (there is a pencil of such conics), then we have correspondingly in π' a conic through O with $A'B'C'$ as a self-conjugate triangle.

Through any point of S_4 there passes a plane pencil of lines incident to both π and π'; the plane of this pencil is the intersection of the solids which join the point to π and π' and meets these planes in two lines passing through O. These lines will not, in general, correspond to one another in the collineation.

The three lines AA', BB', CC' have a common transversal meeting them in P, Q, R. Now take S, any point of the line PQR; the plane of the pencil of lines through S will meet π in a line l through O and π' in a line l' through O. The three planes π, π', $OPQR$ determine a quadric point-cone with vertex O, and the four planes $OAA'P$, $OBB'Q$, $OCC'R$, $Oll'S$ are planes of the opposite system of this cone. Hence the two pencils $O\{ABCl\}$ and $O\{A'B'C'l'\}$ are homographic, so that l and l' are corresponding lines in the collineation between π and π'.

The pencil of lines through S incident to π and π' meets l and l' in two ranges in perspective. For a general position of S on the line PQR there will be two points of l which are in perspective from S with their corresponding points on l', and these include O. Hence there is one line, other than SO, through S which joins a pair of corresponding points of π and π'.

The lines BC, $B'C'$, QR lie in the solid determined by $BB'Q$ and $CC'R$; this solid contains P on the line QR. Hence there is a line PDD' meeting BC in D and $B'C'$ in D'. The plane $PDD'AA'$ meets π in the line AD and π' in the line $A'D'$, so that AD, $A'D'$ must intersect in O. Then the lines OAD, $OA'D'$ are corresponding lines and the points D, D' are corresponding points. We have therefore two lines PAA' and PDD' other than PO which join P to a pair of corresponding points of π and π'; there must then be an infinite number of such lines through P.

Through each of the points P, Q, R there passes a pencil of lines incident to π and π' in corresponding points; every line through one of these three points which meets both π and π' does so in a pair of corresponding points.

If X is the harmonic conjugate of O in regard to A and D, any conic through O having ABC as a self-conjugate triangle must pass through X. Similarly we have X' in π', and XX' passes through P. We also have QYY' and RZZ' in the same way.

Returning to the point S, let SUU' be the line through it which joins corresponding points U and U' of π and π'. There is a definite conic passing through O and U for which ABC is a self-conjugate triangle; to this corresponds the conic through O and U' for which $A'B'C'$ is a self-conjugate triangle. The points of these two conics are in (1, 1) correspondence with a united point O; hence the lines joining corresponding points of the two conics form a cubic ruled surface in S_4. The four lines XX', YY', ZZ', UU' are generators of this surface, so that P, Q, R, S are on the surface. Hence $PQRS$ is its directrix line.

Through eight points of general position on this surface there passes a rational quintic C with the directrix for its trisecant*.

Take then points a, b, c, d on the conic $OUXYZ$ such that bc, ad pass through A; ca, bd pass through B; ab, cd pass through C. Similarly, take points e, f, g, h on the conic $OU'X'Y'Z'$ such that fg, eh pass through A'; ge, fh pass through B'; ef, gh pass through C'. Then there is a rational quintic passing through a, b, c, d, e, f, g, h with the directrix for its trisecant.

The lines PAA', QBB', RCC' must lie on the V_3^6 formed by the chords of the curve, as each meets it in a triple point and two double points. Hence these are three axes of the curve, which must meet its trisecant in P, Q, R.

There is a quadric point-cone whose vertex is O and which contains the planes $OAA'P$, $OBB'Q$, $OCC'R$, as already mentioned above. The planes π, π', $OPQR$ belong to the opposite system. The cone therefore meets the quintic curve in at least eleven points, and so contains it entirely. It is the cone projecting the cubic ruled surface from O.

Hence we have constructed in S_4 a rational quintic which lies, together with three of its axes and trisecant, on a quadric point-cone.

This shews that for surfaces of the type III (A) we can have a bitangent developable consisting of three quadric cones; all the cones having a common tangent plane, while any two have a second common tangent plane.

Also in surfaces of the type III (B) we can have a double curve consisting of three conics; all the conics have a point in common, while any two of them have a second intersection.

107. In the type III (C) the curve C meets every plane ϖ through O in three points, every plane ρ through O in two points, and has a double point, O lying on a chord of C.

An arbitrary plane ρ meets T in a line; the plane ϖ through this line is the plane joining it to O, which contains three points and therefore three chords of C. The plane joining the line to the double point P meets Ω in a second line through P, and there will be two further chords of C meeting the line.

Hence the double curve consists of the directrix R counted three times, a double generator G, and a conic.

R and G intersect. R and the conic also intersect; their point of intersection is represented on Ω by the ϖ-plane which contains the chord of C passing through O. The conic meets G also.

* Marletta, *loc. cit.* p. 102. No five of the points must be on the same conic and no two on the same generator.

The tangent prime of Ω at P meets T in a solid passing through O and meeting C in four points at P. Thus it meets the curve in one further point Q, and the plane OPQ is a ϖ-plane. Hence G is met by one other generator g only, and this passes through the point RG.

Through any point of R there pass three generators.

An arbitrary plane ϖ meets T in a line; the plane ρ through this line is the plane joining it to O, which contains two points and therefore one chord of C.

Hence the bitangent developable consists of the two pencils of planes through R and G, together with a developable of the fourth class.

There is a plane of this developable passing through R; it is represented on Ω by the ρ-plane which contains the chord of C passing through O. The developable has the plane Gg as a double tangent plane; this is represented by the plane ρ_1 through PQ. Any plane ϖ which meets ρ_1 in a line meets T in a line intersecting PQ; this line is met by three chords of C other than PQ*, but one of these lies in the ρ-plane which joins the line to O. Correspondingly, through any point of the plane Gg there pass only two planes of the developable besides Gg.

108. The ruled surface formed by the chords of C which lie on a quadric containing it is, in general, of order 10 with C for a triple curve, and has a double generator*. But in surfaces of the type III (C) this surface will clearly break up into two distinct parts, one formed by those chords which lie in ϖ-planes through O and the other formed by those chords which lie in ρ-planes through O.

The chords of C which lie in the ρ-planes through O join the pairs of points of an involution on C and therefore form a cubic ruled surface†. There is a generator of this surface passing through P, and the plane ϖ through this generator represents the point of intersection of G with the double conic. Thus the ruled surface formed by the chords of C which lie on Ω breaks up into a cubic ruled surface and a ruled surface of the seventh order, this latter having C for a double curve and having also a double generator‡. The section of this composite ruled surface by a solid consists of a twisted cubic and a septimic having six double points. The two curves lie on a quadric and form its curve of intersection with a surface of the fifth order; the cubic meets all generators of one system in one point and all of the other system in two points, so that the septimic meets all generators of one system in four points and all of the other system in three points. If then the septimic is projected on to a plane we obtain a curve with six

* Cf. § 102.

† The pair of points of C on its two branches at P is a pair of the involution, so that we have a cubic ruled surface—the projection of a quartic ruled surface in [5] from a point of itself.

‡ Cf. § 103.

double points, one triple point and one quadruple point, and this curve is of genus $15 - 6 - 3 - 6 = 0$, so that it is rational.

The cubic passes through five of the double points of the septimic and meets it in one other point. This other point is on the chord of C which passes through O; this chord is a common generator of the two ruled surfaces.

109. In surfaces of the type III (D) the double curve consists of a directrix R, a double generator G and a quartic. This quartic is rational, having a double point on G, this being the point of intersection of G with the only other generator which meets it. The quartic meets R. The bitangent developable consists of the planes through R counted three times, the planes through G, and a quadric cone; one tangent plane of this cone passing through R and another through G.

Through each point of R there pass two generators; there is one point of R at which the plane of the two generators contains R, it is represented on Ω by the ϖ-plane containing the chord of C which passes through O, and is the intersection of R with the double conic. Each plane through R contains three generators.

110. In the type III (E) C meets every plane ϖ through O in three points and every plane ρ through O in two points, while two chords of C pass through O. We have a rational quintic ruled surface in [3] with a directrix line R; through any point of R there pass three generators, while any plane through R contains two generators. There are two and only two planes through R such that the two generators in either plane intersect in a point of R.

An arbitrary plane ρ meets T in a line; the plane ϖ through this line is the plane joining it to O, which contains three points and therefore three chords of C. There are three other chords of C meeting the line, so that the double curve of the ruled surface consists of the directrix R counted three times together with a twisted cubic. R is a chord of the cubic. The two points in which R meets the cubic have, in fact, already been noticed; they are the two points of R in which pairs of generators meet and at the same time lie in a plane with R. The tangents of the cubic at these two points lie in the planes of the pairs of generators.

An arbitrary plane ϖ meets T in a line, and the plane ρ through this line is the plane joining it to O, which contains two points and therefore one chord of C. There will be five other chords of C meeting the line. Hence the bitangent developable consists of the planes through R together with a developable of the fifth class. There are two planes of this developable passing through R represented by the ρ-planes of Ω containing the two chords of C which pass through O; it has also a tritangent plane, this being represented on Ω by the plane ρ through the trisecant of C.

111. In the type III (F) we have a rational quintic ruled surface in [3] with a directrix line R; through any point of R there pass two generators, while any plane through R contains three generators. The double curve consists of R and a quintic; this quintic has a triple point and meets R in two points. The bitangent developable consists of the planes through R, counted three times, together with a developable of the third class, two planes of this latter developable passing through R.

112. Consider now the genus of this quintic curve; we know that it must be rational, having a triple point.

The trisecant t of C is joined to O by a ρ-plane; it therefore meets every ϖ-plane through O in one point. The chords of C form the locus V_3^6 with the double surface F_2^7; a ϖ-plane through O meets F_2^7 in two points of C, one other point on the chord joining these two points, three points at the intersection of the plane with t, and also in O; while a ρ-plane through O meets F_2^7 in three points of C, three other points on the chords joining the pairs of these, and also in O*.

The intersection of F_2^7 with the quadric point-cone, vertex O, on which C lies, consists of C, t counted three times, and a sextic curve with a double point at O and meeting every chord of C in one point†. It is clear that this sextic meets every ϖ-plane through O in one point and every ρ-plane through O in three points other than O; it is thus a rational curve.

Here again the ruled surface formed by the chords of C which lie on Ω breaks up. The ϖ-planes through O meet C in pairs of an involution, so that the chords in these planes form a quartic ruled surface with a double point at O, the projection of a normal quartic ruled surface in [5] from a point. The section of this ruled surface by any solid lying in T is a rational quartic lying on a quadric, meeting all generators of one system in three points and all of the other system in one point.

The chords of C which lie in the ρ-planes through O form a ruled surface of order 8 with C as a double curve and t as a triple line. By considering the intersections of the planes of Ω through O with the surface F_2^7 it is easily seen that there is no other multiple curve on this ruled surface. The section by a solid gives an octavic curve having five double points and one triple point; it lies on a quadric, meeting all the generators of one system in three points and all of the other system in five points. Hence the genus of this curve is

$$21 - 5 - 3 - 3 - 10 = 0,$$

so that it is a rational curve. Thus the quintic double curve of the ruled surface in [3] is a rational curve.

The chords of C which lie in the ϖ-planes through O correspond to the points of the line R regarded as part of the double curve and to the planes

* Cf. § 95. † Cf. § 96.

of the developable of the third class regarded as part of the bitangent developable; the chords of C which lie in ρ-planes through O correspond to the points of the quintic curve and to the triple pencil of planes through R; this last must be regarded as a rational family of planes.

The ruled surface is formed by the chords of the quintic curve which meet R; clearly two such chords pass through any point of the curve and three lie in any plane through R. We thus take a rational quintic with a triple point and one of its chords, and we at once obtain a surface of this type.

There are similar results for the surface of the type III (E).

Surfaces with a directrix line which is also a generator

113. In surfaces belonging to the type IV we have a directrix line R which is also a generator, this being represented by the point O of Ω; C lies in the tangent prime of Ω at O and passes through O.

In IV (A) C meets every ϖ-plane through O in three points and every ρ-plane through O in one point other than O. Through every point of R there pass three generators other than R, while every plane through R contains one generator other than R.

An arbitrary plane ρ meets T in a line, and the plane ϖ through this line is the plane joining it to O. This contains four points and therefore six chords of C, and no other chords meet the line. Hence the double curve is the line R counted six times. An arbitrary plane ϖ meets T in a line, and the plane ρ through this line joins it to O. This contains two points and therefore one chord of C; there will be five other chords meeting the line. Hence the bitangent developable consists of the planes through R together with a developable of the fifth class. Two planes of this latter pass through R, and it has a tritangent plane represented on Ω by the plane ρ passing through the trisecant of C. The ϖ-plane through the tangent of C at O meets C in two other points; the two ρ-planes containing the chords of C which join these points to O represent the two planes of the quintic developable which pass through R.

In IV (B) we have another type of surface; R is both a directrix and a generator, through any point of R there passes one generator other than R, while any plane through R contains three generators other than R. The double curve consists of R and a quintic with a triple point, R being a chord of the quintic; the bitangent developable consists of the planes through R counted six times.

114. In IV (C) C meets every plane of Ω through O in two points other than O and has a double point P; P will represent a double generator G of the ruled surface. Through every point of R there pass two generators other than R, while every plane through R contains two generators other than R.

Any plane of Ω meets T in a line; the plane of the opposite system through this line passes through O, containing three points and therefore three chords of C. The plane joining the line to P meets Ω in a second line through P, while there are two other chords of C meeting the line. The double curve therefore consists of G, R counted three times, and a conic. R and G intersect. The ρ-plane through the tangent of C at O meets C in another point, and the ϖ-plane, which contains the line joining this point to O, represents a point of intersection of R and the conic. G and the conic also intersect. Similarly the bitangent developable consists of the planes through G, the planes through R counted three times, and the tangent planes of a quadric cone, one tangent plane of this cone passing through R and another through G.

The ruled surface formed by the chords of C which lie on Ω here breaks up into a quartic cone with vertex O passing through C and having the double generator OP, together with two cubic ruled surfaces both passing through C.

115. In IV (D) the trisecant of C passes through O, C meeting every plane of Ω through O in two points other than O. Again, we have a surface for which the line R is both a directrix and a generator; every plane through R contains two generators other than R, while through every point of R there pass two generators other than R. The difference between this surface and one of the type IV (C) lies in the fact that there is a plane through R which contains two generators meeting in a point of R, while in the former type of surface we only have the plane through R and a double generator.

Any plane of Ω meets T in a line; the plane of the opposite system through this line joins it to O, containing three points and therefore three chords of C. There are three other chords of C meeting the line. Hence the double curve consists of the line R counted three times together with a twisted cubic. R is a chord of the cubic. One of the common points of R and the cubic is represented on Ω by the ϖ-plane through the trisecant of C. The other is represented by the ϖ-plane which contains that chord of C which joins O to the remaining intersection of C with the ρ-plane containing its tangent at O. Similarly the bitangent developable consists of the planes through R counted three times together with a developable of the third class, two of whose planes pass through R.

116. If C lies in a tangent prime T of Ω and has a double point at O we have a rational quintic ruled surface in [3] with a directrix line R which is also a double generator.

For the type V (A) C meets every ϖ-plane through O in two points and every ρ-plane through O in one point other than O. An arbitrary plane ρ meets T in a line; the plane ϖ through this line joins it to O, and meets

C in the double point O and two points A and B. The chords OA, OB, AB are the only chords of C meeting the line, since OA and OB are double on the locus V_3^5 formed by the chords of C*. Hence the double curve is the line R counted six times. An arbitrary plane ϖ meets T in a line; the plane ρ through this line joins it to O and contains one other point of C, so that there will be three chords of C meeting the line which do not lie in this ρ-plane. Hence the bitangent developable consists of R counted three times and a developable of the third class. There are two planes of this developable passing through R. The ϖ-plane through either tangent of C at O meets C in one other point; the ρ-plane through the chord of C joining this point to O represents a plane of the developable passing through R.

Through any point of R there pass two generators other than R, while any plane through R contains one generator other than R.

For a surface of the type V (B) we have a directrix R which is also a double generator; through any point of R there passes one generator other than R, while any plane through R contains two generators other than R. The double curve consists of the triple line R together with a twisted cubic having R for a chord; the bitangent developable consists of the planes through R counted six times.

The ruled surface, formed by the chords of C which lie on Ω, breaks up into the cubic cone which projects C from O, counted twice, together with a quartic ruled surface passing through C.

Surfaces whose generators belong to a linear congruence

117. Suppose now that C lies on the quadric Q in which Ω is met by a solid S_3, the two tangent primes of Ω through S_3 touching it in O and O'. Then O and O' represent lines R and R', in [3], which are both directrices of the surface.

If C belongs to the type VI (A) it meets all generators of Q of one system in four points and all of the other system in one point. We can suppose that the generators of the first system lie in the ϖ-planes through O and the ρ-planes through O'; those of the other system lying in the ϖ-planes through O' and the ρ-planes through O. Then through every point of R there pass four generators of the ruled surface which lie in a plane through R', while conversely every plane through R' contains four generators which meet in a point of R.

The rational quintic in S_3 has six apparent double points. An arbitrary plane ρ meets S_3 in a point of Q; the six chords of C through this point all coincide with the generator of Q which is quadrisecant to C, the projection of C from this point on to a plane in S_3 being a quintic with a quadruple point. The plane ϖ through this generator passes through O,

* Cf. § 102.

so that the double curve of the surface consists of the line R counted six times. Similarly the bitangent developable consists of the line R' counted six times.

118. If C belongs to the type VI (B) it meets all generators of Q of one system in three points and all of the other system in two points, having two double points. These represent two double generators G and H of the surface. Any point of R is the intersection of three generators lying in a plane through R', while conversely any plane through R' contains three generators meeting in a point of R. Through any point of R' there pass two generators lying in a plane through R, while any plane through R contains two generators meeting in a point of R'.

An arbitrary plane ρ meets S_3 in a point of Q; the six chords of C through this point consist of the lines to the two double points, the generator of Q meeting C in two points, together with the trisecant generator counted three times. Hence the double curve consists of G, H, R' together with R counted three times. The bitangent developable consists of the planes through G, H and R together with those through R' counted three times.

119. Now suppose that C lies on the quadric cone in which Ω is met by a solid touching it at a point V.

In the type VII (A) C passes through V and meets every generator of the cone in two points other than V. The surface has a directrix line R which is also a generator. Since each generator of the cone is the intersection of two planes of Ω, of opposite systems, both lying in the tangent prime at V, through each point of R there pass two other generators which lie in a plane with R, while each plane through R contains two other generators meeting in a point of R. C has two double points, so that the surface has two double generators G and H.

Any plane of Ω meets S_3 in a point of the cone. The projection of C from this point on to a plane of S_3 gives a rational quintic with two double points, and a triple point at which two branches touch each other. This latter is equivalent to four double points, being formed by the union of two double points and a tacnode. The six chords of C which can be drawn from any point on the cone consist of the generator of the cone, counted four times, together with the lines to the two double points.

The double curve of the surface consists of G and H with R counted four times, while the bitangent developable consists of G and H considered as pencils of planes together with the planes through R counted four times.

This surface is really a degeneration of the type VI (B) when the two directrices R and R' of that type coincide. The plane sections will be rational quintic curves with double points on G and H and triple points (at which two branches have a common tangent) on R.

120. In the type VII (B) C has a triple point at V and meets every generator of the cone in one point other than V. The surface has a directrix line R which is also a triple generator; through any point of R there passes one other generator, while any plane through R contains one other generator. Clearly the double curve consists of the points of R counted six times, the bitangent developable of the planes through R counted six times.

121. We have now found twenty-four different kinds of rational quintic ruled surfaces in [3]; these are exhibited in tabular form on p. 304.

SECTION II

RATIONAL QUINTIC RULED SURFACES CONSIDERED AS PROJECTIONS OF NORMAL SURFACES IN HIGHER SPACE

The general surface in [6]

122. The rational quintic ruled surface is normal in [6]; there are two distinct kinds of surfaces, one with a directrix line λ, and the most general one with a directrix conic Γ*.

The rational quintic ruled surfaces f of ordinary space Σ can all be obtained by projection from the normal surfaces F in [6]. The projection will be from a plane ϖ which must not meet F; the solids joining ϖ to the points of F meet Σ in the points of f, while the [4]'s joining ϖ to the generators of F meet Σ in the generators of f.

Let us now consider the general surface F with a directrix conic Γ. A prime through ϖ meets F in a rational normal quintic, six of whose chords meet ϖ; so that there are six solids in this prime which pass through ϖ and meet F in two points. Projecting on to Σ we see that in any plane there are six points in which two generators of f intersect, so that the double curve is a sextic.

123. Consider now the five-dimensional locus M_5 formed by the chords of F.

This locus M_5 contains any solid K which contains a directrix cubic Δ of F; for through any point of K there passes a chord of Δ. Also M_5 contains any solid K' which contains a pair of generators g, g' of F; for through any point of K' there passes a transversal of g and g'.

Conversely, through any point of M_5 there passes a chord of F; this meets F in two points through which† there passes a directrix cubic Δ, while the points themselves lie on two generators g and g'. Hence every

* § 43. † § 45.

point of F lies in a solid K and also in a solid K', so that M_5 can be generated either by the ∞^2 solids K or by the ∞^2 solids K'.

If any solid K is taken, a prime through it will meet F in the directrix cubic of K and in two generators; these two generators lie in a solid K' which meets the plane of Γ in the line joining the points where the two generators meet Γ. Taking three different solids K, each of them is the base of a doubly-infinite system of primes; and we can establish a projectivity between the primes of these three systems, two primes of different systems corresponding when they join the respective solids K to the same line in the plane of Γ. Then corresponding primes of the three systems meet in a solid K', and all the solids K' are given in this way.

Hence M_5, being generated by the solids K', is generated by three doubly-infinite systems of primes projectively related to each other. This proves that M_5 is a *cubic* primal $M_5{}^3$; for if we take the section by an arbitrary solid we obtain a surface generated by three projectively related "stars" of planes, the vertices of the stars being the points in which the arbitrary solid is met by the three solids K. We have thus the well-known generation of the *cubic* surface.

When the cubic surface in [3] is generated by three projective stars of planes there are six sets of three corresponding planes of the stars which have a line in common instead of a point only; these lines lie on the cubic surface and form half of a double-six. Hence, given an arbitrary solid in the [6] containing F, there are six solids K' meeting it in lines. In particular, we may take this arbitrary solid to contain the plane ϖ from which we are projecting F on to Σ. Then, through a given point of Σ there pass six planes, each of which contains a pair of generators of f; so that the bitangent developable of f is of the sixth class. The projected surface f has one tritangent plane; this being the intersection of Σ with the prime containing ϖ and Γ.

The chords of F meet ϖ in the points of a cubic curve c_3, this being the intersection of ϖ with $M_5{}^3$. Since no two chords of F can intersect (except on F itself or at a point in the plane of Γ) this curve has no double point and is therefore elliptic. Hence the double curve and bitangent developable of f are both elliptic; the points of the double curve and the planes of the bitangent developable both being in (1, 1) correspondence with the points of c_3.

124. Algebraically, suppose that the surface is generated by a (1, 1) correspondence between its directrix conic Γ in the plane $x_0 = x_1 = x_2 = x_3 = 0$ and one of its directrix cubics Δ in the solid $x_4 = x_5 = x_6 = 0$. Then we may take the coordinates of corresponding points to be

$$(0, 0, 0, 0, \theta^2, \theta, 1) \text{ and } (\theta^3, \theta^2, \theta, 1, 0, 0, 0),$$

so that any point of F has coordinates

$$(\theta^3, \theta^2, \theta, 1, \lambda\theta^2, \lambda\theta, \lambda),$$

and the equations of the surface are

$$\frac{x_0}{x_1}=\frac{x_1}{x_2}=\frac{x_2}{x_3}=\frac{x_4}{x_5}=\frac{x_5}{x_6},$$

the generators being given by $\theta = \text{const.}$

The chords of F are ∞^4 in aggregate and form a locus M_5 whose equation can at once be written down. For, taking any two points

$$(\theta^3, \theta^2, \theta, 1, \lambda\theta^2, \lambda\theta, \lambda) \text{ and } (\phi^3, \phi^2, \phi, 1, \mu\phi^2, \mu\phi, \mu)$$

on F, the coordinates of a point on the chord joining them are

$$(\theta^3+\kappa\phi^3,\quad \theta^2+\kappa\phi^2,\quad \theta+\kappa\phi,\quad 1+\kappa,\quad \lambda\theta^2+\kappa\mu\phi^2,\quad \lambda\theta+\kappa\mu\phi,\quad \lambda+\kappa\mu),$$

and these may be taken as the coordinates of any point of M_5. The coordinates are thus expressed in terms of five parameters. They satisfy the relations

$$\begin{aligned} x_0-(\theta+\phi)\,x_1+\theta\phi x_2&=0,\\ x_1-(\theta+\phi)\,x_2+\theta\phi x_3&=0,\\ x_4-(\theta+\phi)\,x_5+\theta\phi x_6&=0,\end{aligned}$$

so that the equation of M_5 is

$$\begin{vmatrix} x_0 & x_1 & x_2 \\ x_1 & x_2 & x_3 \\ x_4 & x_5 & x_6 \end{vmatrix} = 0,$$

a primal M_5^3 of the third order.

Since the equation of M_5^3 is given by equating a determinant to zero it follows at once that it can be generated by systems of spaces in two different ways; it contains two doubly-infinite systems of solids.

The solid whose equations are

$$\begin{aligned} \alpha x_0+\beta x_1+\gamma x_2&=0,\\ \alpha x_1+\beta x_2+\gamma x_3&=0,\\ \alpha x_4+\beta x_5+\gamma x_6&=0,\end{aligned}$$

lies on M_5^3 for all values of $\alpha:\beta:\gamma$. This solid meets F in points for which

$$\alpha\theta^2+\beta\theta+\gamma=0,$$

i.e. in two generators.

Conversely, the solid containing the two generators given by $\theta=\theta_1$ and $\theta=\theta_2$ is determined by the four points

$$(\theta_1^3, \theta_1^2, \theta_1, 1, 0, 0, 0), \qquad (0, 0, 0, 0, \theta_1^2, \theta_1, 1),$$
$$(\theta_2^3, \theta_2^2, \theta_2, 1, 0, 0, 0), \qquad (0, 0, 0, 0, \theta_2^2, \theta_2, 1),$$

so that its equations are

$$\begin{aligned} x_0-(\theta_1+\theta_2)\,x_1+\theta_1\theta_2 x_2&=0,\\ x_1-(\theta_1+\theta_2)\,x_2+\theta_1\theta_2 x_3&=0,\\ x_4-(\theta_1+\theta_2)\,x_5+\theta_1\theta_2 x_6&=0,\end{aligned}$$

all other primes through the solid being linear combinations of these three. Thus the solid lies on M_5^3; M_5^3 can be generated by the solids K'.

We also have the conjugate generation of M_5^3; the solid whose equations are

$$\begin{aligned} ax_0+bx_1+cx_4&=0,\\ ax_1+bx_2+cx_5&=0,\\ ax_2+bx_3+cx_6&=0,\end{aligned}$$

lying on M_5^3 for all values of $a:b:c$. This solid meets F in points for which θ and λ are connected by the relation

$$a\theta+b+c\lambda=0.$$

Since this is linear in λ it represents a directrix curve meeting each generator $\theta =$ const. in one point; in fact it is a directrix cubic Δ given by

$$\{c\theta^3, \quad c\theta^2, \quad c\theta, \quad c, \quad -\theta^2(a\theta+b), \quad -\theta(a\theta+b), \quad -(a\theta+b)\}.$$

We have thus the ∞^2 curves Δ on F, and $M_5{}^3$ can be generated by the solids K containing these curves.

All these curves Δ can be obtained by means of prime sections through any two fixed generators; for the prime, whose equation is

$$a\{x_0 - (\theta_1+\theta_2)x_1 + \theta_1\theta_2 x_2\} + b\{x_1 - (\theta_1+\theta_2)x_2 + \theta_1\theta_2 x_3\} \\ + c\{x_4 - (\theta_1+\theta_2)x_5 + \theta_1\theta_2 x_6\} = 0,$$

contains the curve and the pair of generators given by $\theta = \theta_1$ and $\theta = \theta_2$.

If we consider the six primes

$$\Sigma_1 \equiv \alpha x_0 + \beta x_1 + \gamma x_2 = 0, \; \Sigma_2 \equiv \alpha x_1 + \beta x_2 + \gamma x_3 = 0, \; \Sigma_3 \equiv \alpha x_4 + \beta x_5 + \gamma x_6 = 0,$$
$$S_1 \equiv a x_0 + b x_1 + c x_4 = 0, \quad S_2 \equiv a x_1 + b x_2 + c x_5 = 0, \quad S_3 \equiv a x_2 + b x_3 + c x_6 = 0,$$

then
$$a\Sigma_1 + b\Sigma_2 + c\Sigma_3 \equiv \alpha S_1 + \beta S_2 + \gamma S_3,$$

so that the six primes have a line in common. Thus a solid K and a solid K' have a line of intersection.

Since all the first minors of the determinant

$$\begin{vmatrix} x_0 & x_1 & x_2 \\ x_1 & x_2 & x_3 \\ x_4 & x_5 & x_6 \end{vmatrix}$$

vanish at a point of F, F must be a double surface on $M_5{}^3$. Since they also vanish at a point of the plane of Γ this plane must be a double plane on $M_5{}^3$.

It follows, as a consequence of the two methods of generating F, that an arbitrary solid of [6] is met in lines by six solids K and also by six solids K', and that these lines

$$\begin{matrix} k_1, & k_2, & k_3, & k_4, & k_5, & k_6, \\ k_1', & k_2', & k_3', & k_4', & k_5', & k_6', \end{matrix}$$

form a double-six on the cubic surface which is the section of $M_5{}^3$ by the arbitrary solid.

The quintic ruled surface F in [6] which has a directrix line has the equations

$$\frac{x_0}{x_1} = \frac{x_1}{x_2} = \frac{x_2}{x_3} = \frac{x_3}{x_4} = \frac{x_5}{x_6},$$

and its chords form the cubic primal

$$\begin{vmatrix} x_0 & x_1 & x_2 \\ x_1 & x_2 & x_3 \\ x_2 & x_3 & x_4 \end{vmatrix} = 0.$$

125. Suppose now that we take two fixed generators, g and g', of F. Then the ∞^4 directrix quartics of F are obtained* by primes through g and also by primes through g', and the system of ∞^4 primes through g is thus related projectively to the system of ∞^4 primes through g'. If we take a pencil of primes through g we obtain on F a pencil of directrix

* § 45. This applies also to the normal surface F with a directrix line λ.

quartics with three common points; these three points being in fact the intersections (other than g itself) of F with the [4] which is the base of the pencil of primes. Corresponding to this [4] we have a [4] through g' containing the same three points of F. *The trisecant planes of F are thus the intersections of corresponding* [4]'s *of the projectivity.* The system of ∞^4 primes through g contains ∞^6 pencils of primes, the bases of these pencils being the [4]'s through g; these, with the corresponding [4]'s through g', give the ∞^6 trisecant planes of F. The surface F itself is generated by the intersections of corresponding planes of the projectivity; there are ∞^4 planes through g and ∞^4 corresponding planes through g', and, since two conditions are necessary in order that two planes in [6] should have a common point, there will be ∞^2 planes through g which meet their corresponding planes through g'; these ∞^2 points are the points of the surface F.

126. We now enquire how many trisecant planes of F there are which meet an arbitrary plane ϖ of [6] in lines; we expect that there will be a finite number*.

The generator g and the plane ϖ determine a [4] S_1; corresponding to this we have a [4] S_1' through g' meeting S_1 in a trisecant plane of F, and this trisecant plane, lying in the [4] S_1 with ϖ, meets ϖ in a point P_1. Similarly, the generator g' and the plane ϖ determine a [4] S_2'; corresponding to this we have a [4] S_2 through g meeting S_2' in a trisecant plane of F, this trisecant plane meeting ϖ in a point P_2.

Suppose now that there is a trisecant plane π of F which meets ϖ in a line. There is then a [5] through S_1 which contains π, so that there must also be a [5] through S_1' containing π. Hence π meets S_1' in a line, and this line will have to meet the line of intersection of π with ϖ, and therefore must pass through P_1, the point of intersection of S_1' and ϖ. Hence π must pass through P_1, and similarly π must pass through P_2. If then there is a trisecant plane meeting ϖ in a line, this line must be P_1P_2.

There are three† chords of F meeting P_1P_2, and these do in fact lie in a plane. For consider one of these chords meeting F in B and C. We have a [4] containing g, P_1P_2 and BC. Now the plane gP_2 is the intersection of S_1 and S_2, so that the corresponding plane through g' is the intersection of S_1' and S_2', i.e. the plane $g'P_1$. Hence the [4] through g' which corresponds to the [4] through g containing P_2 and BC must contain P_1 and BC, and therefore the plane P_1P_2BC. We thus have corresponding [4]'s through g and g' meeting in the plane P_1P_2BC, which is therefore a trisecant plane of F. If A is its third point of intersection with F the three chords of F which meet P_1P_2 are BC, CA, AB.

There is then *one trisecant plane of F which meets ϖ in a line.*

* § 53. † § 123.

127. Any prime through ϖ contains six chords of F, so that those chords of F which meet ϖ meet F in the points of a curve C_{12} of order 12; this projects from ϖ into the double curve of f. C_{12} has three double points at A, B, C, and, since the [4] through ϖ and any generator meets F in three further points, C_{12} must meet each generator of F in three points. It cannot have any other double points, so that it is a curve $C_{12}{}^4$ of genus* 4.

The (3, 1) correspondence between $C_{12}{}^4$ and Γ shews† that there are twelve generators of F touching $C_{12}{}^4$; hence there are twelve generators of f touching the double curve.

Also the (2, 1) correspondence between $C_{12}{}^4$ and c_3, the elliptic cubic curve in ϖ, shews† that there are six tangents of $C_{12}{}^4$ meeting ϖ. Hence *the tangents of F form a locus $M_4{}^6$ of the sixth order*‡.

128. *Rational quintic ruled surfaces in* [4]. Before proceeding to investigate the surfaces f of [3] it will be convenient to interpolate here a few remarks upon the rational quintic ruled surface in [4]; this is obtained by projecting the general surface F in [6] from a line l which does not meet it. Some of the properties that we shall obtain are given by Severi ||, but it is instructive to deduce them directly by projection.

We have seen that there are three points a, b, c on l through which there pass chords aa_1a_2, bb_1b_2, cc_1c_2 of F. The S_4 determined by these three chords must meet F in a directrix quartic, and on projecting from l on to the space [4] this becomes a plane quartic curve with three double points.

There is a solid K containing a directrix cubic of F which passes through a_1 and a_2; K containing the chord aa_1a_2. On projection this cubic becomes a plane cubic curve with a double point, this being at the same point as one of the double points of the quartic. We thus obtain three rational plane cubic curves on the surface in [4]; any two of these cubics intersect in the point of intersection of their planes, this being the projection of the point of intersection of the corresponding twisted cubics on F.

* § 17. † By Zeuthen's formula, § 16.

‡ The order of M_4 is obtainable at once by elementary methods. For suppose F to be generated by a (1, 1) correspondence between Γ and one of the directrix cubics Δ. The tangents of Γ and Δ are also in (1, 1) correspondence, and the tangent solids of F are determined by the pairs of corresponding tangents. But the ∞^1 solids determined by corresponding generators of two ruled surfaces, of orders 4 and 2, whose generators are in (1, 1) correspondence, form a locus of order $4+2=6$.

Similarly, the tangents of a rational ruled surface of order n form an $M_4{}^{2n-4}$.

|| See the footnote on p. 49 of his paper, "Intorno ai punti doppi impropri di una superficie generale dello spazio a quattro dimensioni e a' suoi punti tripli apparenti," *Palermo Rendiconti*, 15 (1901), 33.

Thus the general rational quintic ruled surface in [4] has three double points. It has a plane quartic on it; this lies in the plane of the three double points and has double points itself at these points. There are, further, three plane cubics, each of which has a double point at one of the double points of the surface. Further still, there is a directrix conic.

Of course we can obtain other surfaces in [4] by specialising the position of l in regard to F. If l lies in a solid K the projected surface has a triple line and is generated by a (1, 3) correspondence between a line and a conic. If l lies in a solid K' the projected surface has a double generator and contains ∞^1 plane cubics with double points on this generator. If l is an axis of a directrix quartic E the projected surface has a double conic. It is generated by two conics in (1, 2) correspondence with a united point. We can also project the surface with a directrix line.

Similarly, ruled surfaces in [5] are obtained by projecting F from a point of [6]; a general point of [6] does not lie on M_5^3, so that the general rational quintic ruled surface in [5] has no double points. But if the point of projection does lie on a chord of F we obtain a surface in [5] with one double point and having a plane cubic on it with a node there, while if the point of projection lies in the plane of Γ we obtain a surface in [5] with a double line, generated by a (1, 2) correspondence between a line and a cubic curve.

The surfaces in [3] *derived by projection from the general surface in* [6]

129. We now proceed to obtain the rational quintic ruled surfaces of [3] by projection from the two normal surfaces in [6], and also to give methods for generating them. Of the twenty-four types which we have enumerated seventeen are obtained from the general surface F, the other seven arise from the surface F with a directrix line.

We have already shewn how to obtain the most general surface f. Since F can be generated by placing its directrix conic Γ in (1, 1) correspondence with any one of its directrix cubics Δ, the most general surface f is generated by a conic and a twisted cubic in (1, 1) correspondence.

130. Suppose that we take an ordinary involution I of pairs of generators on F. If we take any directrix quartic E on F, I will determine an involution on E; the chords of E joining the pairs of the involution form a cubic ruled surface lying in the S_4 determined by E. This has a directrix line l, and a general plane ϖ will not contain this line*; but let us choose ϖ to pass through such a line.

The plane ϖ will meet M_5^3 in l and a conic ϑ. The chords of F which meet l will meet F in the points of the quartic E, while those which meet

* The lines of [6] are ∞^{10} in aggregate and include ∞^6 lines l.

ϑ will meet F in the points of an octavic C_8, meeting each generator of F in two points. The involution on E has two double points, so that there are two tangents of E which meet l; hence there must be four tangents of C_8 meeting ϑ, the (2, 1) correspondence between C_8 and ϑ having four double points. Applying Zeuthen's formula to this correspondence we at once find that C_8 is an elliptic curve, and then applying Segre's formula for the genus of a curve on a ruled surface we see that C_8 has one double point A. There are two chords of F passing through A, meeting C_8 again in B and C, and as these cannot be double points on C_8 they must be intersections of C_8 with E. The two chords of F which pass through the points common to l and ϑ are chords both of C_8 and E, so that we have four other intersections of these curves. There are, in fact, precisely six intersections*.

Projecting from ϖ on to the solid Σ we obtain a surface f with a double curve consisting of a conic (the projection of E) and a quartic (the projection of C_8); the quartic is rational since its points are in (1, 1) correspondence with those of ϑ; it has a double point (the projection of A, B and C) lying on the conic and meets the conic in two other points†.

F can be generated by placing Γ and E in (1, 1) correspondence with a united point. Hence f can be generated by two conics Γ_1 and Γ_2 in (1, 2) correspondence with a united point P. To P, regarded as a point of Γ_1, there correspond two points P, P' of Γ_2 one of which is P; to P regarded as a point of Γ_2 corresponds the point P of Γ_1.

Γ_1 meets the plane of Γ_2 in a second point Q; to Q there correspond two points Q', Q'' of Γ_2. The pairs of points of Γ_2 which correspond to the points of Γ_1 are the pairs of an involution; their joins all pass through O, the intersection of PP' and $Q'Q''$. The planes of the pairs of generators which intersect in the points of the double conic Γ_1 are therefore formed by the points of Γ_1 and the corresponding lines of a plane pencil in (1, 1) correspondence with Γ_1; there is one united element, the point P of Γ_1 lying on the line PP' of the pencil which corresponds to it. Thus‡ these planes touch a quadric cone E_2. This quadric cone is part of the bitangent developable of the surface.

The plane of Γ_2 is a tritangent plane of the ruled surface since it contains the three generators PP', QQ', QQ''. It is a tangent plane of E_2 as joining Q to the line $OQ'Q''$. The vertex of the cone E_2 is O.

131. If any directrix quartic E is taken on F all the axes l arising from this lie on the cubic locus formed by the chords of E, and no two involutions on E can have the same axis||.

* See the formula for i given in the footnote to § 97.

† Cf. § 92.

‡ § 22.

|| For the configuration of the axes of E see Segre, "Sulle varietà cubiche dello spazio a quattro dimensioni," *Memorie Torino* (2), 39 (1889), 3; in particular § 43.

Any two directrix quartics E, E' intersect in three points; the plane of these three points is the plane of intersection of the two [4]'s which contain the curves. If then an axis of E coincided with an axis of E' it would lie in a trisecant plane of either curve, which is impossible.

If a plane ϖ contains two axes of the same curve E it must be contained in the S_4 to which E belongs; it then occupies a special position. The type of surface f arising by projection from such a plane will be subsequently considered.

Thus to obtain a surface f with two double conics we try to find a plane ϖ containing an axis l_1 of a directrix quartic E and an axis l_2 of a directrix quartic E'. This we can certainly do; we have merely to take a common chord of E and E' and an axis of each curve passing through any point of this chord*. The plane ϖ meets $M_5{}^3$ in the lines l_1 and l_2 together with a third line l_3, and the chords of F which pass through the points of l_3 meet it in a third directrix quartic E''. The curves E' and E'' have a common chord passing through the intersection of l_2 and l_3 and have also a third common intersection A, and we have similar points B and C arising from the other two pairs of curves. The plane ABC meets ϖ in a line; the chords BC, CA, AB all meeting ϖ.

Projecting from ϖ on to a solid Σ we obtain a rational quintic ruled surface f with three double conics. The conics all pass through one point, while any two of them have a second intersection.

The surface F can be generated by a (1, 1) correspondence between E and E' with three united points. Thus to generate a surface f with two (and therefore three) double conics we take two conics Γ_1 and Γ_2 in Σ with two common points P, Q and place them in (2, 2) correspondence. To the point P regarded as a point of Γ_1 there correspond two points of Γ_2 which both coincide with P, while to the point P regarded as a point of Γ_2 there correspond two points of Γ_1 which both coincide with P. To the point Q regarded as a point of Γ_1 there correspond two points of Γ_2, one of which coincides with Q, while to the point Q regarded as a point of Γ_2 there correspond two points of Γ_1, one of which coincides with Q. The lines joining corresponding points of Γ_1 and Γ_2 generate a rational quintic ruled surface with two double conics Γ_1 and Γ_2.

132. We have seen that the prime $\varpi\Gamma$ contains three generators of F; in general there will not be a solid passing through ϖ and meeting each of these generators. But we may clearly choose ϖ so that this happens, and then the surface f, instead of being of the type I, is specialised and is of the type II (A).

* There are two axes of each curve passing through any point of the chord (Segre, *loc. cit.*).

Take any three points of Γ and the three generators through them. These determine a prime containing Γ; take points X, Y, Z one on each of the three generators and a line l lying in the plane XYZ. Then if we take any plane ϖ passing through l and lying in the prime and project from it on to Σ we obtain a surface f of the type II (A), having three generators passing through a point and lying in a plane.

When a surface f is generated by a conic and a twisted cubic in (1, 1) correspondence the plane of the conic is the tritangent plane. But, if we specialise the correspondence so that the lines which join the three points in which the cubic meets the plane of the conic to their corresponding points are concurrent, the three generators in the tritangent plane meet in the triple point.

This type of surface can be further specialised so as to have one or two double conics.

If, in the generation given in § 130, the correspondence between Γ_1 and Γ_2 is so specialised that PO passes through Q we obtain a surface with a double conic Γ_1 which is of the type II (A).

In the generation at the end of § 131 the point Q is a triple point of the ruled surface; one generator through Q lies in the plane of Γ_1 and a second in the plane of Γ_2. As a point approaches Q along one conic one of its corresponding points on the other conic must also approach Q; the limiting position of the line joining the two points is the third generator through Q. If the correspondence is specialised so that these three generators lie in a plane we have a surface belonging to the type II (A).

133. A solid K' through two generators does not meet F again. If we choose ϖ to pass through a line l of K' which does not meet either generator, and then project on to Σ, we obtain a surface f with a double generator G.

ϖ meets M_5^3 in a line l and a conic ϑ; the chords of F which meet ϖ will meet F in two generators and a curve C_{10} of order 10 meeting each generator in three points; C_{10} meets every solid K' in six points and every solid K in four points.

There are six tangents of C_{10} meeting ϑ, and applying Zeuthen's formula to the (2, 1) correspondence between C_{10} and ϑ we find that C_{10} is a hyperelliptic curve of genus 2; the g_2^1 on C_{10} consists of the pairs of points which correspond to the points of ϑ. Applying Segre's formula we see that C_{10} must have one double point A.

There are two chords of C_{10} passing through A and meeting ϖ; these meet C_{10} again in points B and C which must be intersections of C_{10} with the two generators of F that we originally selected. The chord BC meets l. On projecting we have a surface f with a double generator and a double quintic curve having a double point on the double generator. The quintic is rational since its points are in (1, 1) correspondence with those of ϑ.

Further, the quintic meets the double generator in two other points, these arising from the chords of F which pass through the intersections of l and ϑ. The generators of f are trisecants of the quintic*. The bitangent developable consists of the planes through G, and a developable of the fifth class whose planes form a rational family in (1, 1) correspondence with the points of ϑ. This developable has one double tangent plane and two ordinary tangent planes passing through G.

The prime $\varpi\Gamma$ necessarily contains the two chosen generators of F, assuming that the planes of ϖ and Γ do not meet.

Hence to generate this surface f in Σ we take a conic and a twisted cubic in (1, 1) correspondence, but we so specialise the correspondence that two of the points in which the cubic meets the plane of the conic have for corresponding points those two points of the conic which lie on the line joining them.

134. Suppose now that ϖ is chosen to meet the plane of Γ in a point O. Then the projected surface f has a directrix line R, the intersection of Σ with the [4] containing ϖ and Γ. A prime through the [4] $\varpi\Gamma$ contains three generators of F, so that a plane through R contains three generators of f. A solid passing through ϖ and lying in the [4] $\varpi\Gamma$ meets two generators of F, so that through any point of R there pass two generators of f. This plainly indicates the types III (D) and III (F).

Suppose that there is a point X on R such that the two generators g_1 and g_2 of f which intersect there are co-planar with R.

The two generators of F which give rise to g_1 and g_2 must clearly lie in a prime containing ϖ and Γ. Such primes form a pencil, and each meets F in Γ and three generators; they thus cut a g_3^1 on any directrix curve of F, the two generators in question passing through two points of a set of this g_3^1.

Further, the two spaces [4] which project the generators from ϖ must meet the [4] $\varpi\Gamma$ in the same solid and therefore must meet the plane of Γ in the same line through O. The lines through O meet Γ in the sets of a g_2^1 and the pairs of generators so determined give a g_2^1 on any directrix curve.

Now, if we are given a g_2^1 and a g_3^1 on a rational curve, there are two† sets of the g_2^1 belonging to sets of the g_3^1. Hence there are, in general, two pairs of generators of F such as we require.

* Cf. § 102.

† The g_2^1 may be regarded as a (1, 1) correspondence, and the g_3^1 as a (2, 2) correspondence; both these correspondences are symmetrical, and are, in fact, involutions. Hence the number of common pairs of corresponding points is 2—half the number given by Brill's formula (see § 15). More generally, the number of pairs of points common to a g_m^1 and a g_n^1 on a curve of genus p is $(m-1)(n-1)-p$.

Hence, in general, there will be two points X on R such that the two generators of f which intersect there are co-planar with R, and then f is of the type III (F).

It may, however, happen that one of the two pairs of generators of F is such that there is a [4] through ϖ containing them. The surface f has then a double generator and is of the type III (D).

If both pairs of generators are special in this way it appears that there is a directrix cubic Δ of F for which the solid K meets ϖ in a line; f is then a type of surface which will be subsequently considered.

For let gg' and hh' be the two pairs of generators; the solids gg' and hh' meeting ϖ in the lines x and y. Take a point P on g and the transversal through P of $gg'x$, meeting g' in Q and x in R. The two points P and Q determine a directrix cubic Δ meeting h and h' in S and T. Through S there passes a transversal of $hh'y$, meeting y in U and h' in T'.

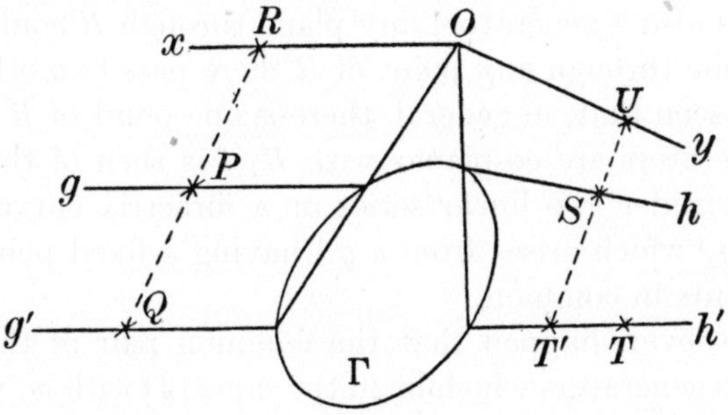

Fig. 5.

Then the ranges (T) and (T') on h' are homographic, and have two common corresponding points. One of these is clearly on Γ; the other gives a curve Δ for which the solid K meets ϖ in a line.

135. The generation of the surfaces f of the preceding article is at once obtained, since F can be generated by a (1, 1) correspondence between Γ and any of its directrix cubics. We take in Σ a line and a twisted cubic in (1, 2) correspondence; the joins of corresponding points give a quintic ruled surface with the line as a double directrix.

The pairs of points of the cubic which correspond to the points of the line form an ordinary rational involution; the chords joining the pairs therefore form a regulus. Hence there will be two of these chords meeting the line in points A and B. Through A passes a chord Aaa', the pair of points aa' corresponding to a point α of the line; through B passes a chord Bbb', the pair of points bb' corresponding to a point β of the line. In general, the surface is of the type III (F); but if either α coincides with A or β with

B we have a surface of the type III (D) with a double generator. If α coincides with A and β coincides with B the surface f degenerates into a type with two directrices.

If a (1, 1) correspondence has been established between the points of a line and the lines of a regulus then the planes containing corresponding elements form a developable of the third class*. If one of the two lines of the regulus meets the line in the point which corresponds to it the planes touch a quadric cone, while if both lines of the regulus which meet the line do so in their corresponding points the planes all pass through a line. This confirms the result found for the bitangent developables of the surfaces III (F), III (D) and VI (B).

136. When ϖ has been chosen to meet the plane of Γ in a point the [4] $\varpi\Gamma$ will not, in general, contain a generator of F, but we may clearly choose ϖ so that it does. Then the projected surface f will have a directrix line R which is also a generator; any plane through R contains two other generators, while through any point of R there pass two other generators.

It is easily seen that, in general, there is one point of R at which these two other generators are co-planar with R; f is then of the type IV (D). We have to consider two linear series on a directrix curve of F; one g_2^1 and a second g_2^1 which arises from a g_3^1 having a fixed point. These have one pair of points in common.

It may, however, happen that the common pair of these two linear series gives two generators which lie in the same [4] with ϖ; we may clearly choose ϖ so that this happens. Then f has a double generator and is of the type IV (C).

137. We again consider F as generated by a (1, 1) correspondence between Γ and one of its directrix cubics Δ. The [4] $\varpi\Gamma$ contains a generator g, and, when we project on to Σ, Γ and Δ become a line and a twisted cubic which intersect in a point P, the projection of the point $g\Delta$. Thus to generate f we take a line and twisted cubic meeting in a point P and establish a (1, 2) correspondence between them. To any point of the line correspond two points of the cubic, while to any point of the cubic corresponds one point of the line, P not being special in any way. We have a surface f of the type IV (D).

The pairs of points of the cubic which correspond to the points of the line give rise to lines forming a regulus meeting the line in two points P and Q. The planes of the pairs of generators issuing from the points of the line thus form a developable of the third class which is part of the bitangent developable of f.

* See § 23 above.

Through Q there passes a chord Qaa' of the cubic; a and a' forming the pair of points corresponding to some point α of the line. If then α coincides with Q we have a surface f with a double generator of the type IV (C); this has a quadric cone as part of its bitangent developable.

138. Further, when ϖ meets the plane of Γ in a point, it may happen that the [4] $\varpi\Gamma$ contains two generators of F. Then f has a directrix line R which is also a double generator; any plane through R contains one other generator, while through any point of R there pass two other generators. Hence f is of the type V (A).

To generate f we take a twisted cubic and one of its chords and place them in (2, 1) correspondence without united points. Those planes of the bitangent developable which do not pass through the chord form a developable of the third class.

139. We have seen that of the ∞^2 solids K there is a singly infinite set meeting a general plane ϖ in points but that there is none meeting it in a line. If, however, we choose ϖ to meet a solid K in a line the projected surface f has a directrix line R, the intersection of Σ with the [4] ϖK. Since any prime through the [4] ϖK meets F in a directrix cubic Δ and two generators we see that any plane through R contains two generators of f, and since any solid passing through ϖ and lying in the [4] ϖK meets F in three points there will be three generators of f passing through any point of R. This indicates the types III (C) and III (E).

Suppose that there is a plane x through R such that the pair of generators which it contains intersect in a point on R.

The two spaces [4] joining ϖ to the two generators of F from which these arise must meet the [4] ϖK in the same solid, and must therefore meet K in the same plane. This plane will contain the line of intersection of ϖ and K, so that the two generators of F meet Δ in a pair of points belonging to a set of a $g_3{}^1$ cut out on Δ by planes of K passing through a line. Also the two generators of F must lie in a prime through ϖ and K; such primes form a pencil, each meeting F in Δ and two generators, giving thus a $g_2{}^1$ on Δ. But the $g_2{}^1$ has two sets belonging to sets of the $g_3{}^1$. Hence, in general, there are two planes x through R such as we are seeking, and f is of the type III (E).

It may happen that one of these two pairs of generators of F is such that there is a [4] through ϖ containing them. Then f has a double generator and is of the type III (C).

If both pairs of generators are special in this way it appears that ϖ must meet the plane of Γ in a point; the surface f then belongs to a type which will be subsequently considered.

For let one pair of generators be g and g', the other pair h and h'. The solid gg' will meet ϖ in a line x; the solid hh' will meet ϖ in a line y. Let G, G', H, H' be the points of intersection of Γ with the four generators. Then GG' and HH' intersect, and this point of intersection is the point common to the two solids gg' and hh' and is therefore also the point of intersection of the lines x, y.

140. Since F is generated by a (1, 1) correspondence between Δ and Γ, f can be generated by a (1, 3) correspondence between a line and a conic; to any point of the line R correspond three points of the conic, while to any point of the conic corresponds one point of the line R.

We have an involution of sets of three points on the conic, and the sets of three joins of all such triads are known to touch a conic Γ_0*. There are two tangents to Γ_0 from the point in which the line R meets its plane; these give the two pairs of generators of f which lie in planes through R and intersect in points of R. The surface is, in general, of the type III (E).

The point of intersection of R with the plane of the conic gives three corresponding points of the conic. If two of these happen to be collinear with the point on R we have a surface f of the type III (C) with a double generator.

141. When ϖ is chosen to meet a solid K in a line the [4] ϖK will not, in general, contain a generator of F, but we may clearly choose ϖ so that it does. Then, on projecting, the surface f has a directrix R which is also a generator. Any plane through R contains one other generator, while through any point of R there pass three generators. Hence F is of the type IV (A).

To generate f we again take a line R and a conic in (1, 3) correspondence, but here they have a point of intersection. This point does not specialise the correspondence in any way.

The point of intersection of R and the conic is the projection from ϖ on to Σ of the point of intersection of Γ with the generator of F which lies in the [4] ϖK.

142. We now investigate a type of surface f to which we have already twice referred. Suppose that ϖ is chosen to meet a solid K in a line and also to meet the plane of Γ in a point O. Then the projected surface f has two directrices; R, the intersection of Σ with the [4] ϖK, and R', the intersection of Σ with the [4] $\varpi\Gamma$.

Any prime through ϖ and K meets F in Δ and two generators which must meet Γ in a pair of points collinear with O. Also any solid through

* Cf. Baker, *Principles of Geometry*, 2 (Cambridge, 1922), 137.

ϖ lying in the [4] $\varpi\Gamma$ meets Γ in two points collinear with O; there is then a prime containing these two generators and ϖ, which necessarily contains K also. Hence any plane through R contains two generators of f meeting in a point of R', while through any point of R' there pass two generators of f lying in a plane with R. Similarly, any plane through R' contains three generators of f meeting in a point of R, while through any point of R there pass three generators lying in a plane with R'.

Now let us enquire whether f has any double generators. This is the same question as whether there exist spaces S_4 through ϖ which contain two generators of F. Such an S_4 would have to meet the plane of Γ in a line through O and the solid K in a plane. Conversely, if we have a pair of generators of F such that the chords of Γ and Δ determined by the pair both meet ϖ, there is an S_4 through ϖ containing the pair of generators. Now the chords of Γ through O determine an involution on Γ and thus also a g_2^1 on Δ; while the planes of K passing through its line of intersection with ϖ determine a g_3^1 on Δ. Hence there are two pairs of generators of F such as we require, and f has two double generators. f is of the type VI (B).

The (1, 1) correspondence between Δ and Γ clearly gives rise to a (2, 3) correspondence between R and R', and f can be generated by means of this correspondence. But this is not the most general (2, 3) correspondence between two lines; it must be specialised in order to give the two double generators.

143. We can give another method of generating this surface of the type VI (B) which leads at once to a generation for a surface of the type VII (A).

ϖ and a generator of F determine a space S_4; any prime through this meets F in the generator and in a directrix quartic E; E meets Γ in one point and Δ in two points. The [4] containing ϖ and Δ will meet the prime containing ϖ and E in a solid which contains ϖ and the two intersections of E and Δ. Hence the line joining these two points must meet ϖ. The S_4 containing E meets ϖ in a line which is met by three chords of E, one of these being already accounted for.

When we project, E gives rise to a plane quartic with three double points; it passes through the point in which R' meets its plane and one of its double points lies at the point in which R meets its plane.

Now F can be generated by means of a (1, 1) correspondence between Γ and E with a united point. Hence, to generate f, we take a plane quartic with three double points and a line R' meeting it in a point P. To any point of R' there correspond two points of the quartic, while to any point of the quartic corresponds one point of R', P being a united point.

But it is necessary that the two points which correspond to any point on R' should be collinear with one of the double points. For, returning to the surface F in [6], we have seen that the prime containing ϖ and two generators g and g', which meet Γ in a pair of points collinear with O, also contains K. It therefore meets E in four points; one on g, one on g', and the two on Δ already mentioned. This shews on projection that, given a point of R', the two corresponding points on the quartic are collinear with the double point on R.

The two other double points of the quartic determine two double generators of f.

The line joining the points in which R and R' meet the plane of the quartic is the generator of f which lies in this plane.

This method of generation at once suggests the following for a surface of the type VII (A).

Take a plane quartic with three double points A, B, C and a line R, not in the plane of the quartic, passing through A. Establish a (1, 2) correspondence between R and the quartic, with a united point, such that to any point of R there correspond two points of the quartic collinear with A: this is at once secured by referring the range of points on R to the pencil (A) of lines through A in the plane of the quartic. The point A, regarded as a point of R, must give rise to two points of the quartic, one of which is A itself: this is secured by making the point A on the range R correspond to one of the tangents of the quartic at A considered as a line of the pencil (A). There will be a second point on R which corresponds to A; this being that point of the range which corresponds to the other tangent of the curve at A considered as a line of the pencil (A). Then we have a ruled surface f with a directrix line which is also a generator; through each point of R there pass two generators lying in a plane with R, while each plane through R contains two generators intersecting in a point of R. There are two double generators passing through the points B and C. This is the surface of the type VII (A).

144. We can examine in closer detail the way in which ϖ may be chosen so as to give a surface of the type VII (A).

Take any two generators g and g' of F meeting Γ in the points G and G', and any point O on the line GG'; also a point X on F. Then there are ∞^1 directrix cubics passing through X and their solids K meet the solid gg' in lines forming a regulus. GG' belongs to this regulus; this line arises from the degenerate cubic consisting of Γ and the generator g_0 through X. Any line through O lying in the solid gg' will meet the regulus in a second point O', the line of the regulus through O' being a chord of a directrix cubic Δ. There are planes through OO' meeting the solid K containing

Δ in lines, and on projection from such a plane we obtain a surface f of the type VI (B).

But suppose that we take a tangent, at O, of the quadric surface on which the regulus lies; and then a plane ϖ through this tangent, containing a line passing through O, and lying in the solid $g_0\Gamma$. On projecting we have a surface f with a directrix R which is also a generator.

Through ϖ and two generators of F which meet Γ in two points collinear with O there passes a prime, which necessarily contains Γ and g_0; so that through any point of R there pass two other generators which lie in a plane with R, and f is of the type VII (A).

145. F has ∞^4 quartic directrices, and ϖ will meet the [4] containing such a directrix in a point. There are, however, ∞^2 quartic directrices such that the [4]'s containing them meet ϖ in lines; in fact, any line of ϖ lies in such a [4], determined by the three chords of F which meet the line. But, in general, there is no [4] so arising which contains ϖ entirely; this is evident when we remember that all directrix quartics can be obtained as residuals of prime sections of F through any fixed generator.

Let us suppose, however, that ϖ is chosen to lie in a space S_4 containing a directrix quartic E. Then the projected surface f has a directrix line R, the intersection of Σ with S_4. Since a prime through S_4 meets F in E and one generator there will be one generator of f contained in any plane passing through R, and since any solid lying in S_4 and passing through ϖ meets E in four points there are four generators of f passing through each point of R. Hence f is of the type III (A).

The cubic locus in S_4 formed by the chords of E is none other than the section of M_5^3 by S_4; in general, ϖ meets this locus in an ordinary non-degenerate elliptic cubic curve, and the bitangent developable of f is non-degenerate and of the sixth class, having a tritangent plane. The planes of the developable form an elliptic family, since they are in (1, 1) correspondence with the points of the cubic curve in ϖ. The tritangent plane is, of course, the intersection of Σ with the prime $\varpi\Gamma$.

But ϖ may be chosen to pass through an axis l of E; the chords of E through the points of l determining an involution on E and thus an involution I of pairs of generators of F. ϖ meets M_5^3 in l and a conic ϑ. We have already seen (§ 130) that the bitangent planes of f which arise from I touch a quadric cone. The residual developable is of the fourth class, with two ordinary tangent planes and one double tangent plane which touch the cone also. This last plane clearly arises from the prime $\varpi\Gamma$; the other two are determined by the chords of F which pass through the two points of intersection of l and ϑ.

Further, ϖ may be chosen to contain two, and therefore three, axes of E, say l_1, l_2, l_3. Then the bitangent developable of f consists of three quadric cones. The prime $\varpi\Gamma$ meets Σ in a plane which touches each cone. Also the chord of F which passes through the intersection of l_2 and l_3, say, meets a pair of generators which give on projection a common tangent plane of the two cones which arise from l_2 and l_3; thus any two of the three cones have a second common tangent plane.

146. F can be generated by placing Γ and E in (1, 1) correspondence with a united point. Hence to generate this type of surface f we take a line R and a conic which meets it, and place them in (1, 4) correspondence with their intersection as a united point. Any plane through R contains one generator, while through every point of R there pass four generators. The plane of the conic contains three generators all passing through the point in which R meets it; it is thus a tritangent plane.

But if the plane ϖ contains an axis of E then, corresponding to each point of R, we have four points of the conic as before; but two of these four points form a pair of a certain involution, so that the line joining them passes through a fixed point O. The bitangent developable of f breaks up into two parts.

The pencil of lines through O in the plane of the conic is related to the range of points on R, and the planes joining the rays of the pencil to the corresponding points on R touch a quadric cone with vertex O, which touches the plane of the conic. Hence the bitangent developable breaks up into this cone and a developable of the fourth class having the plane of the conic for a double tangent plane.

The joins of the sets of an involution of sets of four points on a conic are known to touch a curve of the third class. In this degenerate case the curve will consist of the point O and a conic, and two tangents of this last conic will pass through O. This shews that the quadric cone and the developable of the fourth class have two other common tangent planes.

Now suppose that the plane ϖ contains three axes of E. Any solid through ϖ meets the cubic locus of chords of E in a four-nodal cubic surface, the nodes being the four points in which the solid meets E. The three axes are the three lines on this surface other than the six edges of the tetrahedron formed by the nodes, and it is a well-known property of the four-nodal cubic surface that each of these three lines meets a pair of opposite edges of the tetrahedron. If, then, any point A is taken on E the solid ϖA meets E again in three points B, C, D such that AB and CD meet one axis, AC and BD meet another, while AD and BC meet the third.

Thus in the correspondence between R and the conic if a, b, c, d are the four points of the conic which correspond to some point of R we have ab and cd belonging to one fixed involution, ac and bd belonging to a second and ad and bc belonging to a third. We thus have three points O_1, O_2, O_3 forming a self-conjugate triangle in regard to the conic; these being the three points through which the joins of pairs of the three involutions respectively pass. The envelope of the third class formed by the joins of the sets of four points here degenerates into the three points O_1, O_2, O_3.

Thus the bitangent developable of f consists of three quadric cones with vertices O_1, O_2, O_3 all touching the plane $O_1O_2O_3$. Any two of the cones have a second common tangent plane.

This completes the determination of those surfaces f which are projections of the surface F with a directrix conic.

The surfaces in [3] derived by projection from the surface in [6] with a directrix line

147. Take now a rational quintic ruled surface F in [6] with a directrix line λ. Any chord of F lies in a solid through λ containing two generators of F, so that the locus M_5 of the chords of F is a five-dimensional cone having a line-vertex and ∞^2 generating solids. If we take a directrix quartic E of F the [4] in which it lies meets M_5 in the cubic locus formed by the chords of E; we have thus a cubic line-cone $M_5{}^3$.

No two generating solids of the line-cone can intersect, unless on the three-dimensional locus formed by the planes through λ containing the generators of F. Since a general plane ϖ does not meet this locus it will meet $M_5{}^3$ in a cubic curve without a double point.

Take now a general plane ϖ of [6] not meeting F and project from ϖ on to a solid Σ. We obtain a rational quintic ruled surface f with a directrix line R, the intersection of Σ with the [4] $\varpi\lambda$. Since a prime through ϖ and λ meets F in λ and four generators there are four generators of the surface f which lie in any plane through R, and since a solid passing through ϖ and lying in the [4] $\varpi\lambda$ meets λ in a point there is one generator of f passing through any point of R. Hence f is of the type III (B).

It is seen as in § 127 that the chords of F which meet ϖ meet F in the points of a curve C_{12} of order 12 and genus 4, having three double points whose plane meets ϖ in a line, C_{12} meeting each generator of F in three points. The double curve of f is an elliptic sextic curve with a triple point.

The locus $M_4{}^6$ formed by the tangents of F is here again of the sixth order, but it is now a line-cone with λ for vertex and has ∞^1 generating solids all passing through λ. It is of the sixth order, because the [4] which contains any directrix quartic E meets $M_4{}^6$ in the ruled surface formed by the tangents of E, and this is known to be of the sixth order*.

This type of surface F contains ∞^4 directrix quartics E; any one of these is determined by four points of F, and any two intersect in three

* Cf. the footnote to § 127.

points. They can all be obtained as residuals of prime sections of F through any fixed generator. Each curve E determines a space [4] containing it. In general, such a space [4] will meet ϖ in a point, but there are ∞^2 of them meeting ϖ in lines, one passing through each line of ϖ. For a general position of ϖ no [4] will contain it entirely.

Now ϖ may clearly be chosen to pass through an axis l of one of these curves E, meeting M_5^3 in l and a conic ϑ. The chords of F meeting l meet F on E itself, those meeting ϑ meet F in an elliptic curve of the eighth order, with one double point, which meets each generator in two points. On projecting we have a surface f of the type III (B) whose double curve consists of a conic and a rational quartic; this quartic has a double point lying on the conic and meets the conic in two other points.

Further, ϖ may be chosen to pass through an axis l_1 of a quartic E and an axis l_2 of a quartic E'. It meets M_5^3 in three lines l_1, l_2, l_3, and l_3 is an axis of a quartic E''. The surface f has a double curve consisting of three conics with a common point, any two of the conics intersecting in one other point*.

148. F can be generated by means of a (1, 1) correspondence between λ and any of its directrix quartics E. Hence to generate the most general surface f belonging to the type III (B) we take a line and a rational skew quartic and place them in (1, 1) correspondence.

If, however, ϖ contains an axis of E then E becomes on projection a double conic of f, so that to generate this surface we take a line and a conic in (2, 1) correspondence.

The construction of the quintic surface with a directrix line and two double conics can be deduced from that for the quintic ruled surface with two double conics without a directrix line† simply by making the (2, 2) correspondence between Γ_1 and Γ_2 express the condition that the generators should all meet a line. Or we can deduce a construction from that of the dual surface; we take a line lying in a tangent plane of a quadric cone and place the planes through the line and the tangent planes of the cone in (1, 4) correspondence. The four planes of the cone which correspond to any plane through the line form pairs of three involutions.

149. Suppose now that ϖ is chosen to lie in a space [4] with one of the directrix quartics E. Then the projected surface f has two directrices; R, the intersection of Σ with the [4] $\varpi\lambda$, and R', the intersection of Σ with the [4] ϖE. A prime through ϖ and λ meets F in λ and four generators, and these must meet E in four points lying in a solid through ϖ. Also, if a solid through ϖ meets E in four points the four generators of F passing through these points all meet λ. Hence any plane through R

* Cf. § 131.

† § 131.

contains four generators of f which meet in a point of R', while through any point of R' there pass four generators of f lying in a plane with R. Similarly any plane through R' contains one generator of f which meets R, while through any point of R there passes one generator of f meeting R'. Hence f is of the type VI (A).

Since F can be generated by a (1, 1) correspondence between λ and E, the surface f can be generated by a (1, 4) correspondence between R' and R.

150. Any prime meets F in a rational normal quintic curve, one point of which lies on λ; the chords of the curve passing through this point form a cone of the fourth order. This shews that the ∞^1 planes joining λ to the generators of F form a locus M_3^4 of three dimensions and the fourth order. In general this has no point in common with a plane ϖ. But if ϖ does meet a plane of M_3^4 we have on projection a surface f with a directrix line R which is also a generator.

Since a prime through ϖ and λ now meets F in three variable generators there are three generators of f which lie in a plane through R other than R itself. Also through any point of R there passes one generator of f other than R. Hence f is of the type IV (B). To generate f we take a line and a rational quartic in Σ which meet, and place them in (1, 1) correspondence without a united point.

We may choose ϖ to meet two planes of M_3^4. Then the surface f has a directrix R which is at the same time a double generator. Any plane through R contains two generators of f other than R, while through any point of R there passes one generator other than R. Hence f is of the type V (B). To generate f we take in Σ a rational quartic and a line meeting it in two points, and place them in (1, 1) correspondence without any united points.

Further, we may choose ϖ to meet three planes of M_3^4. Then f has a directrix R which is also a triple generator. Any plane through R contains one other generator, while through any point of R there passes one other generator. Hence f is of the type VII (B). To generate f we take in Σ a rational quartic and one of its trisecants, placing them in (1, 1) correspondence without any united points.

SECTION III

QUINTIC RULED SURFACES WHICH ARE NOT RATIONAL

Elliptic quintic ruled surfaces considered as curves on Ω

151. *Elliptic quintic curves on* Ω. The elliptic curve of the fifth order is normal in [4]*. Also we can have on a quadric in [3] an elliptic quintic curve meeting all the generators of one system in three points and all of the other system in two points, the curve having a double point; it is the intersection of the quadric with a cubic surface passing through one of its generators and touching it in a point. Similarly we can have an elliptic quintic curve lying on a quadric cone; the curve has a double point and passes through the vertex, meeting every generator of the cone in two points other than the vertex.

We can thus write down the following types of elliptic quintic curves C which lie on Ω, numbering them consecutively with the types of rational quintic curves.

VIII. The normal elliptic quintic curve C lying in a [4] which does not touch Ω.

IX. C lies in a tangent prime T touching Ω in a point O but does not pass through O.

(A) C meets every plane ϖ through O in three points and every plane ρ through O in two points, a chord of C passing through O.

(B) C meets every plane ϖ through O in two points and every plane ρ through O in three points, a chord of C passing through O.

X. C lies in the tangent prime T touching Ω in a point O and passes through O, meeting every plane of Ω in two points other than O.

XI. C lies on the quadric Q in which Ω is met by a space S_3 through which pass two tangent primes. C has a double point, meeting all the generators of one system of Q in three points and all of the other system in two points.

XII. C lies on the quadric cone in which Ω is met by a space S_3 which itself touches Ω in a point V. C has a double point, passes through V, and meets every generator of the cone in two points other than V.

152. *The general type of surface.* Suppose that we have a normal elliptic quintic C in [4]. The projection of C from any line on to a plane is a quintic curve with five double points, so that any line is met by five chords of C. Hence the chords of C form a locus V_3^5 of three dimensions and the fifth order.

* § 8.

Hence if C belongs to the type VIII any plane of Ω meets the [4] containing C in a line which is met by five chords of C. Hence we have a ruled surface in [3] whose double curve is of the fifth order and whose bitangent developable is of the fifth class.

If C is projected on to a plane from a line which meets it we obtain a quartic with two double points, so that the line is met by two chords other than those passing through its intersection with C. Hence C is triple on V_3^5. If C is projected from one of its chords on to a plane we obtain an elliptic cubic without a double point; thus there will not be any double surface on V_3^5.

The intersection of Ω with V_3^5 is a surface F_2^{10} on which C is a triple curve; this is the ruled surface formed by the chords of C which lie on Ω, three such chords passing through any point of C. The section of this ruled surface by a solid is a curve of order 10 with five triple points; the curve lying on a quadric and meeting every generator in five points. Projecting from a point of this quadric on to a plane we obtain a curve of order 10 with five triple points and two quintuple points which is therefore of genus

$$36 - 15 - 20 = 1.$$

But this curve is representative of the double curve and bitangent developable of the surface in [3]; hence the double curve is an elliptic quintic curve, while the planes of the bitangent developable form an elliptic family.

If we take an elliptic quintic curve in ordinary space then, on projecting it from a point of itself on to a plane, we obtain a quartic with two double points; hence there are two trisecants of the curve passing through any point of it, assuming that the curve itself has not a double point. The surface is, in fact, generated by the trisecants of an elliptic quintic curve without a double point*.

153. Suppose now that C belongs to the type IX (A). The point O represents a line R which is a directrix of the ruled surface.

An arbitrary plane ρ meets T in a line which is met by five chords of C. The plane ϖ through this line joins it to O and contains three points and therefore three chords of C. There are two other chords meeting the line. Hence the double curve of the corresponding ruled surface consists of the line R counted three times and a conic. R and the conic intersect, their point of intersection being represented on Ω by the ϖ-plane through the chord of C which passes through O.

An arbitrary plane ϖ meets T in a line, and the plane ρ through this line contains two points and therefore one chord of C. Four other chords

* See the reference to Zeuthen in § 89.

of C meet the line. Hence the bitangent developable consists of the planes through R and a developable of class four. There is a plane of this developable passing through R; it is represented on Ω by the ρ-plane which contains the chord of C passing through O.

154. The ruled surface formed by the chords of C which lie on Ω must clearly break up into two parts; one will consist of the chords joined to O by ρ-planes and the other of the chords joined to O by ϖ-planes.

The chords of C which lie in ρ-planes join the pairs of an ordinary rational involution on C; hence they form a cubic ruled surface*. The plane ρ which passes through the directrix of this surface represents the plane of the double conic. Then the chords of C which lie in ϖ-planes must form a ruled surface of order seven with C for a double curve.

We now take the section of this composite ruled surface by a solid lying in T; the solid meets Ω in a quadric, and we have on this quadric a cubic curve meeting every generator of one system in two points and every generator of the other system in one point, together with a septimic curve meeting every generator of the first system in three points and every generator of the other system in four points. This septimic has five double points through which the cubic passes. The cubic is rational but the septimic is elliptic, for on projecting it from a point of the quadric on to a plane we obtain a plane curve of order seven with one quadruple point, one triple point and five double points, and therefore of genus

$$15 - 6 - 3 - 5 = 1.$$

Two points of C which lie in a ρ-plane through O represent two generators of the ruled surface whose plane passes through R and whose point of intersection lies on the double conic; the conic is a rational curve and the pencil of planes through R is a rational family. But R regarded as a triple line must be considered an elliptic curve, while the planes of the developable of the fourth class form an elliptic family.

If we apply a general result for the number of intersections of two curves lying on the same quadric† we find that the cubic and septimic intersect in eleven points; ten of these are accounted for by the five double points on the septimic, the other arises from the chord of C passing through O.

155. If C is of the type IX (B) we have a ruled surface with a directrix line R; through every point of R there pass two generators, while every plane through R contains three generators. The double curve consists of

* See the footnote to § 19.

† If there are two curves on a quadric of which one meets all generators of one system in x points and all of the other system in y points, while for the second curve the corresponding numbers are x' and y', the number of intersections of the two curves is $xy' + x'y$.

the line R and an elliptic quartic curve which meets R; the bitangent developable consists of the planes through R counted three times together with the tangent planes of a quadric cone, one tangent plane of this cone passing through R.

This surface can be generated by taking an elliptic quartic curve and a line R meeting it in a point; the generators of the surface are those chords of the curve which meet R.

156. Suppose now that C is of the type X. Then the ruled surface has a directrix line R which is itself a generator; through each point of R there pass two generators other than R, while each plane through R contains two generators other than R.

Any plane of Ω meets T in a line and the plane of the opposite system through this line joins it to O; this contains three points and therefore three chords of C, so that two other chords will meet the line. Hence the double curve consists of R counted three times and a conic, while the bitangent developable will consist of the planes through R counted three times together with the tangent planes of a quadric cone. The conic will meet R and a tangent plane of the cone will pass through R.

The ruled surface formed by the chords of C which lie on Ω here breaks up into two cubic ruled surfaces and the elliptic quartic cone projecting C from O.

157. Now let C be of the type XI. There are two tangent primes of Ω through S_3, which touch it in points O and O'. These represent two lines R and R' which are both directrices of the ruled surface. C has a double point P which represents a double generator G.

Suppose that the generators of Q which are trisecants of C lie in the ϖ-planes through O and the ρ-planes through O'. Then the generators of the other system will lie in the ρ-planes through O and the ϖ-planes through O'. Through any point of R there pass three generators of the surface which lie in a plane through R'; any plane through R' contains three generators meeting in a point of R. Any plane through R contains two generators meeting in a point of R', while through any point of R' there pass two generators lying in a plane through R.

Any plane of Ω meets S_3 in a point of Q. C has five apparent double points, but the five chords which can be drawn from a point of Q consist of the trisecant generator through the point counted three times, the other generator through the point, and the line to the double point.

The double curve of the ruled surface consists of R' and G together with R counted three times; the bitangent developable consists of the planes through R and G together with those through R' counted three times.

158. Finally, suppose that C is of the type XII. Then the ruled surface has a directrix R which is itself a generator; through any point of R there pass two generators other than R which lie in a plane with R; any plane through R contains two generators which intersect in a point of R.

C has five apparent double points. But if C is projected from a point of the cone on to a plane we obtain an elliptic quintic with a double point, and a triple point at which two branches touch. Hence the five chords of C which pass through a point of the cone consist of the line to the double point P, and the generator counted four times.

The double curve of the ruled surface thus consists of the double generator G, together with the directrix R counted four times; the bitangent developable consists of the planes through G, and the planes through R counted four times.

A plane section of the surface is an elliptic quintic curve with a double point on G and a triple point, at which two branches touch, on R.

159. We have now obtained six different types of elliptic quintic ruled surfaces in [3]; these are exhibited in tabular form on p. 305.

Elliptic quintic ruled surfaces in [3] *considered as projections of normal surfaces in higher space*

160. A ruled surface of the fifth order which belongs to a space [6] is rational, its prime sections being rational normal quintic curves.

Suppose now that we have a ruled surface of the fifth order belonging to a space [5]. If the surface is elliptic a prime through one of its generators meets it again in an elliptic quartic curve, unless the surface is a cone. The elliptic quartic curve lies in a [3]; through this [3] there passes a pencil of primes. The surface must be contained in one of these primes, since otherwise each prime of the pencil would contain a generator of the surface, which would then be rational*. Hence *an elliptic quintic ruled surface which is not a cone belongs to a space of dimension* 3 *or* 4.

Suppose now that we have an elliptic quintic ruled surface in [3]; a quadric which contains one of its generators g will meet it again in a curve C_9 of order 9. This curve meets each generator of the surface in two points, and those two points where it meets g are points of contact of the quadric and the ruled surface. The quadric can be chosen so that it does not touch the ruled surface elsewhere, so that the only double points of C_9 will be on the double curve of the ruled surface. Hence† C_9 will be of genus 5.

* The generators would be in (1, 1) correspondence with the primes of a pencil and therefore with the points of a line.

† § 17.

Now a curve C_9 of genus 5 in [3] is the projection* of a normal curve of order 9 and genus 5 in [4]. The generators of the ruled surface in [3] join pairs of points of an elliptic involution on $C_9{}^5$; these are the projections of the joins of pairs of points of an elliptic involution on the normal curve, and these joins are generators of an elliptic ruled surface in [4]. Since we have on this ruled surface a curve of order 9 and genus 5 meeting each generator in two points the surface must be of order† 5; the elliptic quintic ruled surface in [3] is then the projection of this elliptic quintic ruled surface in [4]. Hence we have the result: *the elliptic quintic ruled surface is normal in* [4]; *and any elliptic quintic ruled surface in* [3] *can be obtained as the projection of a normal surface in* [4].

We now consider the normal elliptic quintic ruled surfaces F of [4]. We find that there are two types of surface, on one of which no two generators intersect, while on the other the generators intersect each other in pairs. By projection we obtain from the first surface two of the types of elliptic quintic ruled surfaces which we have just obtained in [3]; the other four types of surfaces in [3] are obtained by projection from the normal surface with a double line.

161. Suppose then that we have, in [4], an elliptic quintic ruled surface F, of which no two generators lie in a plane. The section of F by a solid will be a directrix (i.e. a curve meeting each generator of the surface in one point) together with, perhaps, a certain number of generators. But since the directrix must be an elliptic curve it cannot be a line or a conic, so that no three generators of F can lie in the same solid.

Any two generators of F determine a solid which must meet F further in a plane cubic curve without a double point; we have ∞^2 solids determined by the pairs of generators of F, while through the plane of any cubic curve on F there pass ∞^1 solids each meeting F again in two generators. We have therefore ∞^1 cubic directrices on F; these will be the directrices of minimum order and there will be a finite number of them passing through any point of F.

Every cubic curve lies in a solid with any fixed generator g of F; to obtain then the cubic curves passing through any point P of F we have to take those solids which contain the plane gP and meet F in another generator. The number of such solids is clearly the number of remaining intersections of the plane gP with F. Now any plane α through g meets F in three points not on g; for a solid through α meets F again in an elliptic quartic curve which meets α in four points, one of these four points is on g and the other three give isolated intersections of α with F. Hence the plane gP meets F in two further points, so that through P there pass two of the cubic curves.

* § 8.

† By the formula of § 17.

We have then the following result: *the normal elliptic quintic ruled surface F without double points has, as directrices of minimum order, ∞^1 plane elliptic cubic curves; through each point of F there pass two of these curves.*

Any two of the cubic curves are put into (1, 1) correspondence by the generators of F; this correspondence must have a united point*, so that any two of the cubic curves intersect. We notice that, in the (1, 1) correspondence between any two of the cubic curves, three collinear points of one curve do not correspond to three collinear points of the other; for if they did we should have three generators of F lying in the same solid.

The planes of the cubic curves form a locus W_3 of three dimensions. The section of this locus by a solid consists of the trisecants of the elliptic quintic curve in which the solid meets F, and is therefore an elliptic quintic ruled surface†. Hence W_3 is a locus W_3^5 of the fifth order. It is elliptic when considered as a family of ∞^1 planes; the planes of W_3^5 are in (1, 1) correspondence with the generators of F, since, if any cubic curve of F is taken, there is one plane of W_3^5 passing through each point of it. The point of intersection of two planes of W_3^5 is the intersection of the two cubic curves which they contain and therefore lies on F; F is a double surface on W_3^5.

162. Now project F from a point O on to a [3] Σ. The lines joining O to the points of F meet Σ in the points of an elliptic quintic ruled surface f, while the planes joining O to the generators of F meet Σ in the generators of f.

A solid through O meets F in an elliptic quintic curve; this has five apparent double points, or five of its chords pass through O. Hence the double curve of f is of the fifth order, a plane section of f being an elliptic quintic curve with five double points.

The class of the bitangent developable of f is the number of solids which contain a given line through O and also two generators of F. Such a solid meets F further in a cubic curve, whose plane must then meet the line through O. Hence the class of the bitangent developable of f is equal to the order of W_3^5; we have a bitangent developable of the fifth class.

We have a surface in [3] of the type VIII.

Since F is generated by two elliptic cubic curves in (1, 1) correspondence with a united point, f is also generated by two elliptic cubic curves (whose planes both lie in Σ) in (1, 1) correspondence with a united point.

163. This surface f is the most general type of elliptic quintic ruled surface in [3] and has been obtained by projecting F from a point O of general position in [4]. But suppose now that for O is taken a point of W_3^5.

* § 19. † § 152.

Then the plane ϖ of W_3^5 in which O lies meets Σ in a line R which is a directrix of f. Since any line of ϖ passing through O meets F in three points there are three generators of f passing through each point of R, and, since any solid through ϖ meets F in two generators, there are two generators of f lying in any plane through R. Hence we have a surface f of the type IX (A).

We can generate F by establishing a (1, 1) correspondence between the cubic curve in ϖ and another cubic directrix, there being a united point. Hence f is generated by means of a (1, 3) correspondence, with a united point, between a line R and an elliptic cubic curve.

These two types of surfaces are the only ones which can be obtained by projection from the normal surface F which we have been considering.

164. We suppose now that we have, in [4], a normal elliptic quintic ruled surface F, two of whose generators intersect. A solid containing the plane of these two generators meets F further in an elliptic cubic curve; we thus obtain ∞^1 directrix cubic curves. Now the plane of any one of these cubic curves Γ meets the plane of the two intersecting generators in a line; this line meets Γ in three points, one on each of the generators. Thus there is a point X in which the plane of the two generators meets Γ and which does not lie on either of them. Then there is a solid containing the plane of the two generators and also the generator through X; the residual intersection with F will be a directrix curve of order 2, and, since the surface is elliptic, this will be a *double line* λ. Hence, if there are two generators of F which intersect, all the generators of F intersect one another in pairs, and the locus of the points of intersection is a line λ.

The solid which we have just considered, containing a pair of intersecting generators and the generator through X, meets F in these three generators together with λ; hence the point X is the only point of F which lies in the plane of the two intersecting generators and not on either of the generators themselves. But each of the ∞^1 directrix cubics of F meets this plane in a point which does not lie on either generator; hence all the cubic curves pass through X. And, since the same argument may be applied to any pair of intersecting generators, the plane of every pair of intersecting generators passes through X.

We have then, in [4], *a normal elliptic quintic ruled surface F with a double line λ; this surface contains ∞^1 plane elliptic cubic curves all passing through the same point X, while through a general point of F there passes one of the cubic curves.*

The surface is generated by a line λ and an elliptic cubic curve in (1, 2) correspondence.

We may of course also generate the surface by means of a (1, 1) correspondence between two of its directrix cubics, X being a united point.

Now if three collinear points are taken on one of the cubics the three generators all meet λ and therefore lie in the same solid; they therefore meet any other one of the directrix cubics in three collinear points, so that the correspondence between any two of the cubic curves is part of a projectivity between their planes. This kind of (1, 1) correspondence between two elliptic cubics will be called *special*. This explains clearly the difference between the two types of normal surface F. If we take, in [4], two elliptic cubic curves with an intersection X and place them in (1, 1) correspondence, then the lines joining pairs of corresponding points generate an elliptic quintic ruled surface F. In general, F is of the former type and has no double point, but if the correspondence is special the surface is of the type which we are now considering and has a double line λ. The pairs of intersecting generators meet either of the cubic curves in pairs of points collinear with X.

The plane containing any cubic curve of F meets the plane containing any pair of intersecting generators in a line through X; the planes containing two cubic curves do not meet, except in X, and the planes containing two pairs of intersecting generators do not meet, except in X. Hence we have the two systems of planes of a quadric point-cone with vertex X. There is a generator through X meeting λ, these forming together a degenerate cubic curve of F; the plane π_0 containing them is met in a line through X by any plane containing a pair of intersecting generators.

The planes joining λ to the generators of F form an elliptic line-cone; this cone is of the third order, a prime section being the cubic cone of lines projecting an elliptic quintic curve from a double point. The plane π_0 belongs to this cone; in fact the plane π_0 and the surface F form together the complete intersection of this cubic line-cone with the quadric point-cone.

165. Let us now project F from a point O, of general position in [4], on to a solid Σ. The plane $O\lambda$ meets Σ in a line R which is a directrix of the projected surface f; through each point of R there pass two generators of f. Also, since any solid through the plane $O\lambda$ meets F in three generators, any plane through R contains three generators of f. Thus f is of the type IX (B).

To generate f we take, in Σ, a line R and an elliptic cubic, and place them in (1, 2) correspondence.

166. Now let us specialise the position of O, so that it lies on the cubic line-cone containing F. Then O lies in a plane containing λ and a generator, so that this plane meets Σ in a line R which is a directrix and also a generator of f. Through any point of R there pass two generators of f other than R itself. Any solid through O and λ meets F in three generators, one of which is the fixed generator lying in the plane $O\lambda$. Hence any plane through R contains two generators of F other than R itself. Thus f is of the type X.

To generate f we take a line R and an elliptic cubic curve; R and the cubic intersect and we place them in (1, 2) correspondence without a united point.

Now let us take O to lie on the quadric point-cone containing F; then it lies in a plane π containing a directrix cubic of F and also in a plane π' containing a pair of intersecting generators of F.

The projected surface f will have two directrices; R, the intersection of Σ with the plane joining O to the double line, and R', the intersection of Σ with π. We have also a double generator, the intersection of Σ with π'.

A prime through the plane joining O to the double line meets π in a line passing through O and F in three generators which meet this line. Thus a plane through R contains three generators of f which meet in a point of R'. Also a prime through π meets the double line in a point and contains the two generators of F which intersect there. Thus a plane through R' contains two generators of f which meet in a point of R.

This surface f is of the type XI. It can be generated by means of a (2, 3) correspondence between R' and R, but this is not the most general (2, 3) correspondence between two lines; it must be specialised to give the double generator.

Now let us choose O in the plane π_0. The plane π_0 meets Σ in a line R which is a directrix and also a generator of f. Also the line OX meets the double line of F, and the plane of the two generators of F intersecting in this point passes through OX. Hence f has a double generator.

Through any point of the double line of F there pass two generators; and the plane of these two generators, which passes through X, meets π_0 in a line. Hence through any point of R there pass two generators of f, other than R which is itself a generator, and the plane of these two generators contains R. This surface f is of the type XII.

To generate this last type of surface we take a line and an elliptic cubic which have a point of intersection and place them in (1, 2) correspondence without a united point. But the two points of the cubic curve which correspond to a point of the line must be collinear with the point in which the line meets the curve. The double generator passes through this point and lies in the plane of the cubic.

The quintic ruled surface of genus 2

167. If we have a quintic ruled surface of genus 2 in a space [3], its generators will be represented by the points of a quintic curve C of genus 2 lying on the quadric Ω in [5]. Now a quintic curve of genus 2 is necessarily contained in a space S_3*, so that we have two possibilities.

* § 8.

XIII. C lies on the quadric Q in which Ω is met by a space S_3 through which pass two tangent primes. C meets every generator of Q of one system in three points and every generator of the other system in two points.

XIV. C lies on a quadric cone in which Ω is met by an S_3 which touches it in a point V. C passes through V and meets every generator of the cone in two points other than V.

If there are two tangent primes through S_3 touching Ω in O and O' then these two points represent lines R and R' of the original space [3] which are both directrices of the ruled surface. Each generator of Q is the intersection of a plane of Ω through O with a plane of the opposite system through O'. Suppose that the generators of Q which are trisecants of C lie in the ϖ-planes through O and the ρ-planes through O'; the other generators will lie in the ϖ-planes through O' and the ρ-planes through O. Through every point of R there pass three generators lying in a plane through R', while through any point of R' there pass two generators lying in a plane through R.

The curve C has four apparent double points, four of its chords passing through any point of S_3. But if this point lies on Q three of the chords coalesce in the trisecant generator through the point, C projecting into a plane quintic curve with a triple point and a double point. The double curve of the ruled surface consists of the line R' together with the line R counted three times.

Similarly the bitangent developable consists of the planes through R' together with those through R counted three times.

This is the surface generated by the most general (2, 3) correspondence between two lines R and R'.

If S_3 touches Ω in a point V then this represents a line R which is a directrix and also a generator of the ruled surface. Through each generator on the cone in which S_3 meets Ω there passes a plane of each system of Ω, and the two planes lie in the tangent prime of Ω at V. Hence through any point of R there pass two generators of the ruled surface which lie in a plane with R.

The curve C has four apparent double points, but the four chords of C which pass through any point of the cone all coincide with the generator through the point; the projection of the curve from this point on to a plane of S_3 is a quintic curve with a triple point at which two of the branches touch each other.

The double curve of the ruled surface is the line R counted four times, while the bitangent developable consists of the planes through R counted four times.

168. Since a quintic curve of genus 2 is necessarily contained in [3] a quintic ruled surface whose prime sections are of genus 2 is necessarily contained in [4]. But those surfaces belonging to [4] are cones*, so that the surface is normal in [3] and the question of projection from higher space does not arise.

The surface cannot contain a directrix line which is not a multiple line, nor a conic, nor a cubic.

Consider the surface with two directrices R and R'. A plane through a generator meets the surface again in a quartic curve with one double point, this double point being on R. The quartic meets the generator again on R' and also in the point of contact of the plane with the surface. We thus obtain ∞^2 plane quartic curves of genus 2 on the surface.

Through two general points of the surface there pass three of these curves, for the line joining the two points meets the surface again in three further points, and there are planes through the first two points and the generator through any one of these last three points. Two of the quartics intersect in three points on the line of intersection of their planes.

169. We can generate the surface by means of a (1, 2) correspondence between a line R' and a plane quartic with one double point P. The quartic must pass through P', the point in which R' meets its plane, and P' must be a united point for the correspondence.

The points of R' will give rise to the pairs of the g_2^1 on the curve, and these are collinear with P†. The points of the range on R' are related projectively to the rays of the pencil through P; the point P' of the range corresponding to the ray PP' of the pencil. The planes joining the corresponding elements will therefore all pass through a line R which passes through P‡. Through any point of R' there pass two generators of the surface which lie in a plane through R, while any plane through R' contains three generators meeting in a point of R. The line PP' is a generator.

To obtain the surface with one directrix we have only to make P and P' coincide. We take a plane quartic with one double point P and a line R passing through P; we then place the line and curve in (1, 2) correspondence, P being one of the two points on the quartic which corre-

* If the surface were not a cone a [3] through a generator would meet it further in a quartic curve of genus 2. This is a plane curve, and we have an argument similar to that of § 160.

† There can only exist one g_2^1 on a curve of genus 2; it is the canonical series of the curve, and for a plane quartic with one double point P it is cut out by the lines through P.

‡ If the point P' did not correspond to the ray PP' then the planes joining corresponding elements would touch a quadric cone.

spond to P regarded as a point of the line. This is at once secured by referring the range of points on R to the pencil of lines through P, so that the point P of the range corresponds to one of the tangents of the curve at P. The other tangent of the curve at P will correspond to some other point of R, and the line R is a generator as well as a directrix. Through any point of R there pass two generators (other than R itself) which lie in a plane through R. The generator of the surface which lies in the plane of the quartic curve is one of the tangents at the double point.

CHAPTER IV

SEXTIC RULED SURFACES

SECTION I

RATIONAL SEXTIC RULED SURFACES

170. We shall in this chapter enumerate completely the different kinds of sextic ruled surfaces in [3]. So far as is known, no serious attempt has been made to solve this problem before, but if we employ the two powerful methods which we have already used in classifying the quintic ruled surfaces it should be possible to arrive at a solution.

In the first place we regard the generators of the ruled surface as the points of a sextic curve on a quadric Ω in [5]; in the second place we regard the ruled surface as the projection of a normal ruled surface in higher space. We have up to the present pursued these two lines of investigation separately; we shall also pursue them separately for the ruled surfaces of the sixth order which are not rational, but since the ruled surfaces of the sixth order which are rational are so numerous we shall for these surfaces pursue the two lines of investigation concurrently, all the information concerning one particular type of surface being then collected together.

The rational sextic curves which lie on quadrics

171. All rational sextic curves can be obtained by projection from the normal curve in [6]. As we are only considering curves which lie on a quadric Ω in [5] this normal curve does not enter directly into our work, but we can always resort to it in order to obtain properties of the actual curves that we are using.

We then divide the rational sextic curves C on Ω into eight classes:

I. C is contained in [5].

II. C is contained in a [4] which does not touch Ω.

III. C lies in a tangent prime T of Ω but does not pass through O, the point of contact of Ω and T.

IV. C lies in T and passes through O.

V. C lies in T and has a double point at O.

VI. C lies in T and has a triple point at O.

VII. C lies in a [3] meeting Ω in an ordinary quadric surface.

VIII. C lies in a [3] meeting Ω in a quadric cone.

We now give a more complete classification of these curves C as follows:

I. (A) C is contained in [5] and has no double point.

(B) C is contained in [5] and has a double point.

II. (A) C is contained in [4] and has no singularity.
(B) C is contained in [4] and has a double point.
(C) C is contained in [4] and has two double points.
(D) C is contained in [4] and has a triple point.

III. (A) C is $\varpi_5\rho_1$*.
(B) C is $\varpi_1\rho_5$.
(C) C is $\varpi_4\rho_2$, three chords of C passing through O.
(D) C is $\varpi_2\rho_4$, three chords of C passing through O.
(E) C is $\varpi_4\rho_2$ with a double point, two chords of C passing through O.
(F) C is $\varpi_2\rho_4$ with a double point, two chords of C passing through O.
(G) C is $\varpi_4\rho_2$ with two double points, a chord of C passing through O.
(H) C is $\varpi_2\rho_4$ with two double points, a chord of C passing through O.
(I) C is $\varpi_3\rho_3$, four chords of C passing through O.
(J) C is $\varpi_3\rho_3$ with a double point, three chords of C passing through O.
(K) C is $\varpi_3\rho_3$ with two double points, two chords of C passing through O.
(L) C is $\varpi_3\rho_3$ with a triple point, a chord of C passing through O.

IV. (A) C is $O\varpi_4\rho_1$.
(B) C is $O\varpi_1\rho_4$.
(C) C is $O\varpi_3\rho_2$, two trisecants of C passing through O.
(D) C is $O\varpi_2\rho_3$, two trisecants of C passing through O.
(E) C is $O\varpi_3\rho_2$ with a double point, a trisecant of C passing through O.
(F) C is $O\varpi_2\rho_3$ with a double point, a trisecant of C passing through O.
(G) C is $O\varpi_3\rho_2$ with two double points.
(H) C is $O\varpi_2\rho_3$ with two double points.

V. (A) C is $O^2\varpi_3\rho_1$.
(B) C is $O^2\varpi_1\rho_3$.
(C) C is $O^2\varpi_2\rho_2$; there being a line through O meeting C in two further points.
(D) C is $O^2\varpi_2\rho_2$ with another double point besides O.

VI. (A) C is $O^3\varpi_2\rho_1$.
(B) C is $O^3\varpi_1\rho_2$.

VII. (A) C is the intersection of a quadric and a quintic surface passing through four generators of the same system; it meets all generators of this system in five points and all of the other system in one point.
(B) C is the intersection of a quadric with a quartic surface touching it in three points and containing two generators of the same

* This notation is self-explanatory: "C is $\varpi_5\rho_1$" means "C meets every plane ϖ of Ω through O in five points and every plane ρ of Ω through O in one point." Similarly, in V (D), "C is $O^2\varpi_2\rho_2$" means "C has a double point at O and meets every plane of Ω through O in two points other than O."

system; it meets all generators of this system in four points and all of the other system in two points, having three double points.

(C) C is the intersection of a quadric with a cubic surface touching it in four points; it meets every generator of the quadric in three points and has four double points.

VIII. (A) C is the intersection of a quadric cone with a cubic surface having a node at the vertex of the cone; it has a quadruple point at the vertex and meets each generator of the cone in one point other than the vertex.

(B) C is the intersection of a quadric cone with a cubic surface passing through the vertex of the cone and touching the cone three times; it has a double point at the vertex and three other double points, meeting each generator of the cone in two points other than the vertex.

(C) C is the intersection of a quadric cone with a cubic surface touching it in four points. It meets each generator of the cone in three points and has four double points.

We have thus divided the rational sextic curves C which lie on a quadric Ω in [5] into thirty-eight classes, and these will form a basis for the classification of the rational sextic ruled surfaces in [3].

172. All these rational sextic curves can of course be obtained by projection from the rational normal sextic in [6]. To obtain, for example, the four classes in II we project the normal curve (*a*) from an arbitrary line in [6], (*b*) from a line meeting one of its chords, (*c*) from a line meeting two of its chords, and (*d*) from a line in one of its trisecant planes.

A prime of [6] meets the normal curve in six points; let us take three chords of the curve joining three pairs of these points. Any other chord of the curve meets the prime in a point through which there passes a plane meeting the first three chords*. Projecting from a line in this plane we obtain in [4] a rational sextic with four concurrent chords. This proves the existence of the type III (I). Similarly, all the other curves C can be obtained by suitable projections†.

Surfaces without either a directrix line or a multiple generator

173. Suppose that we have on Ω a curve C of the type I (A). The chords of C form a three-dimensional locus, and, since the projection of C from a plane is a plane sextic with ten double points, there will be ten chords of C meeting an arbitrary plane. Thus the chords of C form a locus M_3^{10}.

* Given three arbitrary lines in [5] there is just one plane through an arbitrary point of [5] meeting the three lines. If O is the point and a, b, c the lines the plane is the intersection of the three [4]'s *Obc, Oca, Oab*.

† For example, to obtain the curve of IV (C) and IV (D) which has two trisecants intersecting in a point of itself, we take two chords of the normal curve and a plane through a point of the curve meeting both these chords. Then projecting from a line in this plane we have the curve in [4] as required. And so on for other types.

C is a quadruple curve on M_3^{10}, and there is also a double curve.

In particular a general plane of Ω is met by ten chords of C; hence C represents a rational sextic ruled surface in [3] whose double curve C_{10} is of order 10 and whose bitangent developable E_{10} is of class 10*.

Through any point of C there pass four chords which lie entirely upon Ω; these chords form a ruled surface R_2^{20} of order 20, the intersection of Ω and M_3^{10}. They set up on C a (4, 4) correspondence of valency 2, so that† there are twenty-four points of C for which two of the four chords which lie on Ω coincide. Also‡ there are eight tangents of C lying on Ω. If C' is a prime section of R_2^{20} we have a correspondence between C and C' for which

$$\alpha = 2, \qquad \alpha' = 4, \qquad p = 0, \qquad \eta = 24, \qquad \eta' = 8,$$

so that C' is of genus 3. Hence the double curve is C_{10}^3 of genus 3 and the bitangent developable is E_{10}^3 of genus 3*.

There are eight trisecant planes of C which lie entirely on Ω||; these are in fact four planes of each system. Hence C_{10}^3 has four triple points and E_{10}^3 four triple planes. These latter are tritangent planes of the ruled surface, each meeting it in three generators and a rational plane cubic.

Through each of the triple points of C_{10}^3 there pass three lines meeting C_{10}^3 in two further points; these are generators of the ruled surface.

This is the most general type of rational sextic ruled surface in [3].

174. Consider now, in [7], the most general rational sextic ruled surface F; this surface contains ∞^1 directrix cubic curves¶. It also contains ∞^3 directrix quartic curves; these can all be obtained by means of primes through any two fixed generators¶. Taking a pencil of primes through the two generators we obtain a pencil of quartic curves; these curves have two common points—the remaining intersections of F with the [5] which is the base of the pencil of primes**.

We have a system of ∞^3 primes through the solid determined by any two fixed generators of F, and the different systems are projectively related to one another when we make those primes which contain the same directrix quartic of F correspond to one another. If we take three fixed pairs of generators of F, the [4]'s which contain the directrix quartics are determined as the intersections of corresponding primes of three projectively related triply infinite systems. A section by an arbitrary solid S gives three projectivities in S; corresponding planes of these projectivities meet, in general, in a point, so that through a general point of S, and hence also through a general point of [7], there passes just *one* [4] which contains a directrix quartic of F.

* § 33. † § 13. ‡ § 32.
|| § 35. ¶ § 45. ** § 46.

Further, the chords of F are determined as the intersections of three corresponding [5]'s of the three projectively related systems. If we take a pencil of primes belonging to one system then we have corresponding pencils of primes belonging to the other two systems; the [5]'s which are the bases of the pencils meet in a line which is a chord of F. The ∞^4 chords of F are all given in this way. Hence the points of intersection of an arbitrary solid S with chords of F are the points of concurrence of three corresponding lines in three projectivities between the planes of S. Such points lie on* a curve $\vartheta_6{}^3$ of order 6 and genus 3.

Hence the chords of F form a locus $M_5{}^6$ of five dimensions and the sixth order; they meet an arbitrary solid S in a curve $\vartheta_6{}^3$ of genus 3.

Suppose that we consider one of the ∞^5 quintic curves of F; it is contained in a space S_5. Then no chord of F, which is not also a chord of the quintic curve, can meet S_5 except in a point of the quintic curve; for we cannot have a prime containing the quintic curve and also two generators. Hence the locus, of three dimensions, in which S_5 meets the locus of five dimensions formed by the chords of F, is simply the locus formed by the chords of the quintic curve. Hence we again find † that the locus of chords of F is of the sixth order, and meets an arbitrary solid in a curve of genus 3.

This argument can also be applied to tangents of F; the four-dimensional locus formed by the tangents of F meets S_5 in the surface formed by the tangents of the quintic curve. Hence the tangents of F form an $M_4{}^8$ of the eighth order; the section of this by an arbitrary [4] is a rational curve.

A directrix cubic Δ of F is determined by a prime through any three fixed generators, so that the solids K containing the curves Δ are determined as the intersections of four corresponding primes belonging to four projectively related pencils of primes. The four-dimensional locus formed by the solids K meets an arbitrary [4] in a curve which is the locus of the intersection of corresponding solids of four projectively related pencils of solids, and this is a rational quartic curve ‡. Hence the solids K form a locus $M_4{}^4$ of the fourth order, and an arbitrary solid S will be met by four of them.

The [4] containing any directrix quartic of F is the base of a doubly infinite system of primes, each prime of the system containing two generators of F. If any directrix cubic Δ is taken the directrix quartic will meet it in one point; so that the primes of the doubly infinite system meet the solid K containing Δ in the star of planes which projects the chords of Δ from a fixed point of itself. Now the star of planes which projects the chords of Δ from any point of itself is projectively related to the star of planes which projects the chords of Δ from any other point of itself, planes of the

* Schur, *Math. Ann.* 18 (1881), 16.

† Cf. § 95.

‡ Veronese, *Math. Ann.* 19 (1882), 219.

two stars corresponding when they contain the same chord of Δ. Hence the system of primes containing any directrix quartic of F is projectively related to the system of primes containing any other directrix quartic of F, primes of the two systems corresponding when they contain the same pair of generators of F.

Hence, taking any four fixed directrix quartics of F, we may say that the solids K' containing the pairs of generators of F are determined as the intersections of corresponding primes of four projectively related doubly infinite systems. If we consider the section by an arbitrary [4] we obtain four projectively related systems of solids, each system having a line as base. These are known to generate, by means of the intersections of corresponding solids, a sextic surface whose curve sections are of genus 3, and which has ten lines on it*; there being ten sets of corresponding solids which have a line in common instead of a point.

The solids K' thus form a locus M_5^6 of five dimensions and the sixth order; it is of course the same locus M_5^6 as that formed by the chords of F. Of the ∞^2 solids K' there are ten which meet any given [4] in lines.

Let us now project F from an arbitrary solid S, which does not meet it, on to a [3] Σ; we obtain a surface f. The chords of F meet S in the points of a curve ϑ_6^3. A prime through S meets F in a rational normal sextic curve, of which there are ten chords meeting S; hence those chords of F which meet S meet F in the points of a curve C_{20} of order 20. Then, on projection, C_{20} becomes the double curve C_{10}^3 of f; C_{10}^3 is of genus 3 since it is in (1, 1) correspondence with ϑ_6^3.

There are eight tangents of F meeting S, so that the (1, 2) correspondence between ϑ_6^3 and C_{20} has eight branch points, and Zeuthen's formula shews that C_{20} is a curve C_{20}^9 of genus 9. Since a [5] determined by S and a generator of F meets F again in four points† the curve C_{20}^9 must meet each generator of F in four points; it must therefore have twelve double points‡. These will lie three in each of four planes meeting S in lines, and the double curve C_{10}^3 of f will thus have four triple points. If we apply Zeuthen's formula to the (1, 4) correspondence between a directrix curve of F and C_{20}^9 we find that there are twenty-four generators of F touching C_{20}^9; thus there must be twenty-four generators of f touching its double curve.

The class of the bitangent developable of f is the number of primes which contain a given [4] through S and also two generators of F; it is therefore the number of solids K' which meet a given [4] through S in lines. We have seen that this number is ten, so that the bitangent developable of f must be of class 10. It is of genus 3, since its planes are in (1, 1)

* Veronese, *Math. Ann.* 19 (1882), 232. White, *Proc. Camb. Phil. Soc.* 21 (1923), 223.

† § 46.

‡ § 17.

correspondence with the points of ϑ_6^3; we have then a bitangent developable E_{10}^3. The number of tritangent planes of f is the number of primes through S which contain three generators of F; such a prime meets F further in a directrix cubic Δ. Then the solid K containing Δ will meet S, and we have already seen that there are four such solids K. Hence f has four tritangent planes.

Since F is generated by a (1, 1) correspondence between two directrix cubics, f is generated by taking two twisted cubics in Σ and placing them in (1, 1) correspondence. We can take either or both of these cubics to be a rational plane cubic instead of a twisted cubic.

Note 1. Algebraically: take two cubics in [7]; let the coordinates of the points of one be $(\theta^3, \theta^2, \theta, 1, 0, 0, 0, 0)$ and the coordinates of the points of the other $(0, 0, 0, 0, \theta^3, \theta^2, \theta, 1)$. Then the general rational sextic ruled surface is given in terms of the parameters λ and θ by $(\theta^3, \theta^2, \theta, 1, \lambda\theta^3, \lambda\theta^2, \lambda\theta, \lambda)$. Its equations are

$$\frac{x_0}{x_1} = \frac{x_1}{x_2} = \frac{x_2}{x_3} = \frac{x_4}{x_5} = \frac{x_5}{x_6} = \frac{x_6}{x_7},$$

and it has ∞^1 directrix cubics Δ given by $\lambda =$ const. The ∞^1 solids K containing these cubics generate the M_4^4 $\frac{x_0}{x_4} = \frac{x_1}{x_5} = \frac{x_2}{x_6} = \frac{x_3}{x_7}$, while the chords of F generate the M_5^6

$$\left\| \begin{matrix} x_0 & x_1 & x_4 & x_5 \\ x_1 & x_2 & x_5 & x_6 \\ x_2 & x_3 & x_6 & x_7 \end{matrix} \right\| = 0.$$

The equations of the solid K' determined by the generators $\theta = \theta_1$ and $\theta = \theta_2$ are

$$\begin{aligned} x_0 - (\theta_1 + \theta_2)\, x_1 + \theta_1\theta_2 x_2 &= x_1 - (\theta_1 + \theta_2)\, x_2 + \theta_1\theta_2 x_3 \\ &= x_4 - (\theta_1 + \theta_2)\, x_5 + \theta_1\theta_2 x_6 = x_5 - (\theta_1 + \theta_2)\, x_6 + \theta_1\theta_2 x_7 = 0, \end{aligned}$$

and the equations of the tangent solid along the generator θ are

$$x_0 - 2\theta x_1 + \theta^2 x_2 = x_1 - 2\theta x_2 + \theta^2 x_3 = x_4 - 2\theta x_5 + \theta^2 x_6 = x_5 - 2\theta x_6 + \theta^2 x_7 = 0.$$

Note 2. It is, of course, essential to our work that we should investigate all the possible positions which the solid S may occupy in regard to F, and the curve ϑ_6^3 in which S meets M_5^6 will break up in many different ways. When we have chosen S to occupy a certain position we shall state the orders and genera of the component curves of ϑ_6^3, and also the number of their mutual intersections; we shall not give the proofs of these statements.

The way in which ϑ_6^3 can break up into separate curves can be seen by making use of the properties of the cubic surface. When ϑ_6^3 is generated by four projective stars of planes with vertices 1, 2, 3, 4 it lies on both the cubic surfaces F_3 and F_4, where F_3 is the cubic surface generated by the stars 4, 1, 2 and F_4 the cubic surface generated by the stars 1, 2, 3. Now, if two corresponding lines of the stars 1 and 2 intersect, this intersection is on both F_3 and F_4, but is not (in general) on ϑ_6^3. Hence ϑ_6^3 is the residual intersection of two cubic surfaces with a cubic curve in common.

Suppose now that we represent one of the cubic surfaces, F_3 say, in the usual way upon a plane. There are six sets of corresponding planes of the stars 1, 2, 3 which meet in lines $a_1, a_2, a_3, a_4, a_5, a_6$ instead of only in points; these lines are represented by *fundamental points* $A_1, A_2, A_3, A_4, A_5, A_6$ in the plane and form one-half of a double-six on F_3. The cubic curve generated by the stars 1 and 2 has these six lines as chords, it is represented on the plane by a quintic with nodes at the fundamental points A. Since the complete intersection of F_3 with another cubic surface is represented on the plane by a curve of order 9 with triple points at the points A, the curve ϑ_6^3 must be represented by a quartic curve through the points A. Hence, in order to find the possible ways in which ϑ_6^3 may break up, we have simply to consider how a plane quartic, with six fixed points, may break up.

Suppose, for example, that ϑ_6^3 breaks up into a line and a quintic curve. The line may be one of the six lines a, or one of the six lines b belonging to the other half of the double-six, or one of the fifteen lines c not belonging to the double-six. If it is a line a we have in the plane a quartic with a double point at a point A; hence, on F_3, a curve ϑ_5^2 with a as a chord. If it is a line b (represented by a conic through five points A) we have in the plane a conic through one of the points A; hence, on F_3, a curve ϑ_5^0 with b as its quadrisecant. If it is a line c (represented by a line joining two points A) we have in the plane a cubic curve through four points A; hence, on F_3, a curve ϑ_5^1 with c for a trisecant. And so on if ϑ_6^3 contains as part of itself a conic or cubic curve, or if it breaks up into more than two parts.

175. If we consider a rational normal sextic in [6], and take any g_2^1 on it, the chords joining the pairs of points form a rational quintic ruled surface with a directrix conic Γ, Γ not meeting the curve. If we then project from a point in the plane of Γ on to a [5] we obtain a rational sextic C, and a g_2^1 giving chords of C which are generators of a rational quintic ruled surface with a double line. There are in [5] ∞^{20} quadric fourfolds; of these there are ∞^7 containing C, and of these latter ∞^4 contain the quintic ruled surface. Let us take one of these last quadrics to be Ω.

The generators of the quintic surface are projected from the double line by planes forming a three-dimensional cubic line-cone; since it contains the quintic surface its residual intersection with Ω must be a plane. Hence Ω contains a plane joining the double line to a generator of the surface. Any general plane of Ω of the same system as this meets the surface in two points, while a plane of the opposite system meets the surface in three points.

The chords of C which lie on Ω form the quintic ruled surface together with a ruled surface R_2^{15}; this latter meets planes of one system of Ω in eight points and planes of the other system in seven points—every plane of Ω being met by ten chords of C. C is a triple curve on R_2^{15}.

The quintic ruled surface gives a (1, 1) correspondence on C, while the surface R_2^{15} gives a (3, 3) correspondence, both these correspondences being symmetrical. It follows, on using Brill's formula (cf. §§ 14, 15), that R_2^5 and R_2^{15} have three common generators.

Of the eight tangents of C which lie on Ω two belong to the quintic ruled surface and the remaining six to R_2^{15}. There are twelve points of C at which two generators of R_2^{15} coincide. Hence, if C' is a prime section of R_2^{15} we have, for the correspondence between C and C',

$$\alpha = 2, \qquad \alpha' = 3, \qquad p = 0, \qquad \eta = 12, \qquad \eta' = 6,$$

so that C' is an elliptic curve.

Suppose, for definiteness, that the plane of Ω which contains the double line and one of the generators of the quintic surface is a ρ-plane. Then the points of C represent the generators of a ruled surface in [3] whose double curve is $C_2 + C_8^1$ and bitangent developable $E_3^0 + E_7^1$. The fact that the two ruled surfaces on Ω have three common generators shews that C_2 and C_8^1 have three common points, while E_3^0 and E_7^1 have three common planes.

Take any one of the four ρ-planes of Ω which are trisecant to C, meeting C in P, Q, R say. Assume for the moment that no one of QR, RP, PQ is a generator of the quintic surface. Then through each of P, Q, R there pass generators of this surface which all meet the double line; and the plane PQR, together with the ρ-plane through the double line, determines a [4] meeting the quintic surface in the double line and four generators, which is impossible. Hence one of QR, RP, PQ must be a generator of the quintic surface, and similarly for each of the other trisecant ρ-planes. Hence E_7^1 has four double planes which are also planes of E_3^0; the two developables having three other planes in common.

Also it will be seen when this surface is obtained by projection that C_2 passes through two double points of C_8^1 and meets it in three further points; C_8^1 has also two triple points.

We might, on the other hand, have taken the plane of Ω which contains the double line and a generator of the quintic ruled surface to be a ϖ-plane. We should then have obtained in [3] a ruled surface with a double curve $C_3^0 + C_7^1$ and bitangent developable $E_2 + E_8^1$. C_7^1 has four double points through which C_3^0 passes, the curves having three other intersections. E_8^1 has two double planes which are also planes of E_2, the two developables having three other planes in common; E_8^1 has also two triple planes.

176. On the normal surface F in [7] there are ∞^3 quartics E. An involution of pairs of generators of F gives rise to a g_2^1 on each of these quartics, and thus to a cubic ruled surface through each of them. Let us then choose S to pass through the directrix line λ of a cubic ruled surface formed by chords of one of these quartics E. There are two tangents of E belonging to this cubic surface.

A prime through S meets F in a rational normal sextic, ten of whose chords meet S; but two of these chords are generators of the cubic ruled surface. Hence the chords of F which meet S meet F in E and a curve C_{16} meeting each generator of F in three points. E and C_{16} have ten intersections*.

S meets M_5^6 in λ and an elliptic quintic ϑ_5^1 of which λ is a trisecant. Through the three intersections of λ and ϑ_5^1 there pass chords of F which are chords both of E and C_{16}; thus six of the intersections of C_{16} with E are accounted for. Let A be another intersection of these two curves. Through A there passes a chord AB of E meeting λ and a chord AC of C_{16} meeting ϑ_5^1. Then the chord BC of F must also meet ϑ_5^1, so that C_{16} passes through B and has a double point at C. There remains a further pair of intersections of E and C_{16}, these are associated in the same way with a double point on C_{16}. There are six tangents of C_{16} which meet ϑ_5^1; hence it is of genus 4. It must then have eight double points. Two of these are already accounted for; the six others lie three in each of two planes which meet S in lines.

Thus when we project from S on to Σ we obtain a ruled surface f whose double curve is $C_2+C_8^1$; C_2 being the projection of E and C_8^1 the projection of C_{16}. C_8^1 has three simple points and two double points on C_2, and has also two triple points.

Since F can be generated by means of a (1, 1) correspondence between E and a directrix cubic Δ with a united point, to generate f we take in Σ a conic and a twisted cubic in (1, 2) correspondence with a united point. The pairs of points of the cubic which correspond to the points of the conic form a g_2^1, so that their joins form a regulus; hence the planes of the pairs of generators which intersect in the points of the conic will form† a cubic developable E_3^0 (since there is a united point). This is part of the bitangent developable of f. The other part is an E_7^1; it is formed by the planes of pairs of generators which intersect in points of the double curve C_8^1.

177. A prime section of F is a rational normal sextic; an involution of pairs of generators of F gives a g_2^1 on this sextic, and the chords joining the pairs of this g_2^1 form a rational quintic ruled surface with a directrix conic Γ, Γ not meeting the sextic. Choose then the solid S to pass through the plane of Γ.

A prime through S meets F in a rational normal sextic, ten of whose chords meet S; but three of these belong to the quintic ruled surface. Thus the chords of F meeting S meet F in the prime section C_6 and a curve C_{14} meeting each generator of F in three points. C_6 and C_{14} meet in fourteen points.

* Cf. the last footnote to § 97.

† § 22.

S meets M_5^6 in Γ and an elliptic quartic ϑ_4^1 having three intersections with Γ. Through these three points pass chords of F which are chords both of C_6 and C_{14}; this accounts for six intersections of C_6 and C_{14}. The other eight fall into four pairs, and with each pair is associated a double point of C_{14}. Since C_{14} has six tangents which meet ϑ_4^1 it is of genus 4, and this shews that it has exactly four double points.

On projection from S on to Σ we obtain a ruled surface f whose double curve is $C_3^0 + C_7^1$; C_3^0 is the projection of C_6, while C_7^1 is the projection of C_{14}. C_3^0 passes through the four double points of C_7^1 and also meets it in three other points.

Since F can be generated by a (1, 1) correspondence between C_6 and a directrix cubic Δ, there being three united points, f can be generated by two twisted cubics in (1, 2) correspondence with three united points. The pairs of points of the second cubic corresponding to the points of the first form a g_2^1 and their joins form a regulus; hence the planes of the pairs of generators which pass through the points of the first cubic are (because of the united points) the tangent planes of a quadric cone E_2. This is part of the bitangent developable of the surface; the remaining part is an E_8^1.

178. On the rational normal sextic curve in [6] there are ∞^2 involutions g_2^1. Each of these gives rise to a quintic ruled surface with a directrix conic; and these conics lie in ∞^2 planes. Let us suppose that two of these planes intersect in a point not on either of their conics. Projecting from such a point on to a [5] we obtain a rational sextic C and two quintic ruled surfaces containing it, each with a double line. There is a quadric Ω containing these two ruled surfaces.

The chords of C which lie on Ω form two quintic ruled surfaces R_2^5 and S_2^5, and a ruled surface R_2^{10} on which C is a double curve. R_2^5 and S_2^5 have one common generator; R_2^{10} has two generators in common with each of R_2^5 and S_2^5. The prime sections of R_2^{10} are rational curves.

For either of the quintic surfaces there is a plane of Ω passing through its double line and containing one of its generators.

First, suppose that both these planes are ρ-planes. Then we have in [3] a ruled surface whose double curve is $C_2 + D_2 + C_6^0$ and bitangent developable $E_3^0 + F_3^0 + E_4^0$. Each of the four ρ-planes of Ω which is trisecant to C must contain a generator of R_2^5 and a generator of S_2^5. Hence there are four planes common to all the developables E_3^0, F_3^0 and E_4^0; E_3^0 and F_3^0 have a further plane in common, while E_4^0 has two further planes in common with each of them. It will be seen that C_2 passes through two double points and two simple points of C_6^0, as also does D_2; C_6^0 has four double points, while C_2 and D_2 have one intersection.

If, on the other hand, both the planes of Ω are ϖ-planes we have a ruled surface in [3] whose double curve is $C_3{}^0 + D_3{}^0 + C_4{}^0$ and bitangent developable $E_2 + F_2 + E_6{}^0$. There are four points common to all the curves $C_3{}^0$, $D_3{}^0$ and $C_4{}^0$; $C_3{}^0$ and $D_3{}^0$ have one other intersection, while $C_4{}^0$ meets each of them in two further points. $E_6{}^0$ has four double planes; two of these are also planes of E_2 and the other two of F_2; $E_6{}^0$ has two further planes in common with E_2 and two with F_2, while E_2 and F_2 have a common plane.

But further: one of the planes of Ω may be a ρ-plane, while the other is a ϖ-plane. We then have in [3] a ruled surface whose double curve is $C_2 + C_3{}^0 + C_5{}^0$ and bitangent developable $E_3{}^0 + E_2 + E_5{}^0$.

179. Take two directrix quartics E and E' on the normal surface F in [7]; they have two intersections. Through these intersections there pass two generators of F; let us take two involutions of generators which both include this pair. Then we have two cubic ruled surfaces each with a directrix line; one line λ lies in the [4] containing E, while the other λ' lies in the [4] containing E'. Both λ and λ' meet the chord of F which joins the intersections of E and E', and we choose the involutions so that they meet this chord in the same point*.

Take a solid S containing λ and λ' and project from S on to Σ. A prime through S meets F in a rational normal sextic; there are ten chords of this curve meeting S, including two chords of E and two chords of E'; thus the chords of F which meet S meet F in E, E' and a curve C_{12} meeting every generator in two points. C_{12} meets each of E and E' in eight points.

S meets $M_5{}^6$ in λ, λ' and a rational quartic $\vartheta_4{}^0$ having λ and λ' as chords. Through the intersections of λ and $\vartheta_4{}^0$ there pass lines which are chords both of E and C_{12}; the other four intersections of E and C_{12} fall into two pairs with each of which is associated a double point of C_{12}. We can thus obtain four double points on C_{12}. There are four tangents of C_{12} meeting $\vartheta_4{}^0$, and the (1, 2) correspondence between $\vartheta_4{}^0$ and C_{12} shews that C_{12} is elliptic, whereupon Segre's formula shews that it has exactly four double points.

Thus we obtain in Σ a ruled surface f with a double curve $C_2 + D_2 + C_6{}^0$. C_2 and D_2 have one intersection; $C_6{}^0$ has four double points, two of which are on C_2 and the other two on D_2, while it has two simple intersections with each of C_2 and D_2.

Since F can be generated by placing E and E' in (1, 1) correspondence with two united points we can generate f by taking two conics C_2 and D_2 with one intersection, placing them in (2, 2) correspondence with a doubly united point. The lines joining the pairs of points of one conic which correspond to the points of the other touch a conic; hence the planes joining

* See the footnotes to § 131.

the points of either conic to the pairs of points on the other which correspond to them form a developable of the third class which is part of the bitangent developable of the surface. We thus have a bitangent developable $E_3^0 + F_3^0 + E_4^0$.

180. Two chords of F determine a [3]; through this [3] there pass ∞^3 primes meeting F in rational normal sextics through four fixed points. On any one of these curves we can regard the two chords as determining an involution, we thus have a quintic ruled surface containing the chords. We can choose the prime so that the directrix conic of the quintic surface meets these chords in assigned points.

Now take a directrix quartic, three of its chords l, m, n and their transversal, meeting them in L, M, N. We can regard l and m as determining an involution of pairs of generators on F and a quintic ruled surface whose directrix conic Γ passes through L and M; similarly, we have another surface whose directrix conic Γ' passes through L and N, the two surfaces having a common generator through L. Let S be the solid containing the planes of Γ and Γ'.

A prime through S meets F in a rational sextic curve, ten of whose chords meet S; of these ten chords three meet Γ and three meet Γ'. Those chords of F which meet S meet F in two prime sections and a curve C_8 meeting every generator in two points and each prime section in eight points.

S meets M_5^6 in Γ, Γ' and a conic ϑ_2 meeting each of Γ and Γ' in two points. There are four tangents of C_8 meeting ϑ_2, so that C_8 is elliptic and has no double points. The chords of F through the intersections of Γ and ϑ_2 are common chords of C_8 and one of the prime sections; there are four other intersections of C_8 with this section to be accounted for. Similarly we obtain four intersections of C_8 with the other prime section. Also there are four points common to the two prime sections other than the two on the chord through L. These three sets of four points are associated with one another; they fall into four triads, each triad includes a point of each set and projects into a single point of Σ.

On projection we have in Σ a ruled surface f whose double curve is $C_3^0 + D_3^0 + C_4^0$; there are four points common to all the curves C_3^0, D_3^0 and C_4^0; C_3^0 and D_3^0 have one further intersection, while C_4^0 meets each of them in two further points.

To generate this surface f we take two twisted cubics C_3^0 and D_3^0 with five common points, placing them in (2, 2) correspondence with four ordinary united points and one doubly united point. The joins of the pairs of points of one cubic which correspond to the points of the other generate a rational quartic ruled surface, so that the planes joining the points of either cubic to the pairs of points of the other which correspond to them touch a quadric cone (because of the five united points). We have a bitangent developable $E_2+F_2+E_6^0$.

181. Take now a prime section C_6^0 of F; an involution of pairs of generators gives chords of C_6^0 forming a quintic ruled surface with a directrix conic Γ. Take any point A of Γ; the chord of F through A meets it in two points through which pass ∞^1 directrix quartics. Take one of these quartics E and an involution of pairs of generators of F such that the resulting cubic ruled surface formed by chords of E has its directrix line λ passing through A, the chord of C_6^0 through A being common to this surface and the quintic surface. Then choose S to be the solid containing λ and Γ.

The chords of F which meet S meet F in E, C_6^0 and a curve C_{10} meeting every generator of F in two points. S meets M_5^6 in Γ, λ and a twisted cubic ϑ_3^0 which meets each of Γ and λ in two points. There are four tangents of C_{10} meeting ϑ_3^0 so that C_{10} is elliptic and has consequently two double points.

C_{10} meets E in six points and C_6^0 in ten points; four of the intersections with E are accounted for by the chords of F through the points common to ϑ_3^0 and λ and four of the intersections with C_6^0 by the chords of F through the points common to ϑ_3^0 and Γ. Four further intersections with C_6^0 are associated in pairs with the two double points of C_{10}; the two remaining ones are associated with the two remaining intersections with E and with the two intersections of E and C_6^0 which do not lie on the chord through A.

Hence on projection we have in Σ a ruled surface f whose double curve is $C_2+C_3^0+C_5^0$. C_5^0 has two double points which lie on C_3^0; it meets C_3^0 in four further points through two of which C_2 also passes, while C_2 and C_3^0 have one other intersection.

Since F is generated by a (1, 1) correspondence between C_6^0 and E with four united points, to generate f we take in Σ a conic C_2 and a twisted cubic C_3^0 with three intersections, placing them in (2, 2) correspondence with two ordinary united points and one doubly united point. The joins of the pairs of points of the conic which correspond to the points of the cubic touch another conic; we thus obtain a quadric cone as part of the bitangent developable. The points of the conic give pairs of points of the cubic whose joins form a quartic ruled surface, and we thus obtain a developable of the third class. Thus the bitangent developable of the surface is $E_3^0+E_2+E_5^0$.

This surface is not strictly self-dual; the planes of the quadric cone are not formed by the generators which intersect in the points of C_2 but by those which intersect in the points of C_3^0.

182. All the ruled surfaces in [3] so far obtained are such that their generators are represented by the points of a curve C on Ω which belongs to the type I (A). Let us now suppose that we have a curve C of the type II (A); since it lies in a [4] the generators of the corresponding ruled surface in [3] belong to a linear complex. The chords of C form an M_3^{10}, so that any plane of Ω meets the [4] containing C in a line which is met by ten chords of C. It is shewn precisely as in § 173 that the chords of C lying on Ω form a ruled surface R_2^{20} whose prime sections are of genus 3; hence the ruled surface in [3] has a double curve C_{10}^3 and a bitangent developable E_{10}^3.

C has four trisecants*: these also lie on Ω. Thus C_{10}^3 has four triple points; through each of these points there pass three generators of the surface, and these lie in a plane which is a triple plane of E_{10}^3.

Since any surface whose generators belong to a linear complex is necessarily self-dual there is no need to seek for the other types of surfaces f when C is of the type II (A).

183. Given a rational sextic C in [5] we can always make some of the ∞^7 quadrics containing it contain also one of its quadrisecant planes. Then the curve C represents a ruled surface in [3] for which either four generators pass through a point or else four generators lie in a plane. The quadrisecant plane of C counts for four among the trisecant planes of C which lie on Ω; we shall have this quadrisecant plane belonging to one system and four trisecant planes belonging to the opposite system.

Take four points, one on each of four generators of the normal surface F, and take S to meet the solid determined by these four points in a plane. If we project from S we have in Σ a surface f with four concurrent generators. The chords of F which meet S meet F in a curve C_{20}^9 with triple points at each of the four selected points, so that the surface has a double curve C_{10}^3 with a sextuple point. To generate f take a plane quartic with a triple point and a twisted cubic passing through the triple point and having one other intersection with the quartic; place them in (1, 1) correspondence with this last intersection as a united point.

To obtain the surface with a quadritangent plane we must project the normal surface with a directrix conic Γ. The chords of this surface also form an M_5^6, meeting an arbitrary solid S in a curve ϑ_6^3, while the tangents form an M_4^8†. The quadritangent plane of the surface f is the intersection

* If we take a rational normal sextic in [6] there are four of its trisecant planes meeting an arbitrary line. If, for instance, the curve is given by

$$x_0:x_1:x_2:x_3:x_4:x_5:x_6 = \theta^6:\theta^5:\theta^4:\theta^3:\theta^2:\theta:1$$

the trisecant planes form the quartic primal

$$\begin{vmatrix} x_0 & x_1 & x_2 & x_3 \\ x_1 & x_2 & x_3 & x_4 \\ x_2 & x_3 & x_4 & x_5 \\ x_3 & x_4 & x_5 & x_6 \end{vmatrix} = 0.$$

† If we set up a correspondence between the points B and C of Γ, the points B and C corresponding when the [5] containing S and the tangent of a given directrix

of Σ with the [6] $S\Gamma$; to generate f we take a conic and a rational skew quartic in (1, 1) correspondence.

Since no two quadrisecant planes of a rational sextic in [5] can intersect we cannot have two quadrisecant planes of the same system on Ω. But it is possible to have two quadrisecant planes on Ω of different systems; then there will be no trisecant planes of C on Ω; the ruled surface in [3] has four concurrent generators and four coplanar generators. This is also obtained by projection from the normal surface with a directrix conic Γ.

Surfaces with a multiple generator but without a directrix line

184. Suppose now that we have a curve C on Ω of the type I (B); C lies in [5] and has a double point P. Correspondingly we shall have in [3] a rational sextic ruled surface with a double generator G. The chords of C form an M_3^9 on which C is a quadruple curve and P a sextuple point; the quartic cone formed by joining P to the other points of C is a double surface on M_3^9. Any plane of Ω is met by nine chords of C; hence, apart from the double generator, the surface in [3] has a double curve of the ninth order and a bitangent developable of the ninth class.

The chords of C lying on Ω form a ruled surface R_2^{18} of order 18, the intersection of Ω and M_3^9. Through any point of C there pass four generators of R_2^{18}, and there are twenty-four points of C at which two of these coincide. These, however, include the point P counted four times*. Also there are eight tangents of C lying on Ω. Hence, for the correspondence between C and a prime section C' of R_2^{18}, we have

$$\alpha = 2, \quad \alpha' = 4, \quad p = 0, \quad \eta = 20, \quad \eta' = 8,$$

and Zeuthen's formula gives $p' = 2$. Hence the ruled surface has a double curve $G + G_9^2$ and a bitangent developable $G + E_9^2$.

The plane of the two tangents of C at P belongs to M_3^9†, so that it meets Ω in two lines which are generators of R_2^{18}. The planes ϖ through these lines represent intersections of C_9^2 and G, while the planes ρ through them represent planes of E_9^2 passing through G.

There are two chords PQ, PR of C which pass through P and lie on Ω.

quartic E, at the point on the generator of F through B, meets the plane of Γ on the tangent at C, we have a (6, 2) correspondence. The eight coincidences give eight tangent solids of F which meet S. Cf. also the footnote to § 127.

* Cf. § 265 below.

† This is seen at once when M_3^9 is regarded as the projection of the M_3^{10} formed by the chords of a rational normal sextic. The tangent [3] of M_3^{10} at a point P contains the tangents of the normal curve at the two points where the chord through P meets it; M_3^{10} has the same tangent [3] at all points of a chord of the curve. The coordinates of a point of M_3^{10} are given parametrically by $(\theta^6 + \kappa\phi^6,\ \theta^5 + \kappa\phi^5,\ \theta^4 + \kappa\phi^4,\ \theta^3 + \kappa\phi^3,\ \theta^2 + \kappa\phi^2,\ \theta + \kappa\phi,\ 1 + \kappa)$; and it is easily seen that the tangent solid at this point does not depend on κ.

The planes of Ω through these lines are to be regarded as trisecant planes of C; thus we have two double points of $C_9{}^2$ on G and two double planes of $E_9{}^2$ through G. There will be two other trisecant planes of C belonging to each system of planes on Ω; hence $C_9{}^2$ has two triple points, and $E_9{}^2$ has two triple planes.

If we project $C_9{}^2$ on to a plane from one of its double points we obtain a curve $C_7{}^2$ with a quadruple point (the intersection of the plane with G) and two triple points, and therefore with one other double point. There is thus one line through either double point of $C_9{}^2$ which meets it in two further points, and this must be a generator of the surface. We thus have the two generators which meet G and are represented on Ω by the points Q and R.

185. Consider again the normal surface F in [7], and take two generators g and g'; let S contain a line l in the solid gg'. Then the projected surface f has a double generator G, the intersection of Σ with the [5] Sgg'.

The directrix cubics Δ of F meet g and g' in related ranges; hence the solids K meet the solid gg' in the lines of a regulus. There are two lines of this regulus meeting l, so that S meets two further solids K. Hence the surface f has two tritangent planes which do not pass through G.

S meets $M_5{}^6$ in l and a curve $\vartheta_5{}^2$ which has l for a chord. The chords of F which meet S meet F in g, g', and a curve C_{18} meeting every generator of F in four points. Since there are eight tangents of C_{18} which meet $\vartheta_5{}^2$ it is of genus 7 and therefore has eight double points. The chords of F which pass through the intersections of l and $\vartheta_5{}^2$ are chords of C_{18}; we thus account for two intersections of C_{18} with each of g and g'. One of the other intersections of C_{18} and g is associated with one of its other intersections with g' and with one of its double points; similarly, for the remaining pair of intersections. The other six double points of C_{18} lie three in each of two planes which meet S in lines.

Hence on projection we have a surface f whose double curve is $G + C_9{}^2$. $C_9{}^2$ has two double points and two ordinary points on G; it has also two triple points.

To generate this surface we take two twisted cubics in (1, 1) correspondence, the correspondence being specialised to give the double generator.

186. On a rational normal sextic there are ∞^1 involutions which contain, as a pair of corresponding points, the ends of a given chord; each of these gives rise to a quintic ruled surface of which the chord is a generator. On projecting from a point of the chord on to a [5] each of these surfaces is projected into a quartic ruled surface, one of whose generators passes through the double point P of the projected curve.

There are ∞^8 quadric fourfolds containing C, and ∞^5 of these contain such a quartic surface*. Take one of these latter to be Ω. The planes of the conics on the quartic surface form a V_3^3; Ω meets this in the quartic surface and in two of its planes, these belonging to opposite systems on Ω. The quartic surface meets a general plane of Ω in two points.

The chords of C which lie on Ω form this quartic ruled surface R_2^4 and a ruled surface R_2^{14} which has C as a triple curve. There are two chords PQ, PR of C which pass through P and lie on Ω; these are double generators of R_2^{14}, and there is one other generator of R_2^{14} passing through P. There are twelve points of C at which two of the three generators of R_2^{14} coincide†; there are two tangents of C belonging to R_2^4 and six belonging to R_2^{14}. Considering then the correspondence between C and a prime section C' of R_2^{14} we have

$$\alpha = 2, \quad \alpha' = 3, \quad p = 0, \quad \eta = 12, \quad \eta' = 6,$$

whence $p' = 1$. R_2^{14} meets a general plane of Ω in seven points; thus we have in [3] a ruled surface whose double curve is given by $C_2 + G + C_7^1$ and bitangent developable by $E_2 + G + E_7^1$.

R_2^4 and R_2^{14} have two common generators‡.

If we take any of the four trisecant planes (two of either system) of C which lie on Ω there is a plane of Ω of the same system meeting R_2^4 in a conic. Then, considering the intersection of R_2^4 with the [4] containing the two planes, we must conclude that the trisecant plane of C contains a generator of R_2^4. G passes through two double points of C_7^1 and meets it in a further point, while also meeting C_2. Also C_2 passes through two double points of C_7^1, while meeting it in two further points: there are exactly similar statements for the bitangent developable.

187. Take an involution of pairs of generators on the normal surface

* It is sufficient to make one of the quadrics through C contain three generators of the quartic surface in order that it should contain the whole of it.

† These coincidences do not include P. If we regard P as two points P_1 and P_2 on different branches of C there are three generators P_1P_2, P_1Q, P_1R of R_2^{14} through P_1 and three others P_2P_1, P_2Q, P_2R through P_2. Thus corresponding to the point of C on either branch at P we have three distinct points.

This may be contrasted with § 24 and with § 184 above and § 265 below.

‡ Not three, as is apparently given by Brill's formula; this includes a false coincidence at P. The tangents of C at P determine a plane containing a generator of R_2^4 and a generator of R_2^{14}, which do not of course coincide. This discrepancy is further illustrated by considering the projections of two quintic surfaces, determined by involutions on the normal curve; projecting from a point of their common generator we have two g_2^1's on C giving two quartic surfaces without a common generator.

F, thus obtaining, by means of a directrix quartic E, a cubic ruled surface with a directrix line λ. Let g, g' be a pair of generators belonging to the involution, and take a line l lying in the solid gg' and passing through the point where λ meets it. Then project from a solid S containing l and λ. S meets M_5^6 in l, λ and an elliptic quartic ϑ_4^1 which meets l and has λ as a chord.

The chords of F which meet S meet F in g, g', E and a curve C_{14} meeting each generator in three points and E in eight points. Since there are six tangents of C_{14} meeting ϑ_4^1 it is of genus 4, so that it must have four double points. The chords of F passing through the intersections of λ and ϑ_4^1 account for four intersections of C_{14}^4 with E; the remaining intersections fall into two pairs, with each of which is associated a double point of C_{14}^4. The other double points of C_{14}^4 are associated with pairs of intersections of C_{14}^4 with g and g'; the remaining pair of these intersections is joined by the chord of F which passes through the common point of l and ϑ_4^1.

Hence on projection the surface f has a double curve $C_2+G+C_7^1$; C_7^1 has two double points and two simple points on C_2, two double points and one simple point on G; G meets C_2.

To generate this surface we take a conic and a cubic in (1, 2) correspondence with a united point; the correspondence being so determined that one point of the conic gives rise to the pair of points of the cubic collinear with it. The joins of the pairs of points on the cubic form a regulus, two lines of which pass through the corresponding points of the conic; thus the planes joining the points of the conic to the pairs of points of the cubic which correspond to them are the tangent planes of a quadric cone. The surface has a bitangent developable $E_2+G+E_7^1$.

188. Let us take two involutions on the rational normal sextic and project on to a [5] from a point of their common chord. Then we obtain a curve C with a double point P and two quartic ruled surfaces containing C; there are ∞^2 quadrics containing both these surfaces R_2^4 and S_2^4; let us take one of these to be Ω. The plane of the tangents to C at P meets Ω in two lines which are generators of R_2^4 and S_2^4 respectively.

The chords of C which lie on Ω form the two ruled surfaces R_2^4, S_2^4 and a third ruled surface R_2^{10} on which C is a double curve. There are four tangents of C belonging to R_2^{10} and there are four points of C at which the two generators of R_2^{10} coincide; this is sufficient to shew that the prime sections of R_2^{10} are rational curves. R_2^{10} meets the planes of Ω in five points. Thus the points of C represent the generators of a ruled surface in [3] whose double curve is $C_2+D_2+G+C_5^0$ and bitangent developable $E_2+F_2+G+E_5^0$.

R_2^{10} has two generators in common with each of R_2^4 and S_2^4, but these two surfaces themselves have not a common generator. Each trisecant plane of C which lies on Ω contains both a generator of R_2^4 and a generator of S_2^4. Hence C_2 and D_2 have two intersections through both of which C_5^0 passes, C_5^0 meeting each of them in two further points. G meets both C_2 and D_2, and passes through two double points of C_5^0. There are exactly similar statements for the bitangent developable.

189. Take two involutions of pairs of generators on the normal surface F. One of these determines, by means of a directrix quartic E, a cubic ruled surface with a directrix line λ; the other similarly determines, by means of a directrix quartic E', a cubic ruled surface with a directrix line λ'. Let us project from the solid S containing λ and λ'.

Let g, g' be the pair of generators common to the two involutions. S contains the line l joining the points where the solid gg' is met by λ and λ'. It meets M_5^6 in l, λ, λ' and a cubic ϑ_3^0 having λ and λ' as chords.

The chords of F which meet S meet F in g, g', E, E', and a curve C_{10} which meets every generator in two points. Since there are four tangents of C_{10} meeting ϑ_3^0 it is an elliptic curve and has two double points; these are associated with its intersections with g and g'. On projection we obtain a ruled surface with a double curve exactly as in the last article.

To generate such a surface we take two conics and place them in (2, 2) correspondence with two united points, the correspondence being specialised to give the double generator. The joins of the pairs of points of either conic which correspond to the points of the other touch another conic, and the planes joining the points of one of the conics to the pairs of points of the other which correspond to them are the tangent planes of a quadric cone. The bitangent developable of the surface thus includes two developables of the second class; it is $E_2 + F_2 + G + E_5^0$.

190. The three types of surfaces so far obtained in this section are all self-dual, and, in fact, there are particular cases of surfaces of these types which belong to a linear complex and are represented on Ω by curves C of the type II (B).

A rational sextic in [4] with a double point P has two trisecants*; its chords form a locus M_3^9 on which C is quadruple, the trisecants triple and P sextuple. Any quadric threefold containing C contains also its trisecants, and any line on this quadric is met by nine chords of C. The chords of C which lie on the quadric form a ruled surface R_2^{18} whose

* The trisecant planes of a rational normal sextic form an M_5^4 on which the chords of the curve are a double locus M_3^{10}. Hence a line meeting a chord of the curve meets two trisecant planes not containing the chord.

prime sections are of genus 2, precisely as in § 184. If we regard the quadric as a prime section of Ω we have in [3] a ruled surface whose generators belong to a linear complex, the double curve is given by $G+C_9{}^2$ and the bitangent developable by $G+E_9{}^2$. $C_9{}^2$ has two triple points; at either of these there intersect three generators of the ruled surface, these lying in a plane which is a triple plane of $E_9{}^2$. G meets $C_9{}^2$ and lies in planes of $E_9{}^2$ just as before.

There are ∞^2 quadrics containing C; the base of this net of quadrics consists of C and the two trisecants.

If we take in [5] a rational sextic with a double point there are ∞^1 involutions on the curve containing the pair of points at the double point; each of these gives a quartic ruled surface. Projecting from a point in the plane of a conic of one of these surfaces we obtain in [4] a rational sextic C, with a double point P, lying on a quartic ruled surface which has a double line; this double line is itself a chord of C. There are ∞^1 quadrics containing this ruled surface, and if one of these is regarded as a prime section of Ω we obtain in [3] a ruled surface whose double curve is $C_2+G+C_7{}^1$ and bitangent developable $E_2+G+E_7{}^1$; but now its generators belong to a linear complex.

Again, we can project from a point of [5] which is common to two planes meeting two different quartic surfaces in conics. We have then two quartic ruled surfaces containing the curve C in [4]; each of these has a double line which is a chord of C. There is a quadric containing C and both these ruled surfaces, and if this is regarded as a prime section of Ω we have in [3] a ruled surface whose generators belong to a linear complex, the double curve being $C_2+D_2+G+C_5{}^0$ and the bitangent developable $E_2+F_2+G+E_5{}^0$.

191. Take an involution of pairs of points on a rational normal sextic in [6] and project on to a [5] from a point of a chord which does not join a pair of the involution. The joins of the pairs of the involution form a rational normal quintic ruled surface through any two points of which there passes a cubic curve; hence on projection we have a curve C with a double point P and a quintic ruled surface with a double point P; there is on this surface a plane cubic curve with a double point at P.

There are quadrics containing this ruled surface. Such a quadric Ω necessarily contains the plane of the cubic curve; this plane and the quintic surface form the complete intersection of Ω and the cubic cone which projects the surface from P. The surface meets all planes of Ω of the same system as this one in two points, all planes of Ω of the opposite system in three points,

There are two chords PQ, PR of C which pass through P and lie on Ω; these are generators of the quintic surface $R_2{}^5$. The chords of C which lie on Ω generate this surface R_2^5 and a surface R_2^{13} on which C is a triple curve; this latter surface meets all planes of Ω of one system in seven points and all planes of the other system in six points. PQ and PR are generators of R_2^{13}, while R_2^{13} and R_2^5 have three other common generators. There are also two generators of R_2^{13} passing through P and lying in the plane of the two tangents to C at P.

There are eight points of C other than P at which two of the three generators of R_2^{13} coincide, and there are six tangents of C which are generators of R_2^{13}. We thus find that the prime sections of R_2^{13} are rational curves.

A trisecant plane of C which lies on Ω contains three generators of R_2^{13} if it is of the opposite system to the plane of the cubic on R_2^5, but if of the same system it must contain a generator of R_2^5.

Suppose that the plane cubic on R_2^5 lies in a ρ-plane of Ω. Then in [3] we have a ruled surface whose double curve is $C_2+G+C_7^0$. G lies in the plane of C_2 and C_7^0 passes through the intersections of G and C_2; C_7^0 meets G in two other points and C_2 in three other points, having two triple points. The bitangent developable is $E_3^0+G+E_6^0$. E_6^0 has two double planes which are planes of E_3^0; it has two planes through G in common with E_3^0 and three further planes in common with E_3^0; it has also two other planes through G.

Similarly, if the plane cubic on R_2^5 lies in a ϖ-plane of Ω we obtain the dual surface in [3]; the double curve is $C_3^0+G+C_6^0$ and the bitangent developable $E_2+G+E_7^0$.

192. Take on the normal surface F in [7] an involution of pairs of generators; then a directrix quartic E gives rise to a cubic ruled surface with a directrix line λ. Choose S to contain λ and to meet the solid containing a pair of generators g, g' in a line l; g, g' not being a pair of the involution. Then the [6] ES contains g and g', so that the surface f has a double generator lying in the plane of a double conic.

S meets M_5^6 in λ, l and a rational quartic ϑ_4^0 having λ for a trisecant and l for a chord.

The chords of F meeting S meet F in g, g', E and a curve C_{14} meeting every generator in three points. There are six tangents of C_{14} meeting ϑ_4^0, so that it is a C_{14}^2 with six double points; these double points lie three in each of two planes meeting S in lines. C_{14}^2 has eight intersections with E; six of these are accounted for by the chords of F which pass through the points where λ meets ϑ_4^0, the other two are the points of E which correspond in the involution to its intersections with g and g'.

Thus on projection we obtain a surface f whose double curve is $C_2+G+C_7^0$; G lies in the plane of C_2 and C_7^0 passes through the two points where it meets C_2; C_7^0 meets G in two other points and C_2 in three other points, and has two triple points.

To generate this surface we take a conic and a twisted cubic in (1, 2) correspondence with a united point. The cubic meets the plane of the conic in two other points; the points of the conic which correspond to these are to be those two points in which it meets the line joining them. The planes which join the points of the conic to the pairs of corresponding points on the cubic form a developable of the third class E_3^0; the bitangent developable of the surface is $E_3^0 + G + E_6^0$.

193. If we take a prime section C_6 of F, an involution of pairs of generators gives a quintic ruled surface with a directrix conic Γ. A solid S through the plane of Γ meets M_5^6 in Γ and an elliptic quartic ϑ_4^1 having three intersections with Γ. This quartic will meet the plane of Γ in a fourth point, and through this point there passes a transversal to two generators g, g' of F (not forming a pair of the involution). Let us take a line l through this point and lying in the solid gg', and then choose S to contain Γ and l. S meets M_5^6 further in a twisted cubic ϑ_3^0 meeting Γ in three points and l in two points.

The chords of F meeting S meet F in C_6, g, g' and a curve C_{12} meeting every generator in three points; there are six tangents of C_{12} meeting ϑ_3^0, so that it is a C_{12}^2, and has two double points. It meets C_6 in twelve points: six of these arise from the three chords of F through the intersections of ϑ_3^0 and Γ; four more are associated as two pairs with the double points of C_{12}^2, while the remaining two are the points of C_6 which correspond in the involution to its intersections with g and g'.

Thus on projection the surface f has a double curve $C_3^0 + G + C_6^0$; G is a chord of C_3^0 and C_6^0 passes through their two intersections, meeting G in two further points and C_3^0 in three further points. Also C_6^0 has two double points on C_3^0.

To generate this surface we take two twisted cubics in (1, 2) correspondence with three united points. The cubics have a common chord; to the points in which this meets the second cubic correspond those in which it meets the first. The planes joining the points of the first cubic to the pairs of points which correspond to them on the second cubic are the tangent planes of a quadric cone. The bitangent developable of the surface is $E_2 + G + E_7^0$.

194. We now pass on to consider curves on Ω of the type II (C); C is contained in a [4] and has two double points P and Q. These represent two double generators G and H of the surface in [3]. The chords of C form a locus M_3^8, there being eight of them meeting an arbitrary line in [4].

If we regard a quadric threefold containing C as a prime section of Ω, every plane of Ω meets the [4] containing C in a line which is met by eight chords of C. Hence the ruled surface in [3] has a double curve $G+H+C_8$ and a bitangent developable $G+H+E_8$.

The chords of C lying on Ω form a ruled surface R_2^{16} (the intersection of Ω and M_3^8) on which C is a quadruple curve. There are apparently twenty-four points of C at which two of the four generators of R_2^{16} coincide, but these include P and Q, each counted four times. There are eight tangents of C which lie on Ω, so that we have a correspondence between C and a prime section C' of R_2^{16} for which

$$\alpha=2, \qquad \alpha'=4, \qquad p=0, \qquad \eta=16, \qquad \eta'=8,$$

whence $p'=1$, and we have a double curve $G+H+C_8^1$ and a bitangent developable $G+H+E_8^1$.

There are two chords PX, PY of C which pass through P and lie on Ω; these are double generators of R_2^{16}. There are two other generators of R_2^{16} passing through P; they lie in the plane containing the two tangents of C at P. C_8^1 has two double points on G and meets it in two further points; E_8^1 has two double planes and also two simple planes through G. Similarly for H.

195. Consider again the normal surface F in [7]; let us take a line l lying in the solid containing a pair of generators g, g' and a line m lying in the solid containing another pair of generators h, h'. Choose S to be the solid lm: the projected surface in Σ has two double generators G and H; the intersections of Σ with the [5]'s Sgg' and Shh' respectively.

The chords of F meeting S meet F in the four generators g, g', h, h' and a curve C_{16} meeting each generator in four points. S meets M_5^6 in l, m and an elliptic quartic ϑ_4^1 having l and m as chords. Since there are eight tangents of C_{16} meeting ϑ_4^1 it is a C_{16}^5, which has four double points. The chords of F passing through the intersections of l and ϑ_4^1 meet F in points common to C_{16}^5 and g or g'; the other four intersections of C_{16}^5 with g and g' are associated in pairs with two of the double points of C_{16}^5.

Hence on projection we obtain a surface f whose double curve is $G+H+C_8^1$; C_8^1 has two double points on G and two double points on H, meeting each of G and H in two further points. The surface is generated by a (1, 1) correspondence between two twisted cubics, the correspondence being specialised to give the double generators.

196. If the quadric containing C is also made to contain the line PQ we have a particular ruled surface for which the double generators G and H intersect. Their point of intersection is a quadruple point of C_8^1 which meets each of them in two further points; the plane containing them is a quadruple plane of E_8^1, which has two further planes passing through each of them.

In order to obtain this surface by projection we take the normal surface in [7] with a directrix conic Γ; take a line l in the solid determined by a pair of generators g, g' and a line m in the solid determined by another pair of generators h, h'. Then project from the solid S containing l and m. We have on projection a surface with two coplanar double generators; their plane meets the surface further in a conic and is the intersection of Σ with the [6] containing S, g, g', h, h' and Γ.

To generate this surface we take a conic and a rational skew quartic in (1, 1) correspondence; the points in which the plane of the conic meets the quartic fall into two pairs, and the pair of points of the conic corresponding to either of these pairs is given by the intersections of the conic with the line joining the pair.

197. Let us project a rational normal sextic in [6] from a point on one of its chords. We obtain a rational sextic in [5] with a double point P. A quintic ruled surface which contains the chord of the normal curve gives on projection a quartic ruled surface with ∞^1 directrix conics; each of these conics meets the projected curve twice, one of them passing through P.

Now let us project this curve on to a [4]; the point of projection is to be chosen in the plane of one of the conics of the quartic surface and also on the chord of the curve which lies in that plane. We obtain in [4] a rational sextic C with two double points P and Q; there is a quartic ruled surface containing the curve, with a double line passing through Q.

There are ∞^3 quadrics containing C, so that there are ∞^1 containing the quartic ruled surface; let us regard one of these latter quadrics as a prime section of Ω.

The chords of C which lie on Ω form the quartic surface R_2^4 and a ruled surface R_2^{12} on which C is a triple curve. Through P there pass two chords of C, PX and PY, which lie on Ω; these are double generators of R_2^{12}. Similarly we have QZ and QT, but these are common generators of R_2^4 and R_2^{12}. The plane of the tangents to C at P meets Ω in a generator of R_2^4 and a generator of R_2^{12}; the plane of the tangents to C at Q meets Ω in two generators of R_2^{12}.

The twelve points of C at which two generators of R_2^{12} coincide include Q counted four times, so that there are eight other points. There are six tangents of C belonging to R_2^{12}, so that we can deduce that the prime sections of R_2^{12} are rational curves. We have thus in [3] a ruled surface whose double curve is $G+H+C_2+C_6^0$ and bitangent developable $G+H+E_2+E_6^0$. H lies in the plane of C_2; C_6^0 passes through the intersections of H with C_2 and meets H in two further points; C_2 and C_6^0 have two further intersections. G meets C_2; it passes through two double points of C_6^0 and meets C_6^0 in one further point.

198. Take an involution of pairs of generators of F; we then have, through any directrix quartic E, a cubic ruled surface with a directrix line λ. Take a line l meeting λ and lying in the solid containing the pair of generators g, g'; this being a pair of the involution. There is a point of the plane $l\lambda$ which is not on either of the lines l or λ and through which passes a chord of F*; we can then take a line m through this point which lies in the solid containing a pair of generators h, h' (not belonging to the involution). Let us project from the solid S containing λ, l and m.

S meets $M_5{}^6$ in l, λ, m and a cubic $\vartheta_3{}^0$ meeting l and having λ and m as chords. The chords of F which meet S meet F in g, g', h, h', E and a curve C_{12} which meets every generator in three points; since there are six tangents of C_{12} meeting $\vartheta_3{}^0$ it is a $C_{12}{}^2$ and therefore has two double points. $C_{12}{}^2$ has six intersections with E; four of these are accounted for by the chords of F passing through the intersections of λ and $\vartheta_3{}^0$. The other two are associated with the points where E is met by the generators which are paired with h and h' in the involution and with points in which $C_{12}{}^2$ meets h and h'. The remaining intersections of $C_{12}{}^2$ with h and h' are accounted for by the chords of F passing through the intersections of m and $\vartheta_3{}^0$. There is also a chord of F passing through the point common to l and $\vartheta_3{}^0$, this accounts for an intersection of $C_{12}{}^2$ with each of g and g'; the other intersections of $C_{12}{}^2$ with these generators are associated with its double points. We thus obtain in Σ a surface with a double curve precisely as in the last article.

To generate this surface we take a conic and a twisted cubic in (1, 2) correspondence with a united point. The points of the conic which correspond to the other two points in which the cubic meets its plane are the intersections of the conic with the line joining these points. Also there is a point of the conic for which the pair of corresponding points on the cubic consists of the ends of the chord through this point. The planes of the pairs of generators which intersect in the points of the conic are the tangent planes of a quadric cone. Hence the bitangent developable is $G+H+E_2+E_6{}^0$.

199. Given any chord of a rational normal sextic there are ∞^1 quintic ruled surfaces which contain it. Through each point of the chord there pass ∞^1 cubic curves on each of these ruled surfaces, and each cubic curve meets the normal sextic in two points. From any point on any chord of the curve we can obtain any other chord of the curve; given any two chords of the curve, through any point of either we have a cubic curve meeting the other in its two intersections with the curve. It will be possible to choose the pair of chords and the points on them so that the

* Cf. § 187.

solids containing the two cubic curves have a plane in common. Then project on to a [4] from the line joining the points in which the cubic curves meet the chords. We obtain a rational sextic C with two double points P and Q. There are two quartic ruled surfaces composed of chords of C, each of these surfaces having a double line; one double line passes through P and the other through Q, and the two double lines intersect.

There are ∞^1 quadric threefolds containing each ruled surface; these two systems are both contained in the system of ∞^2 quadrics which contain C and the intersection of the double lines of the two surfaces. Hence there is a quadric containing both the ruled surfaces; let us regard this quadric as a prime section of Ω.

The chords of C which lie on Ω form three ruled surfaces; a ruled surface R_2^8 on which C is a double curve, a quartic ruled surface R_2^4 with a double line through P and a quartic ruled surface S_2^4 with a double line through Q. The two chords PX, PY of C, which pass through P and lie on Ω, are common generators of R_2^8 and R_2^4, while the plane of the two tangents of C at P meets Ω in two lines, one of which is a generator of R_2^8 and the other of S_2^4. Similarly, the two chords QZ, QT of C which pass through Q and lie on Ω are common generators of R_2^8 and S_2^4, while the plane of the two tangents of C at Q meets Ω in two lines, one of which is a generator of R_2^8 and the other of R_2^4. There is another generator common to R_2^8 and R_2^4 and another common to R_2^8 and S_2^4; R_2^4 and S_2^4 also have a generator in common. There are four points of C at which the two generators of R_2^8 coincide, while there are four tangents of C which are generators of R_2^8; whence the prime sections of R_2^8 are rational curves.

We thus have in [3] a ruled surface whose double curve is $G+H+C_2+D_2+C_4^0$ and bitangent developable $G+H+E_2+F_2+E_4^0$.

The plane of C_2 contains G; C_4^0 passes through the intersections of C_2 and G, meeting each of G and C_2 once further. The plane of D_2 contains H; C_4^0 passes through the intersections of D_2 and H, meeting each of H and D_2 once further. C_2 and D_2 have one intersection. There are similar statements for the bitangent developable.

200. Take two pairs of generators g, g' and h, h' of the normal surface F in [7]. An involution containing the pair gg' gives an axis λ of a directrix quartic E, while another involution containing the pair hh' gives an axis μ of another directrix quartic E'. We take the common pair of the two involutions to be the generators through the two intersections of E and E' and take λ and μ to intersect in a point of the common chord of E and E'.

The [5] $\lambda\mu gg'$ meets the [5] $\lambda\mu hh'$ in a [3] S; S contains a line l in the [3] gg' and a line m in the [3] hh'. We project from S on to Σ. S meets

M_5^6 in the four lines λ, μ, l, m and a conic ϑ_2 which meets each of these lines once. l meets λ and m meets μ.

The chords of F which meet S meet F in g, g', h, h', E, E' and a curve C_8 meeting every generator in two points. There are four tangents of C_8 meeting ϑ_2 so that it is an elliptic curve without double points. It meets E in four points; two of these are accounted for by the chord of F passing through the intersection of ϑ_2 and λ; the others are associated with the points in which E is met by the generators corresponding to h and h' in the first involution and with intersections of C_8 with h and h'. Similarly for the intersections of C_8 with E'. On projection we have in Σ a surface whose double curve is $G+H+C_2+D_2+C_4^0$ precisely as in the last article.

To generate this surface we place two conics C_2 and D_2 in (2, 2) correspondence with a doubly united point. To the other point in which C_2 meets the plane of D_2 correspond a pair of points of D_2 collinear with it, and to the second point in which D_2 meets the plane of C_2 correspond a pair of points of C_2 collinear with it. The planes joining the points of either conic to the pairs of points of the other conic which correspond to them are the tangent planes of a quadric cone. We thus have a bitangent developable $G+H+E_2+F_2+E_4^0$.

201. We now consider the curve C on Ω of the type II (D); we have a rational sextic in [4] with a triple point P—the projection of a normal sextic from a line in one of its trisecant planes. The chords of C form a locus M_3^7 on which C is a quadruple curve and P a sextuple point.

The chords of C which lie on Ω form a ruled surface R_2^{14}, the intersection of Ω with M_3^7; there are no lines through P lying on Ω and meeting C again but there are six generators of R_2^{14} passing through P, viz. the lines in which Ω is met by the three planes containing the pairs of tangents of C at P.

There are apparently twenty-four points of C at which two of the four generators of R_2^{14} coincide; but these include P counted twelve times*. There are eight tangents of C which are generators of R_2^{14}, and we deduce that the prime sections of R_2^{14} are rational curves. We have in [3] a ruled surface whose double curve is $3G+C_7^0$ and bitangent developable $3G+E_7^0$; the triple generator G being represented on Ω by the point P. G meets C_7^0 in six points, while six planes of E_7^0 pass through G.

202. Take now the normal surface F in [7], and let S be chosen to lie in the [5] containing three generators g_1, g_2, g_3. The solids containing the pairs of generators g_2g_3, g_3g_1, g_1g_2 meet S in lines l_1, l_2, l_3 respectively. The projected surface has a triple generator G, the intersection of Σ with the [5] containing S, g_1, g_2, g_3.

* There are three different branches of C passing through P.

The curves Δ meet g_1, g_2, g_3 in related ranges, so that the solids K containing them meet the [5] containing the three generators in the planes of a V_3^3. Thus S meets the M_4^4 formed by the solids K in a cubic curve ϑ_3^0; it meets M_5^6 in ϑ_3^0, l_1, l_2, l_3, and l_1, l_2, l_3 are chords of ϑ_3^0.

The chords of F which meet S meet F in the generators g_1, g_2, g_3 each counted twice and in a curve C_{14} meeting each generator of F four times. There are eight tangents of C_{14} meeting ϑ_3^0, so that it is a C_{14}^3 and has no double points. A chord of F through an intersection of ϑ_3^0 and l_1 meets F in two points on C_{14}^3, one of which is on g_2 and the other on g_3. Hence on projection we have a surface f with a double curve $3G+C_7^0$; G meets C_7^0 in six points.

To generate this surface we take two rational plane cubics in (1, 1) correspondence, there being three pairs of corresponding points on the line of intersection of their planes.

Surfaces with a directrix line which is not a generator

203. Consider on Ω a curve C of the type III (A); it lies in the tangent prime at a point O, meeting every plane ϖ through O in five points and every plane ρ through O in one point. Then we have in [3] a ruled surface with a directrix line R; through every point of R there pass five generators, while any plane through R contains one generator.

Any plane ρ of Ω meets the tangent prime at O in a line, and the plane ϖ containing this line joins it to O; all the ten chords of C meeting the line are contained in this plane ϖ. Thus the double curve of the ruled surface in [3] is its directrix R counted ten times.

A plane ϖ of Ω meets the tangent prime at O in a line which is met by ten chords of C. The chords of C lying on Ω form a ruled surface, and the genus of the prime sections of the ruled surface is found to be three as in former instances. Hence the surface in [3] has a bitangent developable E_{10}^3.

The four trisecants of C are all joined to O by ϖ-planes; the ρ-planes through these trisecants represent four planes which are triple planes of E_{10}^3 and tritangent planes of the ruled surface.

Dually, for a curve C of the type III (B), we have a double curve C_{10}^3 with four triple points and a bitangent developable $10R$.

204. To obtain the first of these surfaces by projection, we take the normal surface F in [7] and project from a solid S which lies in a [5] containing a rational quintic curve of F (there are ∞^5 such curves on F). Then the [5] meets Σ in a line R which is a directrix of f; through any point of R there pass five generators, while any plane through R contains one generator. The only chords of F which meet S are those of the quintic curve, we thus have a $\vartheta_6{}^3$ in S. These chords meet F in the quintic curve counted four times, four of them passing through each point of the curve.

To generate f we take a twisted cubic and one of its chords, placing them in (5, 1) correspondence with two united points.

To obtain the second surface we must project the normal surface in [7] which has a directrix line λ. Projecting on to Σ from a solid S we obtain a surface f with a directrix line R—the intersection of Σ with the [5] $S\lambda$; through each point of R there passes one generator, while every plane through R contains five generators. To generate f we take a line and a rational quintic in (1, 1) correspondence.

The chords of this surface F also form an $M_5{}^6$ meeting S in a $\vartheta_6{}^3$. Also the tangent solids of F meet an arbitrary [5] in the tangents of a rational normal quintic, so that they form an $M_4{}^8$. We have on F a curve $C_{20}{}^9$, eight of whose tangents meet $\vartheta_6{}^3$; it has twelve double points which lie three in each of four planes which meet S in lines. Thus the double curve of the projected surface is a $C_{10}{}^3$ with four triple points.

205. Take now a curve C on Ω of the type III (C). The ρ-planes through O cut out a $g_2{}^1$ on C; of the eight tangents of C which lie on Ω two lie in ρ-planes and the other six in ϖ-planes. We find that the ruled surface in [3] has a double curve $6R+C_4{}^0$ and a bitangent developable $R+E_9{}^1$. R is a trisecant of $C_4{}^0$; its three intersections with $C_4{}^0$ are represented on Ω by the ϖ-planes which contain the chords of C passing through O. Similarly, $E_9{}^1$ has three planes passing through R. Also $E_9{}^1$ has four triple planes; these are represented on Ω by the ρ-planes through the four trisecants of C, which are all joined to O by ϖ-planes.

To obtain this surface by projection we choose the solid S to meet a [4] containing a directrix quartic E of the normal surface F in a plane. Then the [5] containing S and E meets Σ in a directrix R of f; through any point of R there pass four generators, while any plane through R contains two generators.

The chords of E meet S in an elliptic cubic $\vartheta_3{}^1$, there are three of the chords passing through each point of E. The chords of F meet S in $\vartheta_3{}^1$ and a twisted cubic $\vartheta_3{}^0$ meeting $\vartheta_3{}^1$ in three points. These chords meet F in E counted three times and a rational curve $C_8{}^0$ meeting each generator of F once only; there are six tangents of E meeting $\vartheta_3{}^1$ and two tangents of $C_8{}^0$ meeting $\vartheta_3{}^0$. $C_8{}^0$ has six intersections with E; these are accounted for by the three chords of F through the intersections of $\vartheta_3{}^1$ and $\vartheta_3{}^0$. Hence, on projection, the double curve of f is $6R+C_4{}^0$, R being a trisecant of $C_4{}^0$. The surface has four tritangent planes since S meets four of the solids K.

To generate f we take a line and a twisted cubic with one intersection, placing them in (1, 4) correspondence with a united point.

206. When C is of the type III (D) we have in [3] a ruled surface whose double curve is $R+C_9{}^1$ and bitangent developable $6R+E_4{}^0$; R is a trisecant of $C_9{}^1$, which has four triple points, and there are three planes of $E_4{}^0$ passing through R.

To obtain this surface by projection we take the normal surface F in [7] which has a directrix conic Γ, and project from a solid S which meets the plane of Γ in a point O. Then the [5] $S\Gamma$ meets Σ in a line R which is a directrix of f; through any point of R there pass two generators, while any plane through R contains four generators.

The chords of F form an $M_5{}^6$ on which the plane of Γ is a triple plane*, and S meets $M_5{}^6$ in an elliptic sextic $\vartheta_6{}^1$ with a triple point at O. The chords which meet S meet F in Γ and a curve C_{18} meeting every generator of F in three points; there are two tangents of Γ passing through O and six tangents of C_{18} meeting $\vartheta_6{}^1$. Thus C_{18} is of genus 4, and has twelve double points; these lie three in each of four planes, each plane meeting S in a line. C_{18} has six intersections with Γ, these lie on three lines through O.

Hence on projection we have in Σ a ruled surface f whose double curve is $R+C_9{}^1$; $C_9{}^1$ has four triple points and meets R three times.

This surface f is generated by a line and a rational quartic in (1, 2) correspondence. The joins of the pairs of points of the quartic which correspond to the points of the line form a cubic ruled surface; thus we have a developable of the fourth class formed by the bitangent planes of the surface which do not pass through R. There are three planes of this developable passing through R since there are three generators of the cubic ruled surface meeting R.

207. Any prime section $C_6{}^0$ of F meets Γ in two points; let us take a $g_2{}^1$ on $C_6{}^0$ containing this pair of points; then we have a quintic ruled surface with a directrix conic γ meeting the plane of Γ in a point O. Let us choose S to contain γ. Then S meets $M_5{}^6$ in γ and a rational quartic $\vartheta_4{}^0$ having a double point at O, $\vartheta_4{}^0$ meeting γ in two other points.

* The equations of F can be put in the form

$$\frac{x_0}{x_1}=\frac{x_1}{x_2}=\frac{x_2}{x_3}=\frac{x_3}{x_4}=\frac{x_5}{x_6}=\frac{x_6}{x_7},$$

and the chords form the $M_5{}^6$

$$\left\|\begin{matrix} x_0 & x_1 & x_2 & x_5 \\ x_1 & x_2 & x_3 & x_6 \\ x_2 & x_3 & x_4 & x_7 \end{matrix}\right\| = 0.$$

A plane meeting the plane of Γ meets $M_5{}^6$ in three further points, since

$$\left\|\begin{matrix} \alpha x_0' + \beta x_0'' & \alpha x_1' + \beta x_1'' & \alpha x_2' + \beta x_2'' & \alpha x_5' + \beta x_5'' + \gamma\xi_5 \\ \alpha x_1' + \beta x_1'' & \alpha x_2' + \beta x_2'' & \alpha x_3' + \beta x_3'' & \alpha x_6' + \beta x_6'' + \gamma\xi_6 \\ \alpha x_2' + \beta x_2'' & \alpha x_3' + \beta x_3'' & \alpha x_4' + \beta x_4'' & \alpha x_7' + \beta x_7'' + \gamma\xi_7 \end{matrix}\right\| = 0$$

has three solutions in $\alpha:\beta:\gamma$ other than $\alpha=\beta=0$.

The chords of F which meet S meet F in Γ, $C_6{}^0$ and a curve C_{12} meeting each generator in two points. There are two tangents of Γ passing through O and two tangents of $C_6{}^0$ meeting γ; so that there are four tangents of C_{12} meeting $\vartheta_4{}^0$. Hence C_{12} is an elliptic curve and has four double points. C_{12} meets $C_6{}^0$ in twelve points; four of these are accounted for by the chords of F through the two intersections (other than O) of γ and $\vartheta_4{}^0$; the rest are associated in pairs with the double points of C_{12}.

On projection we have in Σ a surface f whose double curve is $R+C_3{}^0+C_6{}^0$. $C_6{}^0$ has four double points, through all of which $C_3{}^0$ passes; these two curves have two other intersections. R meets $C_3{}^0$ once and $C_6{}^0$ twice.

The surface is generated by a line R and a twisted cubic $C_3{}^0$ with one intersection, these being in (2, 2) correspondence with a doubly united point. The pairs of points of the cubic corresponding to the points on the line give chords of the cubic which form a quartic ruled surface, one generator of this surface meeting the line in the point which gives rise to it. Hence the bitangent planes of the surface which do not pass through R form a rational developable $E_4{}^0$, three of whose planes pass through R.

We have also the dual surface whose double curve is $6R+C_4{}^0$ and bitangent developable $R+E_3{}^0+E_6{}^0$. To generate this we take a line R and a twisted cubic in (1, 4) correspondence with a united point; but now the $g_4{}^1$ on the cubic is such that each of its sets is made up of two pairs of an involution. The planes joining R to the pairs of points of this involution give the developable $E_3{}^0$, one of whose planes passes through R.

208. Consider now a normal sextic ruled surface F in [7] and two of its prime sections. Suppose that we have an involution of pairs of generators of F, thus obtaining a quintic ruled surface through one prime section, while another involution of pairs of generators gives similarly a quintic ruled surface through the other prime section. Let us suppose further that the directrix conics of these two quintic surfaces have two intersections; in what circumstances can the solid S containing the planes of these two conics be chosen as a solid from which we can project F on to Σ?

The restriction on S is that it must not meet F; hence we immediately conclude that the two involutions must be different and that the solid containing the pair of generators common to them necessarily passes through one of the two intersections of the conics. Through the other intersection O there will pass two chords of F, so that the four generators of F so determined all meet the same plane and lie in a [6]. Hence F has a directrix conic Γ, the plane of Γ being that of the two chords through O, and S meets the plane of Γ in O.

Taking then the normal surface with a directrix conic Γ let us choose S in this way; it meets the plane of Γ in O and contains two conics γ and δ which pass through O and have another intersection. S meets M_5^6 further in a third conic ϑ_2, which also passes through O and meets γ and δ each in one other point. The chords of F meeting S meet F in Γ and three prime sections; on projection we have a surface f whose double curve consists of a directrix R and three twisted cubics; R meets all the twisted cubics which have four points in common, any two of them having a further intersection. The bitangent developable is again $6R+E_4^0$.

We have also the dual surface whose double curve is $6R+C_4^0$; the bitangent developable consisting of the pencil of planes through R and three cubic developables. This is also generated by a line R and a twisted cubic in (1, 4) correspondence with a united point; but now the g_4^1 on the cubic is such that each of its sets is made up of pairs of three different involutions. If $a_1a_2a_3a_4$ typifies a set of the g_4^1 then a_1a_2, a_3a_4 are pairs of one involution; a_1a_3, a_2a_4 are pairs of another and a_1a_4, a_2a_3 are pairs of a third. The planes joining the points of R to the pairs of any involution which correspond to them form a cubic developable with a plane passing through R.

209. We now consider a curve C of the type III (E); two of its chords pass through O and it has a double point P; it meets every ϖ-plane through O in four points and every ρ-plane through O in two points. The ρ-planes cut out a g_2^1 on C, the two points on the different branches of C at P forming a pair of this g_2^1. Hence the chords of C lying in the ρ-planes form a quartic ruled surface. An arbitrary plane ρ meets the [4] containing C in a line and the ϖ-plane containing this line joins it to O; this contains six chords of C meeting the line; the other three are generators of the quartic ruled surface. We thus have in [3] a double curve $6R+G+C_3^0$. There is a generator of the quartic ruled surface through P, and the two chords of C passing through O are also generators of this surface; hence C_3^0 meets G once and R twice.

The chords of C which lie in the ϖ-planes form a ruled surface R_2^{14} on which C is a triple curve, there are six tangents of C which are generators of this surface. There are twelve points of C at which two of the three generators of R_2^{14} coincide (these do not include P) so that the prime sections of R_2^{14} are elliptic curves. An arbitrary plane ϖ meets the [4] containing C in a line; one chord of C meeting this line is contained in the ρ-plane joining it to O, the other eight are all generators of R_2^{14}. Hence the surface in [3] has a bitangent developable $R+G+E_8^1$.

The two chords of C which lie on Ω and pass through P are double generators of R_2^{14}; there is another generator of R_2^{14} passing through P. Hence G lies in two double planes and one ordinary plane of E_8^1.

Also R is an axis of $E_8{}^1$; the two planes of $E_8{}^1$ through R are represented on Ω by the ρ-planes containing the two chords of C which pass through O. Again, the two trisecants of C are joined to O by ϖ-planes, so that $E_8{}^1$ has two triple planes represented on Ω by the ρ-planes through these trisecants.

210. To obtain this last surface by projection we choose S to meet the [4] containing a directrix quartic E of the general normal surface F in a plane; the chords of E meet this plane in an elliptic cubic $\vartheta_3{}^1$. But further, S is so chosen that it lies in a [5] with a pair of generators g, g'; the chord of E, joining the points where it is met by g and g', meets $\vartheta_3{}^1$. S meets the solid containing g and g' in a line l meeting $\vartheta_3{}^1$. It meets $M_5{}^6$ in $\vartheta_3{}^1$, l and a conic ϑ_2, meeting l once and $\vartheta_3{}^1$ twice. The chords of F which meet S meet F in the quartic E counted three times, g, g' and a prime section $C_6{}^0$. The intersections of $C_6{}^0$ with g and g' lie on the chord of F through the intersection of l and ϑ_2; the four intersections of $C_6{}^0$ and E lie in pairs on the chords of F through the intersections of $\vartheta_3{}^1$ and ϑ_2. Hence on projection we have a surface with a double curve $6R+G+C_3{}^0$ precisely as in the last article.

To generate f we take a line R and a twisted cubic in (1, 4) correspondence with a united point; one of the points of the line gives rise to four points of the cubic which include the two intersections of the cubic with the chord G through it.

211. If we have on Ω a curve C of the type III (F) we have in [3] a ruled surface whose double curve is $R+G+C_8{}^1$ and bitangent developable $6R+G+E_3{}^0$. R and G intersect; $C_8{}^1$ has two triple points, it has also two double points which lie on G, G meeting it in a further point; R is a chord of $C_8{}^1$. There is a plane of $E_3{}^0$ passing through G and there are two planes of $E_3{}^0$ passing through R.

In order to obtain this surface by projection we take the normal surface F with a directrix conic Γ, and project from a solid S which meets the plane of Γ in a point O. But here S is further chosen to lie in a [5] with two generators g, g' of F. Since this [5] is not to be the same as the [5] through S and Γ the two points in which Γ is met by g and g' must lie on a line through O. The solid gg' meets S in a line l passing through O.

S meets $M_5{}^6$ in l and an elliptic quintic $\vartheta_5{}^1$ with a double point at O, $\vartheta_5{}^1$ meeting l again. The chords of F which meet S meet F in Γ, g, g' and C_{16}, where C_{16} meets every generator in three points. There are six tangents of C_{16} meeting $\vartheta_5{}^1$, so that it is of genus 4; it has eight double points. Six of these double points lie three in each of two planes meeting S in lines; if A is either of the others then we have two chords AB and AC of C_{16} meeting $\vartheta_5{}^1$; the chord BC meets l, B being on g and C on g'. Thus we account for two intersections of C_{16} with each of g and g'; the remaining pair is given by the chord of F through the intersection of l and $\vartheta_5{}^1$. C_{16} meets Γ in four points which lie on two lines through O. Hence on projection we have in Σ a surface f with a double curve $R+G+C_8{}^1$ as required.

To generate f we take a line and a rational quartic in (1, 2) correspondence; one point of the line giving rise to a pair of points of the quartic collinear with it. The joins of the pairs of points on the quartic form a cubic ruled surface, one generator of which passes through the point of the line which gives rise to it; hence the bitangent planes of the surface which do not pass through the line or the double generator form a developable of the third class $E_3{}^0$, two of whose planes pass through the line. We have a bitangent developable $6R+G+E_3{}^0$.

212. Take a point O in the plane of Γ; then a line l passing through O and lying in the solid which contains a pair of generators g, g' meeting Γ in a pair of points collinear with O; then a conic ϑ_2 passing through O, this being the directrix conic of the quintic ruled surface determined by an involution on a prime section $C_6{}^0$ of F. Project on to Σ from the solid S containing l and ϑ_2.

S meets $M_5{}^6$ in l, ϑ_2 and a twisted cubic $\vartheta_3{}^0$; $\vartheta_3{}^0$ passes through O, meeting l once again and ϑ_2 twice again. The chords of F meeting S meet F in Γ, g, g', $C_6{}^0$ and an elliptic curve $C_{10}{}^1$, four of whose tangents meet $\vartheta_3{}^0$; $C_{10}{}^1$ meeting every generator in two points. It meets Γ twice and $C_6{}^0$ ten times, having two double points.

A pair of intersections of $C_{10}{}^1$ with g and g' are given by the chord of F through the intersection (other than O) of l and $\vartheta_3{}^0$; the other pair is associated with the intersections of $C_6{}^0$ with g and g' and with two intersections of $C_6{}^0$ with $C_{10}{}^1$. Four other intersections of $C_6{}^0$ and $C_{10}{}^1$ are given by the chords of F passing through the two intersections (other than O) of ϑ_2 and $\vartheta_3{}^0$; the remaining four are associated in pairs with the two double points of $C_{10}{}^1$.

Hence on projection we have a surface f with a double curve $R+G+C_3{}^0+C_5{}^0$. R meets each of G, $C_3{}^0$ and $C_5{}^0$; G is a chord of $C_3{}^0$ and $C_5{}^0$ passes through their two intersections, meeting G in one other point; $C_5{}^0$ has two double points through each of which $C_3{}^0$ passes, $C_3{}^0$ and $C_5{}^0$ having two further intersections.

The surface is generated by a line R and a twisted cubic $C_3{}^0$ in (2, 2) correspondence with a doubly united point; one point of the line giving rise to the intersections of $C_3{}^0$ with the chord which passes through it.

The lines joining the pairs of points of the cubic form a quartic ruled surface, there being two generators of this surface passing through points of the line which give rise to them. Hence the bitangent planes of the surface which do not pass through R or G form a developable $E_3{}^0$, two of whose planes pass through R. We have thus a bitangent developable $6R+G+E_3{}^0$; two planes of $E_3{}^0$ passing through R and one through G, while R and G are co-planar.

We have also the dual surface whose double curve is $6R+G+C_3{}^0$ and bitangent developable $R+G+E_3{}^0+E_5{}^0$. To generate this surface we take a line R and a twisted cubic in (1, 4) correspondence with a united point, one of the points of the line giving rise to four points of the cubic which include the two intersections of the cubic with the chord G through it. But here the $g_4{}^1$ on the cubic is such that each of its sets consists of two sets of an involution (which does not contain the extremities of this chord as a pair of corresponding points). The joins of the pairs of the involution give a regulus, and there is a (1, 2) correspondence between the points of R and the lines of this regulus, there being one united element. We thus have a developable $E_3{}^0$, two of whose planes pass through G and one through R.

213. Now take S to meet the plane of Γ in a point O and to contain an axis λ of a directrix quartic E. The lines through O in the plane of Γ determine an involution of pairs of generators of F, while the generators of the cubic ruled surface having λ for its directrix determine another. If g, g' is the pair of generators common to these two involutions the solid gg' meets S in a line l passing through O and meeting λ.

S meets $M_5{}^6$ in λ, l and a rational quartic $\vartheta_4{}^0$ which has a double point at O and meets λ twice. The chords of F meeting S meet F in E, Γ, g, g', and an elliptic curve $C_{12}{}^1$, four of whose tangents meet $\vartheta_4{}^0$; $C_{12}{}^1$ meets every generator in two points. It has four double points, and meets Γ in four points (collinear with O in pairs) and E in eight points. Four of these intersections with E are given by the chords of F through the two intersections of λ and $\vartheta_4{}^0$; the remaining four are associated in pairs with two of the double points of $C_{12}{}^1$. The other two double points are associated with the intersections of $C_{12}{}^1$ with g and g'.

Thus on projection from S we have in Σ a surface f whose double curve is $R+G+C_2+C_6{}^0$. R meets G and is a chord of $C_6{}^0$, while G and C_2 intersect. $C_6{}^0$ has four double points, two of which are on G; the other two are on C_2, which meets $C_6{}^0$ in two other points.

To generate f we take a line R and a conic C_2 in (2, 2) correspondence; to a branch point of the correspondence on R there corresponds a branch point of the correspondence on C_2 and the line G joining these points is a double generator. The joins of the pairs of points of C_2 which correspond to the points of R touch another conic; there are two tangents of this latter passing through the point in which R meets the plane of C_2. Hence those bitangent planes of the surface which do not pass through R or G give a developable $E_3{}^0$, two of whose planes pass through R and one through G. The bitangent developable is $6R+G+E_3{}^0$.

There is also the dual surface whose double curve is $6R+G+C_3{}^0$ and bitangent developable $R+G+E_2+E_6{}^0$. To generate this surface we take a line R and a twisted cubic in (1, 4) correspondence with a united point; one of the points of R gives rise to a set of four points on the cubic which includes its intersections with the chord through this point of R. And here the $g_4{}^1$ on the cubic is such that each of its sets consists of two pairs of points of an involution, which includes the intersections of the cubic with the chord just mentioned as a pair of corresponding points. The joins of the pairs of the involution give a regulus and there is a (1, 2) correspondence with two united elements between the points of R and the lines of this regulus. We thus have a quadric cone with one of its tangent planes passing through the double generator.

214. Take again the normal surface F with a directrix conic in [7], and an involution of pairs of generators giving a quintic ruled surface through a prime section $C_6{}^0$; the directrix conic ϑ_2 of this surface meeting the plane of Γ in a point O. It is possible to take a solid S through ϑ_2 which also contains an axis λ of a directrix quartic E, where λ meets ϑ_2, and a line l through O, meeting λ, which lies in a solid containing a pair of generators g, g' of F.

S meets $M_5{}^6$ in l, λ, ϑ_2 and another conic ϕ_2 passing through O; ϕ_2 meeting ϑ_2 again and also meeting λ. The chords of F meeting S meet F in Γ, g, g', E, $C_6{}^0$ and another prime section $D_6{}^0$. It is easily seen how the mutual intersections of these curves arise; so that on projection we have a surface whose double curve is $R+G+C_2+C_3{}^0+D_3{}^0$. R meets G, $C_3{}^0$ and $D_3{}^0$, while G meets C_2 and passes through two intersections of $C_3{}^0$ and $D_3{}^0$. There are two points common to all of C_2, $C_3{}^0$, $D_3{}^0$; C_2 meeting each of $C_3{}^0$ and $D_3{}^0$ in one further point; also there is one more intersection of $C_3{}^0$ and $D_3{}^0$. We have again a bitangent developable $6R+G+E_3{}^0$.

The dual surface has a double curve $6R+G+C_3{}^0$ and a bitangent developable $R+G+E_2+E_3{}^0+F_3{}^0$. It is generated by a line R and a twisted cubic in (1, 4) correspondence with a united point; one of the points of R giving rise to four points of the cubic which include the two intersections of the cubic with the chord G through it. Here, however, the $g_4{}^1$ on the cubic is such that each of its sets consists of two pairs of points of three different involutions*. One of the involutions contains the ends of the chord G as a pair of corresponding points; this gives a developable E_2 with a plane passing through G. Each of the other two involutions gives a developable of the third class with two planes through G and one through R, and we get the same two planes through G for each of these two developables.

215. Take now a curve C of the type III (G) with two double points P and Q; it meets every ϖ-plane through O in four points and every ρ-plane through O in two points, a chord of C passing through O. The ρ-planes cut out a g_2^1 on C which includes the pairs of points on the two branches of C at P and on the two branches of C at Q. Hence the chords of C lying in the ρ-planes form a cubic ruled surface R_2^3†. The chords of C lying in the ϖ-planes through O form a ruled surface R_2^{13} on which C is a triple curve, there being six tangents of C which are generators of R_2^{13}. There are twelve points of C at which two of the three generators of R_2^{13} coincide (these do not include P or Q); so that the prime sections of R_2^{13} are elliptic curves.

A ρ-plane of Ω meets the [4] containing C in a line, and the ϖ-plane through this line joins it to O and contains six chords of C. The two other chords meeting the line are generators of R_2^3, and we have in [3] a ruled surface whose double curve is $6R+G+H+C_2$. There are generators of R_2^3 passing through P and Q, and the chord of C through O is also a generator of R_2^3. Hence C_2 meets G, H, R each in one point. G and H both meet R.

A ϖ-plane of Ω meets the [4] containing C in a line, and the ρ-plane through this line joins it to O and contains a chord of C. The other seven chords meeting the line are generators of R_2^{13}. We have then for the bitangent developable of the surface $R+G+H+E_7^1$. The two chords of C which pass through P and lie on Ω are double generators of R_2^{13}, which has also another generator passing through P. Hence there are two double planes and a simple plane of E_7^1 passing through G. Likewise there are two double planes and a simple plane of E_7^1 passing through H; there is also a plane of E_7^1 passing through R, represented on Ω by the ρ-plane which contains the chord of C passing through O.

216. We now obtain this surface by projection. We take the general normal surface F in [7] with ∞^1 directrix cubics Δ and choose the solid S to meet the [4] containing a directrix quartic E in a plane. We also suppose that there are two pairs of generators g, g' and h, h' such that each

* Cf. § 208.

† The projection of a quintic ruled surface in [6] from a line meeting two of its generators.

pair lies in a [5] with S. The solid gg' meets S in a line l and the solid hh' meets S in a line m. The chords of E meet S in the points of a plane cubic ϑ_3^1, and as we assume that the [5] containing S and E does not contain a generator of F the two lines l and m must meet ϑ_3^1. S meets M_5^6 in ϑ_3^1, l, m and a line λ, which is a transversal of l and m, meeting ϑ_3^1. The chords of F meeting S meet F in E counted three times, g, g', h, h' and another directrix quartic E'. Hence we have on projection a surface f with a double curve $6R+G+H+C_2$; C_2 meeting G, H and R, while G and H both meet R.

To generate f we take a line R and a twisted cubic in (1, 4) correspondence with a united point. There are two points of R giving rise to sets of four points on the cubic which include the two intersections of the cubic with the chords, G and H, which pass through the respective points.

217. We have in [3] the dual surface whose double curve is $R+G+H+C_7^1$ and bitangent developable $6R+G+H+E_2$. G and H meet R, while there is a plane of E_2 passing through each of G, H and R. C_7^1 has two double points and one ordinary point on each of G and H and it also meets R.

To obtain this surface by projection we take the normal surface F with a directrix conic Γ. Take two pairs of generators g, g' and h, h', and let the chords of Γ determined by these pairs of generators meet in O. Take a line l through O lying in the solid gg' and a line m through O lying in the solid hh'; then project from a solid S containing l and m.

S meets M_5^6 in l, m and an elliptic quartic ϑ_4^1 passing through O and meeting each of l and m in a further point. The chords of F meeting S meet F in Γ, g, g', h, h' and C_{14}, this latter curve meeting every generator in three points. There are six tangents of C_{14} meeting ϑ_4^1, so that it is of genus 4; hence it has four double points. C_{14} meets Γ in two points collinear with O; the chord of F through the intersection of l and ϑ_4^1 other than O passes through intersections of C_{14} with g and g'; the remaining intersections of C_{14} with g and g' are associated in pairs with two of its double points. Similarly for its intersections with h and h'.

Hence on projection we have a surface with a double curve $R+G+H+C_7^1$ precisely as required.

To generate this surface we take a line and a rational quartic in (1, 2) correspondence; two points of the line give rise to pairs of points of the quartic whose joins respectively pass through them. The joins of the pairs of points of the quartic form a cubic ruled surface, two of whose generators meet the line in the points which give rise to them; there is one other generator of the cubic ruled surface meeting the line. Hence the planes joining the points of the line to the pairs of points of the quartic which correspond to them touch a quadric cone one of whose tangent planes passes through the line. There is also a tangent plane through each of the double generators. We have a bitangent developable $6R+G+H+E_2$.

218. Consider again the surface F with a directrix conic, and take two involutions of pairs of generators; the first of these gives a pencil of lines in the plane of Γ passing through a point O, while the second, by means of any directrix quartic E, gives a cubic ruled surface with a directrix line λ. There is a pair of generators g, g' common to the two involutions; the solid containing them meets λ and passes through O. Take a solid S containing O and λ; it meets the solid gg' in a line l passing through O and meeting λ; further, we choose S to meet the solid containing another pair of generators in a line m passing through O.

S meets M_5^6 in l, m, λ and a twisted cubic ϑ_3^0 passing through O; ϑ_3^0 meets m again and meets λ twice. The chords of F meeting S meet F in Γ, g, g', h, h', E and an elliptic curve C_{10}^1 four of whose tangents meet ϑ_3^0. C_{10}^1 meets every generator in two points and has two double points; it meets Γ in two points collinear with O, and E in six points. Four of these intersections with E are accounted for by the two chords of F through the intersections of λ and ϑ_3^0; either of the others is associated with an intersection of E with h or h' and with an intersection of C_{10}^1 with h' or h respectively. The other intersections of C_{10}^1 with h and h' are on the chord of F through the intersection (other than O) of m and ϑ_3^0; the intersections of C_{10}^1 with g and g' are associated in pairs with the double points.

Hence on projection from S we obtain a surface f with a double curve $R+G+H+C_2+C_5^0$. R meets G, H and C_5^0. H is a chord of C_2, and C_5^0 passes through their intersections meeting H in one other point and C_2 in two other points. G meets C_2 and passes through two double points of C_5^0.

The surface is generated by a line R and a conic C_2 in (2, 2) correspondence. To the point in which R meets the plane of C_2 corresponds a pair of points on C_2 whose join H passes through this point, while there are mutually corresponding double points on R and C_2. The joins of the pairs of points of C_2 which correspond to the points of R touch another conic; the planes joining the points of R to these pairs of points touch a quadric cone with a tangent plane passing through each of R, G and H. The bitangent developable is $6R+G+H+E_2$.

There is also in [3] the surface dual to this one whose double curve is given by $6R+G+H+C_2$ and bitangent developable by $R+G+H+E_2+E_5^0$. This surface is generated by a line R and a twisted cubic in (1, 4) correspondence as in § 216; there are two points of R giving rise to sets of four points on the cubic which include the two intersections of the cubic with the chords G and H passing through these points. But here the g_4^1 on the cubic is such that each of its sets consists of two pairs of an involution, which includes as a pair of corresponding points the intersections of the cubic with either G or H, say with G. The joins of the pairs of this involution form a regulus, and the planes joining the points of R to the corresponding pairs of the involution touch a quadric cone which has one tangent plane through G and two tangent planes through H.

219. Take an involution of pairs of generators on the normal surface F with a directrix conic Γ, and let this give a quintic ruled surface, through a prime section C_6^0 of F, whose directrix conic ϑ_2 meets the plane of Γ in a point O. Then we can choose a solid S to contain ϑ_2, to meet the solid containing a pair of generators g, g' in a line l through O and to meet the solid containing another pair of generators h, h' in a line m through O. Of course neither of the pairs g, g', h, h' need belong to the involution. S meets M_5^6 in l, m, ϑ_2 and a conic ϕ_2 which meets l and m each once and ϑ_2 twice.

The chords of F meeting S meet F in Γ, g, g', h, h', C_6^0 and an elliptic curve C_8^1 four of whose tangents meet ϕ_2. This curve meets every generator of F twice and has no double points. C_8^1 does not meet Γ, but it meets C_6^0 in eight points; four of these are given by the two chords of F through the intersections of ϑ_2 and ϕ_2. The other intersections of C_8^1 and C_6^0 are associated with the intersections of C_6^0 with g, g', h, h' and with intersections of C_8^1 with g', g, h', h (one with each). The other intersections of C_8^1 with these four generators are given by the chords of F through the intersections of ϕ_2 with l and m.

We thus have in Σ a surface f whose double curve is $R+G+H+C_3^0+C_4^0$. R meets G, H and C_3^0. G and H are chords of C_3^0; C_4^0 passes through the four intersections, meeting each of G and H in one other point and C_3^0 in two other points.

To generate this surface we take a line R and a twisted cubic C_3^0 in (2, 2) correspondence with a doubly united point; there are two points of R which give rise to pairs of points of C_3^0 on the chords G and H which pass through them. The pairs of points of C_3^0 which correspond to the points of R are joined by lines forming a quartic ruled surface; the planes joining the points of R to these lines touch a quadric cone, there being tangent planes of this cone through G, H and R. We have a bitangent developable $6R+G+H+E_2$.

We have also the dual surface whose double curve is $6R+G+H+C_2$ and bitangent developable $R+G+H+E_3^0+E_4^0$. To generate this surface we take a line R and a twisted cubic in (1, 4) correspondence giving two double generators G and H as in § 216; but here the g_4^1 on the cubic is such that each of its sets consists of two pairs of an involution, which does not contain the pair of intersections of the cubic with either G or H as a pair of corresponding points. The pairs of points of this involution give lines forming a regulus; there is thus set up a (1, 2) correspondence between the points of R and the lines of this regulus, and the planes joining the points of R to the lines of the regulus give (because of the united point) the developable $E_3{}^0$, which has a plane passing through R and two planes through each of G and H.

220. Take the surface F with a directrix conic Γ, and any two of its directrix quartics E and E'. Take an axis λ of E and an axis μ of E', these intersecting on the common chord of E and E'. Then choose a solid S containing λ and μ and meeting the plane of Γ in a point O. S also contains a line l, passing through O and meeting λ, which lies in the solid containing a pair of generators g, g', and a line m, passing through O and meeting μ, which lies in the solid containing a pair of generators h, h'. S meets $M_5{}^6$ in l, m, λ, μ and a conic ϑ_2 passing through O and meeting λ and μ. The chords of F meeting S meet F in E, E', Γ, g, g', h, h' and a prime section $C_6{}^0$. On projection from S we have in Σ a surface whose double curve is $R+C_2+D_2+G+H+C_3{}^0$. R meets G, H and $C_3{}^0$. C_2 meets G and has H for a chord, $C_3{}^0$ passing through the intersections of H with C_2 and meeting C_2 again. D_2 meets H and has G for a chord, $C_3{}^0$ passing through the intersections of G with D_2 and meeting D_2 again. C_2 and D_2 have one intersection.

There is also the dual surface whose double curve is $6R+G+H+C_2$ and bitangent developable $R+E_2+F_2+G+H+E_3{}^0$. This is generated by a line R and a twisted cubic in (1, 4) correspondence as in § 216, but here the $g_4{}^1$ on the cubic is such that each of its sets consists of two pairs of points of three different involutions. One of these involutions contains the pair of points in which G meets the cubic; the regulus arising from this involution gives, when taken with R, the developable E_2 which has a plane through G and two planes through H. Similarly another of the involutions contains the pair of points in which H meets the cubic; we have then the developable F_2 with a plane through H and two planes through G. The third involution does not contain the extremities either of G or of H; we thus have the developable $E_3{}^0$ with a plane through R and two planes through each of G and H. The planes of $E_3{}^0$ through G are the same as the planes of F_2 through G, and the planes of $E_3{}^0$ through H are the same as the planes of E_2 through H.

221. We now proceed to consider the curve C of the type III (I) on Ω; it meets every plane of Ω through O in three points and has four of its chords passing through O. The chords of C which lie in either system of planes form a ruled surface R_2^{10} on which C is a double curve, and there are four tangents of C which are generators of this ruled surface. Also there are four points of C at which the two generators of the ruled surface coincide; and the prime sections of R_2^{10} are rational curves.

Any plane of Ω meets the [4] containing C in a line, and the plane of the opposite system through this line joins it to O and contains three chords of C; there are seven other chords of C meeting the line. Hence we have in [3] a ruled surface whose double curve is $3R + C_7^0$ and bitangent developable $3R + E_7^0$. C_7^0 meets R in four points; these are represented on Ω by the ϖ-planes through the four chords of C which pass through O; similarly E_7^0 has four planes passing through R.

Of the four trisecants of C two lie in ϖ-planes and two in ρ-planes; C_7^0 has two triple points and E_7^0 two triple planes. The section of R_2^{10} by a solid is a rational curve of order 10 lying on a quadric; it meets all generators of one system in three points and all of the other system in seven points, having six double points and two triple points.

222. In order to obtain this surface by projection we take in [7] the normal surface F with ∞^1 directrix cubics and project from a solid S which meets the solid K containing one of these cubics Δ in a line l. Then S meets the M_4^4 formed by the solids K in two further points* so that the surface f in Σ has two tritangent planes not passing through its directrix. Its directrix is the line R in which Σ is met by the [5] containing S and K; through any point of R there pass three generators of F, while any plane through R contains three generators of F.

S meets M_5^6 in l and a rational quintic ϑ_5^0 of which l is the quadrisecant. There are two chords of Δ passing through any point of it and meeting l, while there are four tangents of Δ meeting l. Hence the chords of F meeting S meet F in Δ counted twice and an elliptic curve C_{14}^1, four of whose tangents meet ϑ_5^0. C_{14}^1 meets every generator of F in two points and has six double points. It meets Δ in eight points; these lie two on each of the four chords of F through the intersections of l and ϑ_5^0. The six double points lie three in each of two planes which meet S in lines.

Hence on projection we have a surface with a double curve $3R + C_7^0$; C_7^0 has two triple points and meets R four times.

This surface is generated by a line R and a twisted cubic in (1, 3) correspondence.

223. We now pass to the curve C on Ω of the type III (J); the chords of C which lie in either system of planes include one trisecant and four tangents and form a ruled surface R_2^9 whose prime sections are rational

* A [5] through S meets M_4^4 in a quartic ruled surface, and any solid through a generator of this surface meets it in two other points.

curves. The ruled surface R_2^9 has C as a double curve, the trisecant as a triple generator and also a double generator passing through the double point of C.

We have in [3] a surface whose double curve is $3R+G+C_6^0$ and bitangent developable $3R+G+E_6^0$. C_6^0 has a triple point and meets R three times; it has a double point on G and meets G in one other point. Similarly for E_6^0. R and G intersect.

To obtain the surface by projection we choose the solid S to meet the solid K containing a directrix cubic Δ of F in a line l and also to meet the solid containing a pair of generators g, g' in a line m. Since S is not to meet F, l and m must intersect, the chord of Δ through their intersection meeting Δ in its intersections with g and g'. The curves Δ meet g and g' in related ranges whose joins form a regulus; this meets m in two points, including its intersection with l. Hence there is only one solid K meeting S in a point not on l or m; so that the projected surface has one tritangent plane passing neither through its directrix nor its double generator.

S meets M_5^6 in l, m and a rational quartic ϑ_4^0 meeting m and having l as a trisecant. The chords of F meeting S meet F in Δ counted twice, g, g' and an elliptic curve C_{12}^1 four of whose tangents meet ϑ_4^0. C_{12}^1 meets every generator of F in two points and has four double points. It meets Δ in six points which lie two on each of the chords of F which pass through the three intersections of l and ϑ_4^0. The chord through the intersection of m and ϑ_4^0 gives intersections of C_{12}^1 with g and g'; the line joining the other pair of intersections does not meet ϑ_4^0 but gives two chords of F which do so, these intersecting in a double point of C_{12}^1. The remaining three double points of C_{12}^1 lie in a plane passing through a trisecant of ϑ_4^0.

Hence on projection we have a surface with a double curve $3R+G+C_6^0$, precisely as required.

To generate this surface take a line R and a twisted cubic in (1, 3) correspondence; one point of R giving rise to a triad of points on the cubic which include the two intersections with the chord G through the point.

224. When C is of the type III (K) the chords which lie in either system of planes include four tangents and form a ruled surface R_2^8; this has C for a double curve and has two double generators, one through each double point of C; there is one other generator through each of these double points. The prime sections of R_2^8 are rational curves. We have in [3] a ruled surface whose double curve is $3R+G+H+C_5^0$ and bitangent developable $3R+G+H+E_5^0$. C_5^0 has a double point and a simple point on G, while E_5^0 has a double plane and a simple plane through G; and similarly for H. R meets G and H. Also R is a chord of C_5^0; the two points of intersection are represented on Ω by the ϖ-planes which contain the two chords of C passing through O. Similarly there are two planes of $E_5{}^0$ passing through R.

To obtain this surface by projection take a line l in a solid containing a directrix cubic Δ of the normal surface F. Through a given point A of l there passes a chord of Δ; through the intersections of Δ with this chord we have a pair of generators g, g' of F, and we can take a line m through A lying in the solid containing these two generators. Similarly we have a line n meeting l in a point B and lying in the solid containing a pair of generators h, h' of F. Then take S to be the solid containing l, m and n. S meets $M_5{}^6$ in l, m, n and a cubic $\vartheta_3{}^0$ which meets m and n and has l for a chord.

The chords of F meeting S meet F in Δ counted twice, g, g', h, h' and an elliptic curve $C_{10}{}^1$, four of whose tangents meet $\vartheta_3{}^0$. $C_{10}{}^1$ meets every generator of F in two points and has two double points. $C_{10}{}^1$ meets Δ in four points; these are on the chords of F through the two intersections of l and $\vartheta_3{}^0$. The chord of F through the intersection of m and $\vartheta_3{}^0$ accounts for an intersection of $C_{10}{}^1$ with each of g and g'; the other pair of intersections is associated with a double point of $C_{10}{}^1$. Similarly for the intersections with h and h'.

Hence on projection we have a surface with a double curve as required.

To generate this surface we take a line R and a twisted cubic in (1, 3) correspondence; there are two points of R for which the corresponding triad of points on the cubic contains the two intersections with the chord through the point.

225. When C is of the type III (L) the chords which lie in either system of planes form a ruled surface $R_2{}^7$ on which C is a double curve; the prime sections of $R_2{}^7$ are rational curves. The triple point P of C represents a triple generator G of the ruled surface in [3]; the ruled surface $R_2{}^7$ has three generators passing through P.

The ruled surface in [3] has a double curve $3R+3G+C_4{}^0$ and a bitangent developable $3R+3G+E_4{}^0$. $C_4{}^0$ meets R and has G for a trisecant, while R and G intersect. $E_4{}^0$ has one plane passing through R and three planes passing through G.

The [5] containing three generators g, g', g'' of the normal surface F meets the solid containing one of its directrix cubics Δ in a plane; take S to lie in the [5] and meet the plane in a line l. The solids $g'g''$, $g''g$, gg' meet S in lines m, m', m'' which all meet l. S meets $M_5{}^6$ in l, m, m', m'' and a conic ϑ_2 meeting these four lines each in one point. There are two chords of F through any point of g, g', g'' or Δ which meet S; hence the chords of F meeting S meet F in Δ, g, g', g'' each counted twice and an elliptic curve $C_8{}^1$ four of whose tangents meet ϑ_2. $C_8{}^1$ meets every generator of F in two points and has no double points.

On projection we have a surface with a double curve $3R+3G+C_4^0$ as required.

The cubics of F meet g, g', g'' in related ranges; hence the solids K meet the [5] containing these generators in planes of a V_3^3. S meets the M_4^4 formed by these solids K in l and the conic ϑ_2; the projected surface f contains ∞^1 plane cubics whose planes pass through G; these cubics have double points at those intersections of the planes with C_4^0 which are not on G.

The surface is generated by a line R and a rational plane cubic in (1, 3) correspondence; to the point in which R meets the plane of the cubic correspond three points of the cubic collinear with it.

Surfaces with a directrix line which is also a generator

226. Take a curve C on Ω of the type IV (A); it gives in [3] a ruled surface with a directrix line R which is also a generator; through any point of R there pass four other generators, while any plane through R contains one other generator. Thus the double curve is the line R counted ten times, while the bitangent developable consists of the pencil of planes through R and a developable of the ninth class. The four trisecants of C are all contained in ϖ-planes, so that this last developable has four triple planes represented on Ω by the ρ-planes through the trisecants. The developable will then necessarily be elliptic. We have a double curve $10R$ and a bitangent developable $R+E_9^1$, where E_9^1 has four triple planes. There are three planes of E_9^1 passing through R; there is a ϖ-plane through the tangent of C at O, and these three planes of E_9^1 are represented on Ω by the ρ-planes which contain the three chords of C joining O to the other three intersections of C with the ϖ-plane through its tangent at O.

To obtain this surface by projection we choose S to lie in the [5] determined by a directrix quartic E and a generator g of the normal surface. This [5] meets Σ in a line R which is a directrix and also a generator of f; through any point of R there pass four other generators, while any plane through R contains one other generator. The surface has four tritangent planes since S meets four of the solids K. It is generated by a line and a twisted cubic with two intersections placed in (1, 4) correspondence with one united point.

227. Dually, when C is of the type IV (B), we have in [3] a ruled surface whose double curve is $R+C_9^1$ and bitangent developable $10R$; C_9^1 has R for a trisecant and has four triple points.

To obtain this surface by projection we take the normal surface F in [7] which has a directrix line λ, and then choose S to meet the plane containing λ and some generator g in a point O. The [5] joining S to λ also contains g, and meets Σ in a line R which is a directrix and also a generator of f; through any point of R there passes one other generator, while any plane through R contains four other generators.

The M_5 containing the chords of F is made up of the ∞^2 solids joining λ to the pairs of generators of F, and meets an arbitrary [5] in the chords of a rational normal quintic c_5. Hence* the chords of F form an M_5^6 which meets an arbitrary solid S in a sextic curve ϑ_6^3 of genus 3. Since the quintic curve c_5 is a triple curve on the locus of its chords, any plane joining λ to a generator is a triple plane on M_5^6. We thus have ∞^1 planes through λ forming an M_3^5 which is a triple locus on M_5^6.

The tangent solids of F all pass through λ and meet the [5] in the tangents of c_5; they thus form a locus M_4^8, there being eight of them which meet an arbitrary solid S. If, however, a line in [5] meets c_5 there are only six further tangents of c_5 meeting the line; so that if S meets a plane of M_3^5 in a point O there are only six tangent solids of F meeting S in points other than O.

Thus the solid S from which we are to project meets M_5^6 in an elliptic† sextic ϑ_6^1 with a triple point at O. The chords of F meeting S meet F in λ, g and a curve C_{18}; since there are six tangents of C_{18} meeting ϑ_6^1 it is of genus 4. It meets every generator of F in three points and λ in three points, and has twelve double points. These lie three in each of four planes containing trisecants of ϑ_6^1. The intersections of C_{18} with g are in perspective from O with its intersections with λ.

Hence on projection we have a surface f with a double curve $R+C_9^1$; C_9^1 has R for a trisecant and has four triple points.

The surface is generated by a line R and a rational quintic with one intersection, these being placed in (1, 1) correspondence without a united point.

228. Suppose now, still considering the normal surface with a directrix line, that we take the directrix conic ϑ_2 of a quintic ruled surface determined by an involution on a prime section C_6^0 of F. There is a generator of the quintic ruled surface passing through the intersection of λ and C_6^0; this meets ϑ_2 in a point O and C_6^0 again on a generator g of F. Thus O lies in

* Cf. § 95. If F is generated by a (1, 1) correspondence between λ and one of its directrix quintic curves (there are ∞^5 such curves on F) its equations can be written

$$\frac{x_0}{x_1}=\frac{x_1}{x_2}=\frac{x_2}{x_3}=\frac{x_3}{x_4}=\frac{x_4}{x_5}=\frac{x_6}{x_7},$$

and the equations of M_5^6 are

$$\left\|\begin{matrix} x_0 & x_1 & x_2 & x_3 \\ x_1 & x_2 & x_3 & x_4 \\ x_2 & x_3 & x_4 & x_5 \end{matrix}\right\| = 0.$$

† If we take a plane through a point of a rational quintic curve in [4], it meets the locus V_3^6 of § 95 in a sextic curve with a triple point at this point. This sextic curve has double points at the six remaining intersections of the plane with F_2^7, so that it is an *elliptic* curve.

the plane containing λ and g; so that if S is chosen to contain ϑ_2 it automatically meets the plane containing λ and g in a point O of ϑ_2.

S meets M_5^6 in ϑ_2 and a rational quartic ϑ_4^0 having a double point at O and meeting ϑ_2 in two other points. The chords of F which meet S meet F in λ, g, C_6^0 and an elliptic curve C_{12}^1, four of whose tangents meet ϑ_4^0; C_{12}^1 meets every generator of F in two points and λ in two points, and has four double points. Its intersections with λ are joined by lines through O to its intersections with g. It meets C_6^0 in twelve points; four of these are given by the chords of F through the two intersections (other than O) of ϑ_2 and ϑ_4^0; the remaining ones fall into four pairs associated with the four double points of C_{12}^1.

On projection we have a surface f with a double curve $R+C_3^0+C_6^0$. R meets C_3^0 and is a chord of C_6^0; C_6^0 has four double points through all of which C_3^0 passes, and it meets C_3^0 in two other points.

The surface is generated by a line R and a twisted cubic C_3^0 in (2, 1) correspondence with a united point.

We have also in [3] the dual surface whose double curve is $10R$ and bitangent developable $R+E_3^0+E_6^0$. This is generated by a line R and a twisted cubic placed in (1, 4) correspondence with one united point, R being a chord of the cubic; but here the g_4^1 on the cubic is such that each of its sets consists of two pairs of an involution. The joins of pairs of this involution form a regulus, and we have a (1, 2) correspondence between the points of R and the lines of this regulus; hence, because of the united point, the planes joining the points of R to the corresponding lines of the regulus form a developable E_3^0, one of whose planes passes through R.

229. We have seen that the directrix conics of all the quintic ruled surfaces given by involutions on prime sections of F necessarily meet one of the planes of M_3^5. Let us enquire whether we can project from a solid S containing two of these conics ϑ_2 and ϕ_2. ϑ_2 meets the plane containing λ and a generator g in a point; hence, since the directrix R of the surface in Σ is to be a simple and not a double generator of f, ϕ_2 must meet the same plane in a point. Moreover, since S is not to meet F, ϑ_2 and ϕ_2 must meet this plane in the same point O. ϑ_2 and ϕ_2 have a second intersection through which passes a common generator of the two quintic ruled surfaces to which they belong.

S meets M_5^6 in ϑ_2, ϕ_2 and a third conic ψ_2 passing through O and meeting each of ϑ_2 and ϕ_2 in one further point. The chords of F meeting S meet F in λ, g and three prime sections B_6^0, C_6^0, D_6^0. Projecting from S we obtain in Σ a surface with a double curve $R+B_3^0+C_3^0+D_3^0$. R meets each cubic in one point; there are four points common to all the cubics, while any two of them have one further intersection.

There is also in [3] the dual surface whose double curve is $10R$ and bitangent developable $R+E_3^0+F_3^0+G_3^0$. To generate this we take a line R and a twisted cubic meeting it in two points and place them in (1, 4) correspondence with one united point; but here the g_4^1 on the cubic is such that each of its sets is made up of two pairs of three different involutions. Any one of the involutions gives ∞^1 chords of the cubic forming a regulus, and there is thus a (1, 2) correspondence between the points of R and the lines of this regulus. We thus have, because of the united point, three developables of the third class, each of which has a plane passing through R.

230. Take now a curve C on Ω of the type IV (C). The ρ-planes through O cut out a g_2^1 on C, so that the ruled surface which is formed by those chords of C lying in the ρ-planes and not passing through O is rational. There are six tangents of C, other than that at O, which lie on Ω*; of these two are in ρ-planes and four in ϖ-planes. Those chords of C which lie in ϖ-planes and do not pass through O form a ruled surface on which C is a double curve, and there are four points of C at which the two generators of this ruled surface coincide. The prime sections of this ruled surface are rational curves†.

A general plane ρ of Ω meets the [4] containing C in a line; the ϖ-plane through this line joins it to O and contains six chords of C; there are four other chords of C meeting the line. Hence the double curve of the ruled surface in [3] is $6R+C_4^0$. R is a trisecant of C_4^0; two of the intersections are represented on Ω by the ϖ-planes through the two trisecants of C which pass through O, the remaining one is represented on Ω by the ϖ-plane through that chord of C which lies in the ρ-plane containing the tangent of C at O.

A general plane ϖ of Ω meets the [4] containing C in a line; the ρ-plane through this line joins it to O and contains three chords of C; there are seven other chords of C meeting the line. Hence the bitangent developable of the surface in [3] is $3R+E_7^0$. There are four planes of E_7^0 passing through R; two of these are represented on Ω by the ρ-planes through the two trisecants of C which pass through O, the other two are represented by the two ρ-planes through those chords of C which join O to the other intersections with C of the ϖ-plane through the tangent of C at O. The two trisecants of C which do not pass through O are joined to O by ϖ-planes; the ρ-planes through these trisecants represent two triple planes of E_7^0.

* For there are six tangents of a rational *quintic* in [3] which lie on a quadric containing the curve.

† Such a prime section is a curve of order 10 lying on a quadric in [3]; it meets all generators of one system in seven points and all of the other in three points, having two triple points and six double points.

231. To obtain this surface by projection we take the normal surface in [7] with ∞^1 directrix cubics and choose S to meet the [4] determined by a directrix cubic Δ and a generator g in a plane. Then this [4] and S determine a [5] through S which meets Σ in a line R, R being a directrix and also a generator of the projected surface f. Through any point of R there pass three other generators, while any plane through R contains two other generators.

S meets the solid containing Δ in a line l. The [4] containing g and Δ meets S in a plane through l, and Δ is projected from g on to this plane into a conic ϑ_2 meeting l twice; through any point of ϑ_2 there passes a line meeting Δ and g. Then S meets M_5^6 in l, ϑ_2 and a twisted cubic ϑ_3^0 which meets ϑ_2 once and l twice. Through any point of g there pass three lines meeting ϑ_2 and Δ; through any point of Δ there pass two of its chords meeting l and one line meeting g and ϑ_2. Thus the chords of F meeting S meet F in Δ and g each counted three times and in a rational curve C_8^0 meeting every generator once. C_8^0 meets Δ in five points; four of these are accounted for by the chords of F through the intersections of l and ϑ_3^0; the other lies, with the intersection of C_8^0 with g, on the chord through the intersection of ϑ_2 and ϑ_3^0.

Hence on projection we have in Σ a surface with a double curve $6R+C_4^0$; C_4^0 having R for a trisecant.

To generate this surface we take a line R and a twisted cubic with one intersection, placing them in (1, 3) correspondence without a united point. Each point of R gives a triad of points on the cubic, the plane of the triad meeting R in another point; we have thus a (1, 1) correspondence between the points of R, there being one triad having its plane passing through any point of R*; there are two coincidences, or two triads whose planes pass through the corresponding points on R. These give the two triple planes of E_7^0. There are four planes of E_7^0 passing through R; two of these arise from the triad of points containing the intersection of R with the cubic. The pencil of planes through R gives a g_2^1 on the cubic, and this has two sets belonging to the g_3^1 given by the triads†; these give the other two planes of E_7^0 through R.

The tritangent planes of f are at once obtained from the projection; S meets the M_4^4 formed by the solids K in l and two other points ‡, the solids K through these other points project from S into the two tritangent planes of f.

The primes through the [5] containing S and Δ—since they all contain the generator g—give pairs of generators of F which give a g_2^1 on Δ; the joins of the pairs of this g_2^1 are lines of a regulus, and there are two of

* There is one of these planes passing through any point of Σ; the equation of the plane is expressible linearly in terms of a parameter.

† Cf. the footnote to § 134. ‡ Cf. § 222.

these joins meeting l. Thus on projection there are two points of R such that, at either of these points, the plane of the pair of intersecting generators passes through R. This is of course clear from the representation on Ω; the points are represented by the ϖ-planes containing the two trisecants of C which pass through O. If, however, it happened that one of these pairs of points on Δ gave a pair of generators whose solid met S in a line, the projected surface would have a double generator and C would be of the type IV (E); similarly we might have two double generators, C being of the type IV (G).

232. The dual of the surface which we have been considering arises when C is of the type IV (D); the double curve is $3R + C_7{}^0$, $C_7{}^0$ having two triple points and having R as a quadrisecant; the bitangent developable is $6R + E_4{}^0$, there being three planes of $E_4{}^0$ passing through R.

To obtain this surface by projection take the normal surface F in [7] with a directrix conic Γ, and take S to lie in a [5] containing Γ and a generator g, S meeting the plane of Γ in a point O. Then the [5] meets Σ in a line R which is a directrix and also a generator of f; through any point of R there pass two other generators, while any plane through R contains three other generators.

The [3] containing g and Γ meets S in a line l passing through O; through each point of l there passes a line meeting g and Γ. S meets $M_5{}^6$ in l and a rational quintic $\vartheta_5{}^0$ which has a double point at O and meets l in two other points.

Through any point of g there pass two lines meeting both l and Γ, while through any point of Γ we have one line meeting l and g and also the line joining the point to O. Thus the chords of F which meet S meet F in Γ and g, each counted twice, together with an elliptic curve $C_{14}{}^1$, *four** of whose tangents meet $\vartheta_5{}^0$. This curve meets every generator of F in two points and Γ in six points; of these intersections with Γ four are collinear with O in pairs, the other two being associated with the intersections of g with $C_{14}{}^1$. $C_{14}{}^1$ has six double points; these lie three in each of two planes meeting S in lines.

Hence the projected surface has a double curve $3R + C_7{}^0$; $C_7{}^0$ has two triple points and has R as a quadrisecant.

The surface is generated by a line R and a rational twisted quartic with one intersection, these being placed in (1, 2) correspondence without a united point. The pairs of points on the quartic corresponding to the points of R give a cubic ruled surface; thus the bitangent planes of the ruled surface other than those through R form a rational developable of the fourth class, which itself has three planes passing through R.

* The tangent solid of F along g meets l.

233. Suppose now that C is of the type IV (E); the double point P represents a double generator G of the ruled surface in [3]. The chords of C lying in either system of planes and not passing through O form a rational ruled surface*.

An arbitrary plane ρ of Ω meets the [4] containing C in a line and the plane ϖ through this line joins it to O; this plane contains six chords of C, and there are three others meeting the line. Hence the surface has a double curve $6R+G+C_3{}^0$. R and G intersect, while R is a chord of $C_3{}^0$. $C_3{}^0$ also meets G.

An arbitrary plane ϖ of Ω meets the [4] containing C in a line and the plane ρ through this line joins it to O; this plane contains three chords of C, and there are six others meeting the line. Hence the surface has a bitangent developable $3R+G+E_6{}^0$; there are three planes of $E_6{}^0$ passing through R, while $E_6{}^0$ has a double plane and an ordinary plane passing through G. The trisecant of C which does not pass through O is joined to O by a ϖ-plane; the ρ-plane containing this trisecant represents a triple plane of $E_6{}^0$.

234. To obtain this surface by projection take a directrix cubic Δ on the normal surface and a line l in the solid containing Δ. Then take a pair of generators h, h' of F which meet Δ at its intersections with one of its chords which meet l, and take a line m meeting l and lying in the solid containing h and h'. Then choose S to pass through l and m and lie in a [5] containing Δ and a generator g. We have as before a conic ϑ_2 whose plane passes through l, and S meets $M_5{}^6$ in l, m, ϑ_2 and a conic ϕ_2 meeting each of l, m, ϑ_2 in one point. The chords of F meeting S meet F in Δ and g both counted three times, h, h' and a prime section $C_6{}^0$. On projection we have a double curve $6R+G+C_3{}^0$ as required.

The projected surface has a tritangent plane, S meeting $M_4{}^4$ in one point not on l or m.

This surface is generated by a line R and a twisted cubic $C_3{}^0$ in (2, 3) correspondence; R is a chord of $C_3{}^0$, there being one doubly united point and one ordinary united point. The correspondence is such that to one of the branch-points on R there corresponds one of the branch-points on $C_3{}^0$; the line joining these points is the double generator G.

* The chords of C which lie in the ρ-planes and do not pass through O form a rational quartic ruled surface; they join the pairs of a $g_2{}^1$ on C which includes the pair of points on the two branches at P.

The chords of C which lie in the ϖ-planes and do not pass through O form a ruled surface of order 9; a prime section of this is a curve of order 9 lying on a quadric, meeting all generators of one system in three points and all of the other system in six points. It has one triple point and seven double points.

235. When C is of the type IV (F) we have a double curve $3R+G+C_6^0$ and a bitangent developable $6R+G+E_3^0$.

Consider now the normal surface with a directrix conic Γ; take a point O in the plane of Γ and a line m through O lying in the solid containing a pair of generators h, h'. Choose S to pass through m and also to lie in a [5] with Γ and a generator g. We have as before a line l in S passing through O; S meets M_5^6 in l, m and a rational quartic ϑ_4^0 passing through O, meeting m once again and l twice again.

The chords of F which meet S meet F in Γ and g both counted twice, h, h' and an elliptic curve C_{12}^1 meeting every generator in two points and having four double points. Three of these lie in a plane containing a trisecant of ϑ_4^0, the other being associated with intersections of C_{12}^1 with h and h'; the remaining intersections of C_{12}^1 with h and h' lie on the chord of F passing through the intersection of m and ϑ_4^0 other than O. Two of the four intersections of C_{12}^1 with Γ are collinear with O; the other two are associated with the intersections of C_{12}^1 with g, lying with them on the two chords of F which pass through the two intersections (other than O) of l and ϑ_4^0.

Thus the projected surface has a double curve $3R+G+C_6^0$; R is a trisecant of C_6^0 while C_6^0 meets G and has also a double point on G. R and G intersect and C_6^0 has a triple point.

This surface is generated by a line R and a rational skew quartic in (1, 2) correspondence; there is one intersection but no united point. The correspondence is specialised to give the double generator; one of the points of R gives rise to a pair of points of the quartic collinear with it. The joins of the pairs of points of the quartic form a cubic ruled surface and the planes joining the points of R to the corresponding pairs form a developable E_3^0 with two planes passing through R and one through G. The bitangent developable is $6R+G+E_3^0$.

236. When C is of the type IV (G) the double curve of the ruled surface is $6R+G+H+C_2$ and the bitangent developable $3R+G+H+E_5^0$. G and H meet R, while C_2 meets each of R, G and H. There are two planes of E_5^0 passing through R, while through G there pass a double plane and a simple plane of E_5^0, as also through H.

To obtain the surface by projection we choose the solid S to lie in a [5] containing a directrix cubic Δ and a generator g of F, there being two pairs of generators g', g'' and h', h'' whose solids meet S in lines m and n. S meets the solid containing Δ in a line l which meets m and n; it meets the [4] containing g and Δ in a plane through l, and Δ is projected from g into a conic ϑ_2 in this plane. Then S meets M_5^6 in l, m, n, ϑ_2 and a line λ which meets m, n and ϑ_2. The chords of F meeting S meet F in Γ and g

both counted three times, g', g'', h', h'' and a directrix quartic E; the double curve of the projected surface is precisely as given above.

The surface is generated by a line R and a twisted cubic which meets it, these being in (1, 3) correspondence without a united point; the correspondence is specialised to give the two double generators. Or it can be generated by R and C_2 in (2, 3) correspondence with a united point, there being two pairs of corresponding double elements.

237. When C is of the type IV (H) the double curve of the ruled surface is $3R+G+H+C_5{}^0$ and the bitangent developable $6R+G+H+E_2$. R meets both G and H; $C_5{}^0$ has two double points, one of which lies on G and the other on H, each of these lines meeting $C_5{}^0$ in a further point. R is a chord of $C_5{}^0$. There is one plane of E_2 passing through each of R, G, H.

To obtain this surface by projection take in [7] the normal surface F with a directrix conic Γ. Take a point O in the plane of Γ and two lines m and n passing through O, m lying in the solid containing a pair of generators g', g'' and n lying in the solid containing a pair of generators h', h''. Then choose S to contain m and n and to lie in a [5] with Γ and a generator g. The solid $g\Gamma$ meets S in a line l through O; and S meets $M_5{}^6$ in l, m, n and a twisted cubic $\vartheta_3{}^0$ meeting m and n and having l as a chord.

The chords of F meeting S meet F in Γ and g each counted twice, g', g'', h', h'' and an elliptic curve $C_{10}{}^1$ meeting every generator of F twice and having two double points. These double points lie one in each of the solids $g'g''$ and $h'h''$ and are thus associated with intersections of $C_{10}{}^1$ with these generators; the remaining intersections of $C_{10}{}^1$ with these generators are given by the chords of F through the points in which $\vartheta_3{}^0$ meets m and n. $C_{10}{}^1$ meets Γ in two points; these are associated with its intersections with g and lie on the chords of F through the intersections of l and $\vartheta_3{}^0$. On projection we have a double curve as above described.

The surface is generated by a line R and a rational skew quartic in (1, 2) correspondence; R meets the quartic, but there is no united point. The correspondence is specialised to give the double generators; there are two points on R which give pairs of points of the quartic collinear with them. The joins of the pairs of points of the quartic form a cubic ruled surface, and the planes joining the points of R to the pairs of points of the quartic which correspond to them touch a quadric cone. There is a tangent plane of this cone passing through R and one through each double generator.

238. We now pass to curves C on Ω of the type V. When C is of the type V (A) we have a ruled surface in [3] with a directrix line R which is also a double generator; through any point of R there pass three other generators, while any plane through R contains one other generator. It is clear how to obtain such a surface by projection; we take S to meet the solid K containing a directrix cubic Δ of the normal surface F in a line l, and so that S lies in the [5] containing Δ and two generators g and h. Then this [5] meets Σ in the line R.

The surface is generated by a twisted cubic and one of its chords in (3, 1) correspondence without any united point.

An arbitrary plane ρ of Ω meets the [4] containing C in a line; this line is joined to O by a ϖ-plane which contains all the chords of C meeting the line; the double curve of the surface is thus the line R counted ten times.

An arbitrary plane ϖ of Ω meets the [4] containing C in a line, and the plane ρ through this line joins it to O. If C is projected on to a plane from this line we obtain a rational sextic with a triple point and therefore with seven other double points. Hence there are seven chords of C which meet the line and do not lie in the plane joining the line to O. Hence the ruled surface has a bitangent developable $3R+E_7$. The chords of C which lie in ϖ-planes and do not pass through O form a ruled surface whose prime sections are rational curves*, so that E_7 is a rational developable $E_7{}^0$. There are four planes of $E_7{}^0$ passing through R; the ϖ-plane through either tangent of C at O meets C in two points other than O, and the ρ-planes containing the chords joining O to these points represent two planes of $E_7{}^0$ which pass through R.

C has two trisecants; these are joined to O by ϖ-planes, and the ρ-planes through them represent two triple planes of $E_7{}^0$.

239. The dual surface, represented on Ω by a curve C of the type V (B), has a double curve $3R+C_7{}^0$ and a bitangent developable $10R$. R is a quadrisecant of $C_7{}^0$, which has two triple points.

This surface is obtained by projection from the normal surface with a directrix line λ; S must be chosen to meet the plane containing λ and a generator g in a point X and to meet the plane containing λ and another generator h in a point Y. Then the [5] containing S and λ also contains g and h, and meets Σ in a line R which is a directrix and also a double generator of f. Through any point of R there passes one other generator, while any plane through R contains three other generators.

The line XY is on the $M_5{}^6$ formed by the chords of F; through every point of XY there passes a transversal to g and h. S meets $M_5{}^6$ in XY and a rational quintic $\vartheta_5{}^0$ with double points at X and Y.

* There are four points of C at which the two generators of this ruled surface coincide and also four tangents of C, other than that at O, lying in ϖ-planes (this being the number of tangents of a rational quartic which lie on a quadric containing it). A prime section of the ruled surface is a curve of order ten lying on a quadric surface, meeting all generators of one system in three points and all of the other system in seven points; it has six double points and two triple points.

Through any point of λ there pass lines through X and Y meeting g and h respectively; through any point of g there passes a transversal to h and XY and also a line through X meeting λ; through any point of h there passes a transversal to g and XY and also a line through Y meeting λ; thus the chords of F which meet S meet F in the lines λ, g, h each counted twice and an elliptic curve C_{14}^1 (four of whose tangents meet ϑ_5^0) meeting every generator of F in two points and λ in four points. This curve has six double points, and these lie three in each of two planes containing trisecants of ϑ_5^0. Hence the double curve of f is $3R + C_7^0$; R is a quadrisecant of C_7^0, which has two triple points.

The surface is generated by a rational quintic and one of its chords in 1, 1) correspondence without a united point.

240. Suppose now that C is of the type V (C); we have a line R which is a directrix and also a double generator of the ruled surface; through any point of R there pass two other generators, while any plane through R contains two other generators. The chords of C which lie in either system of planes and do not pass through O join pairs of points of a g_2^1 and form a rational quintic ruled surface.

An arbitrary plane of Ω meets the [4] containing C in a line, and the plane of the opposite system through this line joins it to O; there are four chords of C which meet the line and do not lie in this plane. Hence the double curve of the ruled surface is $6R + C_4^0$ and the bitangent developable $6R + E_4^0$.

R is a trisecant of C_4^0; the ϖ-plane containing the line through O which meets C in two further points represents one of the three intersections. The ρ-plane through either tangent of C at O meets C in another point, and the ϖ-plane containing the line joining this point to O represents one of the other intersections.

Similarly there are three planes of E_4^0 passing through R.

241. To obtain this surface by projection we take the normal surface which has a directrix conic Γ, and choose S to lie in a [5] containing Γ and two generators g and h. Then S meets the plane of Γ in a point O, and the [5] meets Σ in the line R. The [4] containing Γ, g and h meets S in a plane passing through O and the solids gh, $g\Gamma$, $h\Gamma$ meet S in three lines l, m, n which lie in this plane, m and n passing through O. S meets M_5^6 in l, m, n and a twisted cubic which passes through O and meets m and n again.

Through any point of Γ there pass a transversal to g and m, a transversal to h and n and a line to O; through any point of g there pass two transversals to Γ and m and a transversal to h and l; through any point of h there pass two transversals to Γ and n and one transversal to g and l. Hence the chords of F which meet S meet F in Γ, g and h each counted three times and a rational curve $C_8{}^0$ meeting each generator once and Γ four times. Two of these intersections with Γ are collinear with O; the other two lie on the chords of F through the other intersections of $\vartheta_3{}^0$ with m and n and are associated with the intersections of $C_8{}^0$ with g and h.

Hence on projection we have a double curve $6R + C_4{}^0$, R being a trisecant of $C_4{}^0$.

The surface is generated by a rational skew quartic and one of its chords placed in (2, 1) correspondence without any united point. The joins of the pairs of points of the quartic form a cubic ruled surface, so that the planes joining the points of the chord to the pairs of points of the quartic which correspond to them form a developable $E_4{}^0$ with three planes passing through R.

242. The pencil of primes through the [5] containing S, Γ, g and h cuts out an involution of pairs of generators on F. There is one pair of this involution meeting Γ in a pair of points collinear with O; these are in fact two intersections of $C_8{}^0$ with Γ.

Now it may happen that the solid containing this pair of generators meets S in a line p through O; in this case the projected surface has a double generator and corresponds to a curve C of the type V (D). S meets $M_5{}^6$ in l, m, n, p and a conic ϑ_2 meeting m, n and p. On F we have Γ, g, h each counted three times and the new pair of generators k, k' together with a prime section $C_6{}^0$.

The surface is generated by a rational skew quartic and one of its chords R placed in (2, 1) correspondence without any united point; but here the correspondence must be specialised to give the double generator G, one pair of points of the quartic having their join G meeting R in the point which gives rise to them. The joins of the pairs of points of the quartic form a cubic ruled surface, and we thus obtain a developable $E_3{}^0$ with two planes passing through R and one through G. The bitangent developable of the surface is $6R + G + E_3{}^0$.

The properties of the surface are also easily deduced from those of the curve on Ω. The double curve is $6R + G + C_3{}^0$.

243. We now suppose that C is of the type VI (A); the chords of C in the ϖ-planes which do not pass through O form a rational quintic ruled surface. An arbitrary plane ρ meets the [4] containing C in a line and the plane ϖ containing this line joins it to O; there are no chords of C meeting the line other than those which lie in this ϖ-plane. Thus the double curve of the ruled surface is $10R$. An arbitrary plane ϖ of Ω meets the [4] containing C in a line; there are four chords of C meeting this line which do not lie in the ρ-plane joining it to O. Hence the bitangent developable of the surface is $6R + E_4{}^0$.

The ϖ-plane through any one of the three tangents of C at O meets C again in another point; the ρ-plane containing the line joining this point to O represents a plane of E_4^0 which passes through R. Thus there are three planes of E_4^0 passing through R.

To obtain this surface by projection we take the normal surface with a directrix conic Γ and choose S to lie in the [5] determined by Γ and three generators g, h, k. Then this [5] meets Σ in a line R which is a directrix and also a triple generator of F; through any point of R there pass two other generators, while any plane through R contains one other generator. S meets M_5^6 in three lines l, m, n passing through the point O in which it meets the plane of Γ and in three other lines λ, μ, ν, where λ meets m and n, μ meets n and l, and ν meets l and m. The double curve of the projected surface is $10R$; the chords of F meeting S meet F in Γ, g, h and k, each counted four times.

The surface is generated by a rational skew quartic and a line R in (2, 1) correspondence; R is a trisecant of the quartic but there are no united points. The joins of the pairs of points of the quartic form a cubic ruled surface, and the planes joining the points of R to the pairs of points of the quartic which correspond to them give a developable E_4^0, three of whose planes pass through R.

244. When C is of the type VI (B) we have the surface dual to this; the double curve is $6R + C_4^0$, where R is a trisecant of C_4^0, and the bitangent developable is $10R$.

To obtain this surface by projection take the normal surface with a directrix line λ; choose S to meet the plane containing λ and a generator g in a point X, the plane containing λ and a generator h in a point Y and the plane containing λ and a generator k in a point Z. Then there is a [5] containing S, λ, g, h, k which meets Σ in a line R which is a directrix and also a triple generator of the surface. Through any point of R there passes one other generator, while any plane through R contains two other generators. S meets M_5^6 in the lines YZ, ZX, XY and a rational cubic ϑ_3^0 passing through X, Y and Z. The chords of F which meet S meet F in λ, g, h, k, each counted three times and in a rational curve C_8^0 meeting each generator once and λ three times, there being two tangents of C_8^0 meeting ϑ_3^0. On projection we have a double curve $6R + C_4^0$, where R is a trisecant of C_4^0.

The surface is generated by a rational skew quintic and one of its trisecants in (1, 1) correspondence without any united point.

Surfaces whose generators belong to a linear congruence

245. Suppose now that C is of the type VII (A); through the solid containing the quadric surface on which C lies there pass two tangent primes of Ω, touching it in O and O'; these represent two lines R and R' in [3] which are directrices of the ruled surface. Through any point of one of these (say R) there pass five generators lying in a plane through R'. Hence the double curve of the ruled surface is $10R$ and the bitangent developable is $10R'$.

To obtain this surface by projection take the normal surface F with a directrix line λ and project from a solid S lying in a [5] which contains one of its directrix quintics. Then this [5] meets Σ in a line R, while the [5] through S and λ meets Σ in a line R'; R and R' are directrices of f; through any point of R there pass five generators lying in a plane through R'.

The surface is generated by two lines R and R' in (1, 5) correspondence.

The solid S meets M_5^6 in the curve ϑ_6^3 in which it is met by the chords of the directrix quintic; the chords of F which meet S meet F in the directrix quintic counted four times.

246. When C is of the type VII (B) the ruled surface has two directrices R and R' and three double generators G, H, K. Through any point of R there pass four generators lying in a plane through R', while through any point of R' there pass two generators lying in a plane through R. The double curve is $6R+G+H+K+R'$ and bitangent developable is $R+G+H+K+6R'$.

To obtain this surface by projection we take the normal surface with a directrix conic Γ; take S to meet the plane of Γ in a point O and to contain a plane π which lies in a [4] containing a directrix quartic E. Then the three double generators arise automatically, there being three pairs of generators whose solids meet S in lines l, m, n passing through O and meeting π*. S meets M_5^6 in l, m, n and a plane cubic ϑ_3^1 lying in π and passing through the intersections of π with l, m, n.

The surface is generated by a (2, 4) correspondence between R and R' specialised to give the three double generators.

The chords of F meeting S meet F in E counted three times, g, g', h, h', k, k' and Γ.

247. In type VII (C) the ruled surface has two directrices R and R' and four double generators G, H, J, K. Through any point of each directrix there pass three generators lying in a plane through the other. The double curve and bitangent developable are both $3R+G+H+J+K+3R'$.

* Through π there pass solids cutting out a g_4^1 on E, while through O there pass lines cutting out a g_2^1 on Γ; there are three pairs of generators such that a pair meets Γ in a set of the g_2^1 and meets E in two points of a set of the g_4^1. These are the three pairs whose solids meet S in lines.

Take the general surface F in [7] and project from a solid S containing a line l in the solid K containing a directrix cubic Δ and a line l' in the solid K' containing a directrix cubic Δ'. Then there are four pairs of generators whose solids meet S in lines m, n, p, q each of which meets l and l'. S meets M_5^6 in l, l', m, n, p, q.

The surface is generated by two lines R and R' in (3, 3) correspondence, the correspondence being specialised to give the four double generators.

248. When C is of the type VIII (A) the surface has a single directrix R which is also a quadruple generator; through any point of R there passes one other generator. To obtain this by projection we take the normal surface in [7] with a directrix line λ and project from a solid S meeting four planes which join λ to four different generators of the surface, giving the surface in Σ as required.

The surface is generated by a rational skew quintic and its quadrisecant in (1, 1) correspondence without any united point.

The double curve and bitangent developable are both $10R$.

249. When C is of the type VIII (B) the surface has a directrix R which is also a double generator; through any point of R there pass two other generators which are coplanar with R.

Take in [7] the normal surface with a directrix conic Γ, and the [4] which contains Γ and two generators. Two primes through this [4] give each two further generators of F, and we thus have two chords of Γ which intersect in a point O. The primes meet in a [5] containing the plane of Γ and also the first two generators; choose S to lie in this [5] and to pass through O. Since there are two of the pencil of primes through the [5] which meet F in pairs of generators whose solid passes through O it follows that all the primes of the pencil must do so, so that we have an infinity of pairs of generators whose solids meet S in O and which meet Γ in pairs of points collinear with O. Hence on projection we have the surface required. The double curve and bitangent developable are both $7R+G+H+K$.

The surface is generated by a (2, 1) correspondence between a rational skew quartic and one of its chords R; the pairs of points of the quartic lying in planes through R. The joins of these pairs of points form a cubic ruled surface of which R is the double line. The range of points on R is thus related to the pencil of planes through R. There is incidentally a (1, 2) correspondence set up between the points of R; through any point of R there pass two chords of the quartic (other than R), while any plane through R gives another chord of the quartic meeting it. There will be three coincidences in this correspondence, thus shewing the existence of the double generators G, H, K.

250. When C is of the type VIII (C) we have a surface with a directrix R; through any point of R there pass three generators which lie in a plane through R. There are four double generators; the double curve and bitangent developable are $6R+G+H+J+K$.

Take a directrix cubic Δ of the normal surface F, and two primes through it. Each meets F further in three generators, giving thus two triads of points on Δ whose planes meet in a line l. Take S to pass through l and to lie in the [5] common to the two primes. Then the pencil of primes through the [5] is such that any one of the primes meets F in Δ and three generators, these generators meeting Δ in a triad of points whose plane passes through l. On projection we have the surface required.

The surface is generated by a line and a twisted cubic in (1, 3) correspondence; the triads of points on the cubic being those cut out by the planes through the line. We thus have a (1, 3) correspondence between the points of the line; there are four coincidences, thus shewing the existence of the four double generators.

251. On pp. 306–308 we give tables of the different types of rational ruled surfaces of the sixth order in [3] (not including developable surfaces). There are eighty-one different types altogether. We have already obtained sixty-seven of these; the remaining ones will be obtained in Chapter VI.

SECTION II

ELLIPTIC SEXTIC RULED SURFACES

252. We first obtain the different types of elliptic sextic ruled surfaces in [3] by means of elliptic sextic curves on Ω; afterwards we obtain them as the projections of normal surfaces in [5].

In the first investigation we shall need to use the properties of certain ruled surfaces formed by chords of an elliptic sextic curve. The elliptic sextic curve is normal in [5]*, all elliptic sextic curves being obtainable as the projections of curves in [5]. On the normal curve there are ∞^1 linear series of pairs of points, the chords joining the pairs of points of such a linear series form a rational quartic ruled surface with, in general, ∞^1 directrix conics, each conic meeting the curve in two points†. To each of these ruled surfaces there belong four tangents of the curve.

* § 8.

† Segre, "Sur les transformations des courbes elliptiques," *Math. Ann.* 27 (1886), 296. Of the ∞^1 series g_2^1 there are nine for which the quartic ruled surface has a directrix line.

Elliptic sextic curves which lie on quadrics

253. We can at once divide the elliptic sextic curves C which lie on a quadric Ω in [5] into the following seven classes:

I. The normal curve in [5].

II. The curve C is contained in a [4].

III. C is contained in a tangent prime T of Ω but does not pass through the point of contact O of Ω and T.

IV. C is contained in T and passes through O.

V. C is contained in T and has a double point at O.

VI. C lies on the quadric in which Ω is met by a [3].

VII. C lies on a quadric cone in which Ω is met by a [3] which touches it.

When C is contained in a space [4] it may or may not have a double point; if it has not a double point it has two trisecant chords*.

We have two kinds of elliptic sextic curves on a quadric in [3]:

(A) The intersection with a quartic surface passing through two generators of the same system and touching the quadric twice. This curve meets all generators of one system in four points and all of the other system in two points; it has two double points.

(B) The intersection with a cubic surface touching the quadric in three points; this curve meets each generator of the quadric in three points and has three double points.

Also we have on a quadric cone:

(A) The intersection with a cubic surface passing through the vertex and touching the cone twice; this curve has a double point at the vertex and also two other double points; it meets every generator of the cone in two points other than the vertex.

(B) The intersection with a cubic surface touching the cone three times; this curve has three double points and meets every generator in three points.

254. We must not overlook the fact that there can exist on a quadric an elliptic sextic curve with a triple point. It is true that such a curve does not lie on a quadric in general, but if the tangents at the triple point are co-planar it will do so, the quadric being then determined by having to touch at the triple point the plane of the three tangents and to pass through six arbitrary points of the curve. The curve meets every generator of the quadric in three points, and we can also have such a curve lying on a quadric cone.

The quintic ruled surface formed by the trisecants of the curve† breaks up into the quadric counted twice and the plane of the tangents at the triple point.

* Berzolari, *Palermo Rend.* 9 (1895), 195; Castelnuovo, *ibid.* 3 (1889), 28.

† § 89.

To obtain such a curve in [3] we must project the normal curve in [5] from a line in a trisecant plane; the three tangents of the curve at the points where it is met by the trisecant plane lying in a [4]. The existence of such planes is at once clear on using elliptic arguments for points of the curve; there are ∞^2 such, four passing through any chord of the curve. Thus the curve in [3] exists for all values of the modulus.

We also have a curve in [4] such that the tangents at the three points where it is met by a trisecant lie in a [3].

255. We are now in a position to give the following more detailed classification of the elliptic sextic curves C on a quadric Ω in [5]. The abbreviations $\varpi_2\rho_4$, $O\varpi_3\rho_2$, etc., are explained in the footnote to § 171.

I. C is a normal curve on Ω.

II. (A) C lies in a [4] which does not touch Ω, and has no double point.

II. (B) C lies in a [4] which does not touch Ω, and has a double point.

III. C lies in a tangent prime T but does not pass through O, the point of contact of Ω and T.

(A) C is $\varpi_2\rho_4$ with two chords through O.

(B) C is $\varpi_4\rho_2$ with two chords through O.

(C) C is $\varpi_2\rho_4$ with a chord through O and with a double point.

(D) C is $\varpi_4\rho_2$ with a chord through O and with a double point.

(E) C is $\varpi_3\rho_3$ with three chords through O.

(F) C is $\varpi_3\rho_3$ with two chords through O and with a double point.

IV. C lies in a tangent prime T and passes through O.

(A) C is $O\varpi_2\rho_3$ with a trisecant through O.

(B) C is $O\varpi_3\rho_2$ with a trisecant through O.

(C) C is $O\varpi_2\rho_3$ with a double point.

(D) C is $O\varpi_3\rho_2$ with a double point.

These four types can be written down at once because when C, which lies on the quadric point-cone with vertex O in which T meets Ω, is projected from O on to a solid in T it becomes an elliptic quintic curve lying on a quadric*. Similarly the curves under III must give elliptic sextics when thus projected†.

V. C lies in a tangent prime T and has a double point at O. It will meet every plane of Ω passing through O in two points other than O.

VI. C lies in a [3] through which two tangent primes of Ω pass; it thus lies on an ordinary quadric surface.

(A) C meets all generators of one system in four points and all of the other system in two points, having two double points.

(B) C meets every generator in three points and has three double points.

(C) C meets every generator in three points and has a triple point.

* Cf. § 151. † Cf. § 253.

VII. C lies in a [3] which touches Ω, and therefore on a quadric cone with vertex V.

(A) C has a double point at V and also two other double points, meeting every generator in two points other than V.

(B) C has three double points and meets every generator in three points.

(C) C has a triple point and meets every generator in three points.

Surfaces whose generators do not belong to a linear complex

256. If we have a normal elliptic sextic curve C in [5] the projection of C from a plane on to a plane is an elliptic sextic curve with nine double points, while the projection from a plane meeting C is an elliptic quintic curve with five double points. Hence the chords of C form a locus $M_3{}^9$ of three dimensions and the ninth order, on which C is a quadruple curve. C has no quadrisecant planes, because an elliptic quartic in [3] has no double points, so that there is no double surface on $M_3{}^9$.

If there is a quadric Ω passing through C every plane of Ω is met by nine chords of C, so that in the most general type of elliptic sextic ruled surface in [3] the double curve C_9 is of order nine and the bitangent developable E_9 of class 9*.

There are four trisecant planes of C which lie on Ω†; there are, in fact, two of these belonging to each system of planes on Ω. Hence C_9 has two triple points and E_9 two triple planes.

The chords of C which lie on Ω form a ruled surface $R_2{}^{18}$ of order 18, the intersection of Ω and $M_3{}^9$; there are four such chords passing through any point of C. A prime section C' of $R_2{}^{18}$ is in (1, 1) correspondence with C_9 and E_9‡.

In the (α, α') correspondence between C and C' determined by the condition that two points correspond when the line joining them is a chord of C we have $\alpha = 2$ and $\alpha' = 4$. The number η' of branch points of this correspondence on C' is the number of tangents of C which lie on Ω, so that $\eta' = 12$‖. Through each point of C there pass four of its chords which lie on Ω; the number η of branch points of the correspondence on C is the number of points of C for which two of these four generators of $R_2{}^{18}$ coincide. But if, through a point P of C, we have the four chords PA, PB, PC, PD lying on Ω, the points A, B, C, D are a set of points on an elliptic curve of a (4, 4) correspondence of valency 2. Hence $\eta = 24$¶.

Zeuthen's formula then shews that $p' = 4$**.

Hence the most general elliptic sextic ruled surface in [3] has a double curve $C_9{}^4$ and a bitangent developable $E_9{}^4$.

* § 33. † § 35. ‡ § 33.
‖ § 32. ¶ § 14. ** § 16.

257. Consider now a quartic ruled surface, with ∞^1 directrix conics, containing the curve; each generator of this surface is a chord of the curve, while each directrix conic meets it in two points.

There are ∞^{20} quadrics in [5], and of these there are ∞^8 containing the curve C of order six and genus 1; a quadric meeting C in twelve general points necessarily containing it entirely*. If, in addition, the quadric is made to contain three generators of the quartic surface it will contain the whole of the surface, so that we have ∞^5 such quadrics†. This quadric contains the planes of two directrix conics of the surface‡; the ∞^1 planes form a V_3^3 which is met by the quadric in two of the planes and in the quartic surface. The planes are of opposite systems on the quadric.

The ruled surface formed by the chords of C which lie on Ω now breaks up into this quartic surface and a ruled surface of the fourteenth order on which C is a triple curve. Every plane of Ω meets the quartic surface in two points and therefore the other surface in seven points. We thus obtain in [3] an elliptic sextic ruled surface whose double curve consists of a conic and a curve of the seventh order and whose bitangent developable consists of a quadric cone and a developable of the seventh class.

Through any point P of C there pass four of its chords which lie entirely on Ω; one of these PQ is a generator of the quartic ruled surface, while the other three PX, PY, PZ are generators of the ruled surface of order 14. Since the set of points $P+Q$ and also the set $2P+Q+X+Y+Z$ vary in two linear series for different positions of P on C so does the set $P+X+Y+Z$. The generators of the ruled surface of order 14 thus set up on C a (3, 3) correspondence of valency 1, so that there are sixteen points of C at which two of the three generators of this ruled surface coincide.

Again, of the twelve tangents of C which lie on Ω there are four belonging to the quartic; there must then be eight belonging to the ruled surface of order 14.

Considering then the correspondence between C and the curve C' in which the ruled surface of order 14 is met by a [4] we have

$$\alpha=2, \quad \alpha'=3, \quad p=1, \quad \eta=16, \quad \eta'=8,$$

whence $p'=3$, so that C' is of genus 3.

Thus we have in ordinary space a ruled surface whose double curve is $C_2+C_7^3$ and bitangent developable $E_2+E_7^3$.

The generators of the quartic surface set up on C a (1, 1) correspondence of valency 1, while those of the ruled surface of order 14 set up a (3, 3)

* The intersections of an elliptic curve with a primal are such that any one of them is determined by the rest.

† That there are six linearly independent quadrics containing the quartic ruled surface follows at once when its equations are written in the form

$$X/Y = Y/Z = X'/Y' = Y'/Z'.$$

‡ Cf. § 91.

correspondence of valency 1; these correspondences are both symmetrical and have therefore two common pairs of points, which means simply that there are two chords of C generators of both ruled surfaces*. This shews that C_2 and C_7^3 intersect in two points.

258. There are ∞^1 quartic ruled surfaces arising from the ∞^1 g_2^1's on C; we have thus ∞^2 conics, lying in planes, on these surfaces. We may call these planes secant planes of M_3^9; they meet M_3^9 in conics, whereas an ordinary plane meets M_3^9 in nine points. There are ∞^2 secant planes; they form a locus of four dimensions. We can use arguments for these planes similar to those used in § 91.

Take any one of the secant planes and the conic Γ therein meeting C in X and Y; take any point P in the plane and let PX, PY meet Γ again in X' and Y'. Then there are chords of C passing through X' and Y', and these joined to X and Y respectively give the two trisecant planes of C which pass through P.

Hence we conclude that if there is a secant plane passing through a point P it must intersect both the trisecant planes of C through P in lines, provided that P is not on the conic in the secant plane.

259. Take a trisecant plane of C lying on Ω, and suppose for the moment that none of the three chords of C which it contains is a generator of the quartic ruled surface. Then there are three generators of the quartic ruled surface passing one through each of the points in which the trisecant plane meets C. The secant plane which belongs to the same system of planes on Ω as that to which the trisecant plane belongs meets the trisecant plane in a point and the quartic ruled surface in a conic; we thus have a [4] meeting the quartic ruled surface in a conic and three generators, which is impossible. We therefore conclude that the trisecant plane contains a generator of the quartic ruled surface. Incidentally, it must meet the other secant plane on Ω in a line.

Suppose now that Ω contains the planes ϖ_1, ϖ_2, ρ_1, ρ_2 trisecant to C and also the secant planes ϖ_0 and ρ_0. Then ϖ_0 meets ρ_1 and ρ_2 in lines, while ρ_0 meets ϖ_1 and ϖ_2 in lines.

Now ρ_0 represents the plane of the double conic C_2. Hence C_7^3 has two double points on C_2 as well as the two simple points already mentioned; they are represented on Ω by the planes ϖ_1 and ϖ_2. The plane of C_2 meets the sextic ruled surface in C_2 counted twice and in two generators (these generators being represented on Ω by the two points in which C is met by ρ_0); these intersect in a point of C_7^3, and all the seven intersections of C_7^3 with the plane of C_2 are thus accounted for. The generators of the surface are trisecant to C_7^3.

* § 15.

The two points in which ρ_0 meets C lie one in ϖ_1 and the other in ϖ_2.

The projection of $C_7{}^3$ on to a plane from one of its double points is a quintic with three double points. Thus there are two lines through the double point of $C_7{}^3$ each of which meets $C_7{}^3$ in two further points, and these are generators of the surface; the third generator through this point lies in the plane of C_2.

There are similar statements for the developable $E_7{}^3$ and the planes ρ_1, ρ_2.

260. Of the ∞^5 quadrics containing C and one secant plane (and therefore two) there are ∞^1 which contain another (and therefore still another) secant plane. Then the ruled surface formed by the chords of C which lie on Ω breaks up into two quartic surfaces and a ruled surface of order ten of which two generators pass through any point of C. By the same argument as in § 257, there are eight points of C for which these two generators coincide, and each ruled surface contains four tangents of C.

Any plane of Ω is met by two generators of each quartic surface and by five generators of the other surface; we have thus in ordinary space a sextic ruled surface whose double curve is $C_2+D_2+C_5$ and bitangent developable $E_2+F_2+E_5$.

Taking a section of the ruled surface of order ten by a [4] we have a curve C' of order ten, and for the correspondence between C and C'

$$\alpha=2, \qquad \alpha'=2, \qquad p=1, \qquad \eta=8, \qquad \eta'=4,$$

whence $p'=2$, and C' is of genus 2.

Thus for the double curve of the ruled surface we have $C_2+D_2+C_5{}^2$ and for the bitangent developable $E_2+F_2+E_5{}^2$.

Each quartic surface sets up on C a (1, 1) correspondence of valency 1, while the ruled surface of order ten sets up a (2, 2) correspondence of valency zero. This shews that, all these correspondences being symmetrical, there are no generators common to the two quartic surfaces, while each quartic surface has two generators in common with the ruled surface of order ten. Hence $C_5{}^2$ has two simple intersections with each of C_2 and D_2, while $E_5{}^2$ has two simple planes in common with each of E_2 and F_2.

261. Suppose that the quadric Ω has $\varpi_1, \varpi_2, \rho_1, \rho_2$ for trisecant planes of C and also contains the secant planes $\varpi_0, \rho_0, \varpi_0', \rho_0'$. Then the two intersections of ϖ_0 with C will lie one on ρ_1 and the other on ρ_2, with similar statements for the other secant planes.

We conclude that C_2 and D_2 have two intersections each of which lies on $C_5{}^2$. The plane of either C_2 or D_2 meets the ruled surface in the double conic and two generators whose point of intersection lies on $C_5{}^2$. All the intersections of $C_5{}^2$ with these planes are thus accounted for. The generators are chords of $C_5{}^2$.

The three generators through one of the two triple points consist of one in the plane of C_2, one in the plane of D_2 and the trisecant of $C_5{}^2$.

The trisecants of $C_5{}^2$ form a quadric surface; the intersection of this with the sextic surface consists of the two particular trisecants just mentioned and the curve $C_5{}^2$ counted twice.

Surfaces whose generators belong to a linear complex which is not special

262. Suppose that we have on Ω an elliptic sextic curve C contained in a prime which does not touch Ω. The curve has two trisecants, and these lie on Ω. We have in [3] correspondingly an elliptic sextic ruled surface with a double curve of order nine which has two triple points at each of which the three generators are co-planar; by the same argument as in § 256 the double curve is a $C_9{}^4$ of genus 4.

Let us obtain this genus in another way.

The chords of C form a locus $M_3{}^9$ on which the two trisecants are triple lines and C is a quadruple curve. Since any chord of C is met by two* chords, other than those which pass through its intersections with C, there is a double surface F_2 on $M_3{}^9$.

The order of F_2 is the number of double points of a plane section of $M_3{}^9$. The genus of such a plane section can be calculated by an application of Zeuthen's formula, and the number of its double points is thereby determined. Take any plane section c of $M_3{}^9$, and consider the correspondence between C and c, points of the two curves corresponding when the line joining them is a chord of C. The correspondence is a (2, 5) correspondence; for through each point of c there passes a chord of C and through each point of C there pass five of its chords which meet c, these lying in the solid determined by the point of C and the plane of c. The number of branch-points of the correspondence on c is the number of tangents of C which meet c; this number is 12—the order of the surface formed by the tangents of C. If P is a branch-point of the correspondence on C then two of the five chords of C which pass through P and meet c must coincide, so that the solid Pc must touch C at a point other than P. The tangent of C at this other point must be one of the 12 tangents of C which meet c, so that the correspondence has 48 branch-points on C. Thus

$$\alpha = 2, \qquad \alpha' = 5, \qquad p = 1, \qquad \eta = 48, \qquad \eta' = 12,$$

and Zeuthen's formula gives $p' = 10$. A plane curve of order nine and genus 10 has 18 double points; hence the double surface on $M_3{}^9$ is a surface $F_2{}^{18}$ of order 18. It can be shewn that C is a double curve on $F_2{}^{18}$; the section of $M_3{}^9$ by, for example, a quadrisecant plane of C consists of six chords of C together with a cubic having a double point and passing through the four points of C in the plane. Thus $F_2{}^{18}$ meets Ω in C counted twice, the trisecants counted three times and a residual curve of order 18.

Hence the chords of C which lie on Ω form a ruled surface of order 18 (the intersection of Ω and $M_3{}^9$) on which C is a quadruple curve and the two trisecants are triple generators, there being also a double curve of order 18. The section of this ruled surface by a solid is a curve of order 18 lying on a

* The projection of C from a chord on to a plane is an elliptic quartic curve with two double points.

quadric and meeting each generator in nine points; it has six quadruple points, two triple points, and eighteen double points. Thus its genus is

$$136 - 72 - 36 - 6 - 18 = 4,$$

so that C_9^4 and E_9^4 are also of genus 4.

263. If we project a normal elliptic sextic curve on to a [4] from a point lying in a secant plane this secant plane meets [4] in a line which intersects the two trisecants of the projected curve C; through any point of the line pass two chords of C, and all these chords form a quartic ruled surface.

There are ∞^{14} quadrics in [4]; hence there are ∞^2 passing through C, which will incidentally contain the two trisecants, and ∞^1 of these contain the quartic ruled surface.

If we consider one of these quadrics as a section of Ω by the [4] containing C, the points of C represent the generators of an elliptic sextic ruled surface in [3] whose double curve is $C_2 + C_7^3$ exactly as in § 257; C_7^3 has two double points and two simple points on C_2. Similarly for the bitangent developable $E_2 + E_7^3$.

264. Given a g_2^1 on the normal elliptic sextic curve the joins of pairs of points form a quartic ruled surface with ∞^1 directrix conics each meeting the curve in two points; but these pairs of points on the conics themselves form a g_2^1, they are cut out by [4]'s passing through two generators of the quartic surface. Given two points on the curve, that g_2^1 is determined in which they form a pair; but there are four series g_2^1 giving rise to quartic ruled surfaces such that this pair of points lies on a conic of the surface; this last statement is at once clear on using elliptic arguments.

The planes of the directrix conics of a quartic ruled surface form a locus V_3^3, and in [5] two loci V_3^3 without a common surface meet in a curve of order nine. It is therefore clear that there are points not lying on the elliptic curve, or on any of its chords, through which there pass two secant planes. If we project from such a point on to a [4] the two secant planes meet [4] in lines, each of which meets both the trisecants of the projected curve C; through any point of either line there pass two chords of C, and all such chords form a quartic ruled surface on which the line is a double line.

Of the ∞^2 quadrics passing through C there is one containing both the quartic ruled surfaces; regarding this as a prime section of Ω the points of C represent the generators of an elliptic sextic ruled surface in ordinary space whose double curve is $C_2 + D_2 + C_5^2$ and bitangent developable $E_2 + F_2 + E_5^2$ exactly as in § 260. Here the generators of the surface belong to a linear complex, and the three generators at a triple point lie in a tritangent plane.

265. Suppose now that the curve C lying on Ω is contained in a [4] and has a double point P. Then P represents a double generator G of the ruled surface. The chords of C form a locus M_3^8, and any plane on Ω meets the [4] containing C in a line meeting this locus in eight points. Thus the ruled surface in [3] has a double curve $G+C_8$ and a bitangent developable $G+E_8$.

The chords of C lying on Ω form a ruled surface of order 16; there are four of them passing through every point of C, except that through P there pass only two PQ, PR, while through Q and R there pass only three. The twelve tangents of C which lie on Ω belong to this ruled surface. We have on C a (4, 4) correspondence of valency 2; there are twenty-four points of C for which two of the four corresponding points coincide. Now these points include P. For we regard the double point of C as lying on two distinct branches of the curve; suppose that it is P_1 regarded as a point of one branch and P_2 regarded as a point of the other. Then the tangent prime of Ω at P_1 meets C twice at P_1, twice at P_2, and once at each of Q and R. Thus corresponding to P_1 we have $Q+R+2P_2$; similarly, corresponding to P_2 we have $Q+R+2P_1$. The point P in fact counts for four among the twenty-four coincidences. The points Q and R are not included, since P_1 and P_2 are on different branches of C. We have then twenty coincidences, which give generators of the surface in [3] touching the double curve C_8.

Taking a section of the ruled surface we have a curve C' of order 16, and in the correspondence between C and C'

$$\alpha=2, \qquad \alpha'=4, \qquad p=1, \qquad \eta=20, \qquad \eta'=12,$$

so that $p'=3$, and C' is of genus 3.

The curve C_8^3 has two double points and two simple points on G*. Through either of the double points there passes one line meeting C_8 in two other points not on G; this is the generator, other than G, which passes through this point; it is represented on Ω by one of the points Q, R.

We can find the genus of C_8^3 and E_8^3 in another way.

The chords of C form a locus M_3^8 on which C is a quadruple curve; the quartic cone projecting C from P is a double surface on M_3^8, and P is a sextuple point. Making use of an argument similar to that of § 262, we find that there is a double surface F_2^{11} on M_3^8, but this is composed of the quartic cone and a double surface F_2^7. C is a simple curve on F_2^7; a quadrisecant plane of C meets M_3^8 in six chords of C and a conic passing through the four points of C; the intersection of Ω and F_2^7 consists of C and an octavic curve, while Ω meets the quartic cone in C and two lines PQ, PR.

Hence the chords of C which lie on Ω form a ruled surface of order 16 with two double generators, a double curve of order 8 and the quadruple curve C. The section of this ruled surface by a solid is a curve of order 16 lying on a quadric and meeting all the generators in eight points; it has six quadruple points and ten double points. Its genus is therefore

$$105-56-36-10=3,$$

and therefore C_8^3 and E_8^3 are also of genus 3.

* Cf. § 102.

266. Let us project a normal elliptic sextic from a point on one of its chords. We obtain a curve C with a double point P, and there are four lines through P which are double lines of quartic ruled surfaces whose generators join pairs of points of four g_2^1's on C. Since there are ∞^3 quadrics passing through C there are ∞^1 containing one of these quartic ruled surfaces.

Now regard one of these as a section of Ω by a [4]. The surface formed by the chords of C which lie on Ω here breaks up into the quartic ruled surface and a ruled surface of order 12; every plane of Ω meets the [4] containing C in a line meeting the former surface in two points and the latter in six. Hence C represents the generators of an elliptic sextic ruled surface in [3] contained in a linear complex; the double curve is C_2+G+C_6 and the bitangent developable E_2+G+E_6.

The quartic surface sets up on C a (1, 1) correspondence of valency 1, while the ruled surface of order 12 sets up a (3, 3) correspondence of valency 1. This gives sixteen as the number of points of C at which two of the three generators of this latter surface coincide; but P is counted four times in this result.

Of the twelve tangents of C which lie on Ω four belong to the quartic ruled surface and eight to the ruled surface of order 12. If we take the section C' by a solid we have a curve of order 12, and for the correspondence between C and C'

$$\alpha=2, \qquad \alpha'=3, \qquad p=1, \qquad \eta=12, \qquad \eta'=8,$$

so that $p'=2$, and C' is of genus 2.

Thus the ruled surface in [3] has a double curve $C_2+G+C_6{}^2$ and a bitangent developable $E_2+G+E_6{}^2$.

The plane of C_2 contains G, and C_6 passes through the two intersections of G and C_2; $C_6{}^2$ also meets G in two other points*. There are two further intersections of $C_6{}^2$ and C_2.

There is one other generator passing through either intersection of C_2 and G; this is the unique line, other than G, passing through the point, which is trisecant to $C_6{}^2$.

There are precisely similar statements for the bitangent developable.

Surfaces with a directrix line which is not a generator

267. If C is of the type III (A) it meets every plane ϖ of Ω through O in two points and every plane ρ of Ω through O in four points; two chords of the curve passing through O. An arbitrary plane ρ of Ω meets T in a line, and the ϖ-plane through this line joins it to O. This contains one chord of the curve; there are eight others meeting the line. We thus

* For this statement cf. § 102.

have in [3] a ruled surface with a directrix line R; through any point of R there pass two generators, while any plane through R contains four generators; the double curve is $R+C_8$.

The pairs of points of C which lie in the ϖ-planes through O form a g_2^1, and so the chords of C in these planes form a quartic ruled surface. The ρ-planes through O cut out on C sets of a g_4^1; they thus set up a (3, 3) correspondence on C of valency 1, and there are sixteen points of C for which two of the three corresponding points coincide.

The curve C is touched by four ϖ-planes and eight ρ-planes; each of these last planes contains two of the sixteen points just mentioned. The ruled surface formed by the chords of C which lie in the ρ-planes is of order 14; take C', a section of it by a [3]. Then for the correspondence between C and C'

$$\alpha=2, \qquad \alpha'=3, \qquad p=1, \qquad \eta=16, \qquad \eta'=8,$$

so that $p'=3$, and C' is of genus 3.

Thus the double curve is $R+C_8^3$. The generators of the ruled surface meet R and are trisecants of C_8^3. Since C has two trisecants C_8^3 has two triple points; R is a chord of C_8^3, the points in which it meets C_8^3 being represented on Ω by the ϖ-planes containing the two chords of C through O.

Any plane ϖ of Ω meets T in a line, and the plane ρ through this line joins it to O. This contains four points and therefore six chords of C; there are three other chords meeting the line. Thus the bitangent developable of the surface is $6R+E_3^0$; the planes of E_3^0 are the planes of the pairs of generators which intersect in the points of R, and two of these planes pass through R, being represented on Ω by the ρ-planes containing the two chords of C through O.

When C is of the type III (B) we have similarly a double curve $6R+C_3^0$ and a bitangent developable $R+E_8^3$. R is a chord of C_3^0; E_8^3 has two triple planes and two of its planes pass through R. Through any point of R there pass four generators, while any plane through R contains two generators.

268. Consider again a normal elliptic sextic in [5] and a g_2^1 thereon. We have a quartic ruled surface, and the planes of the directrix conics of this form a V_3^3. Now project on to a [4] from a point of this V_3^3 which is not on a chord of the curve. The projection of V_3^3 is a quadric point-cone* and C, the projected curve, lies on this cone, meeting all the planes of one system in two points and all of the other system in four points; but each of these sets of four points consists of two pairs of the same g_2^1.

We can then regard this quadric point-cone as the section of Ω by a tangent prime T, and C is evidently of the type III (A) or III (B).

* § 99.

Consider for definiteness a curve C of the type III (A). The four points in which C is met by a ρ-plane form two pairs of the same g_2^1; hence the chords of C which lie in ρ-planes now form a quartic ruled surface Q_ρ and a ruled surface R_2^{10} of order ten on which C is a double curve; the chords of C in ϖ-planes form as before a quartic ruled surface Q_ϖ. The trisecants of C are generators of Q_ρ and double generators of R_2^{10}. The surface R_2^{10} sets up on C a symmetrical (2, 2) correspondence of valency zero, and we can deduce that R_2^{10} and Q_ρ have two common generators.

The number of points of C at which the two generators of R_2^{10} coincide is eight; also, of the twelve tangents of C which lie on Ω four belong to Q_ϖ, four to Q_ρ and four to R_2^{10}. Hence, considering the correspondence between C and a section C' of R_2^{10} by a solid,

$$\alpha = 2, \qquad \alpha' = 2, \qquad p = 1, \qquad \eta = 8, \qquad \eta' = 4,$$

so that $p' = 2$.

A plane ρ of Ω meets T in a line; the nine chords of C meeting this line consist of the chord in the plane ϖ joining the line to O, of two generators of Q_ρ and six of R_2^{10}. Thus the ruled surface has a double curve $R + C_2 + C_6^2$; C_6^2 has two double points through both of which C_2 passes, while C_6^2 and C_2 have two further simple intersections. C_6^2 meets R in two points, but R and C_2 do not meet. The bitangent developable is still $6R + E_3^0$.

Similarly, if C is of the type III (B) we have in [3] an elliptic sextic ruled surface whose double curve is given by $6R + C_3^0$ and bitangent developable by $R + E_2 + E_6^2$; there are properties of this developable dual to those already given for the double curve of the ruled surface just mentioned.

269. There are still more special examples of surfaces in [3] belonging to the types III (A) and III (B).

Consider again the elliptic normal sextic curve in [5]. We can have sets of four points α, α', β, β' upon the curve such that α and α' form a pair of a g_2^1 including also the pair $\beta\beta'$, while the pairs $\alpha\beta$ and $\alpha'\beta'$ belong to a second g_2^1*. Consider the quartic surface formed by the first g_2^1; the second g_2^1 gives an involution of pairs of generators on this surface; the joins of pairs of points in which these pairs of lines meet any directrix conic of the surface thus pass through a fixed point. In fact the solids determined by the sets of four points such as α, α', β, β' (such a set being determined by one point) have a line in common lying on the V_3^3 formed by the planes of the directrix conics.

* We take the elliptic arguments so that

$$\alpha + \alpha' \equiv c, \qquad \beta + \beta' \equiv c, \qquad \alpha + \beta \equiv c + \tfrac{1}{2}\omega, \qquad \alpha' + \beta' \equiv c + \tfrac{1}{2}\omega,$$

where ω is a period of the elliptic functions. Any three of these congruences involve the fourth.

Let us then project on to a [4] from a point of this line. We obtain an elliptic sextic curve lying on a quadric point-cone, meeting all planes of one system in four points and all of the other system in two points; but the sets of four points are such that, if $\alpha, \alpha', \beta, \beta'$ is one of them, the pairs $\alpha\alpha'$ and $\beta\beta'$ belong to one g_2^1, while the pairs $\alpha\beta$ and $\alpha'\beta'$ belong to another.

Suppose, for definiteness, that C is of the type III (A). The chords of C lying in the ϖ-planes through O form as before a quartic ruled surface Q_ϖ; those which lie in the ρ-planes through O form two quartic ruled surfaces Q_ρ and Q_ρ' and a sextic ruled surface R_2^6. The trisecants of C are generators of each of the three surfaces Q_ρ, Q_ρ', R_2^6. The surface R_2^6 gives on C a (1, 1) correspondence of valency -1, so that this surface has two generators in common with each of the surfaces Q_ρ, Q_ρ' as well as the trisecants.

An arbitrary plane ρ meets T in a line; this meets Q_ρ in two points, Q_ρ' in two points, R_2^6 in four points and is met by the chord of C lying in the ϖ-plane joining it to O. Also it is easily seen that the surface R_2^6 is elliptic.

We have thus in [3] a surface whose double curve is $R + C_2 + D_2 + C_4^1$; C_2 and D_2 have two intersections through each of which C_4^1 passes, while C_4^1 meets each conic in two other points. R is a chord of C_4^1. The plane of either conic meets the surface in this conic counted twice and a pair of generators which intersect on R.

The bitangent developable is again $6R + E_3^0$.

Similarly we have a surface reciprocal to this when C is of the type III (B).

270. If C is of the type III (C) it meets every plane ϖ of Ω through O in two points and every plane ρ of Ω through O in four points; it has a double point P and one of its chords passes through O.

An arbitrary plane ρ of Ω meets T in a line; the plane joining this line to P meets Ω again in a second line passing through P. The plane ϖ joining the line to O contains one chord of C, and there are seven others meeting the line. Hence we have in [3] a ruled surface with a double generator G; the double curve is $R + G + C_7$.

The chords of C which lie in the ϖ-planes through O form a quartic ruled surface Q_ϖ, while those which lie in the ρ-planes through O form a ruled surface R_2^{12} of order 12 on which C is a triple curve. The generators of R_2^{12} set up on C a symmetrical (3, 3) correspondence of valency 1; this shews that there are sixteen points of C at which two of the three generators of R_2^{12} coincide. Through P there pass two chords PQ, PR of C which lie on Ω; the point P is not included among the sixteen coincidences. To the point P_1 on one branch of C there correspond three distinct points Q, R, P_2, while to the point P_2 on the other branch there correspond three distinct points Q, R, P_1.

C is touched by four ϖ-planes and eight ρ-planes through O. Taking a section C' of R_2^{12} by a solid we have, for the correspondence between C and C',

$$\alpha = 2, \qquad \alpha' = 3, \qquad p = 1, \qquad \eta = 16, \qquad \eta' = 8,$$

so that $p' = 3$, and C' is of genus 3. Hence the double curve is $R + G + C_7^3$.

The plane of the two tangents of C at P meets the ϖ-plane through OP in a generator of Q_ϖ and the ρ-plane through OP in a generator of R_2^{12}. The plane ϖ through this generator of R_2^{12} represents a point of intersection of C_7^3 and G. C_7^3 has also two double points on G; these are represented on Ω by the ϖ-planes through the two double generators of R_2^{12}, PQ and PR.

R and G intersect. Also C_7^3 meets R, the point of intersection being represented on Ω by the ϖ-plane which contains the chord of C through O.

An arbitrary plane ϖ of Ω meets T in a line; the plane ρ through this line joins it to O and contains six chords of C; there are two other chords of C meeting the line. Hence the ruled surface has a bitangent developable $6R + G + E_2$. There is a plane of E_2 passing through R; it is represented on Ω by the ρ-plane containing the chord of C passing through O.

Similarly, when C is of the type III (D) we have a double curve $6R + G + C_2$ and a bitangent developable $R + G + E_7^3$. R and G intersect; C_2 meets R. E_7^3 has two double planes and one ordinary plane passing through G and one ordinary plane passing through R.

271. Consider again a normal elliptic sextic curve in [5]. Through any one of its chords there pass four secant planes; consider any one of these and the ∞^1 others belonging to the same quartic ruled surface and forming a V_3^3. Projecting from a point of the chord on to a [4] we have an elliptic sextic curve C with a double point and lying on a quadric point-cone; it meets all the planes of one system in two points and all of the other system in four points. Regarding the cone as a section of Ω by a tangent prime T we have clearly a curve C of one of the types III (C) and III (D); but here the four points of C in a plane of the cone consist of two pairs of the same g_2^1.

Suppose then that C is of the type III (C). The chords of C lying in the ϖ-planes form a quartic ruled surface Q_ϖ, while those lying in the ρ-planes form a quartic ruled surface Q_ρ together with a ruled surface R_2^8 of order eight on which C is a double curve.

An arbitrary plane ρ meets T in a line; this line is met by one generator of Q_ϖ, two of Q_ρ and five of R_2^8. Hence the ruled surface in [3] has a double curve $R + G + C_2 + C_5$.

The surface R_2^8 sets up on C a symmetrical (2, 2) correspondence of valency zero. R_2^8 and Q_ρ have two common generators. Also there are eight points of C at which the two generators of R_2^8 coincide, and of the twelve tangents of C which lie on the point-cone four belong to Q_ϖ, four to Q_ρ and four to R_2^8. Thus, if C' is the section of R_2^8 by a solid, we have a correspondence between C and C' for which

$$\alpha=2, \qquad \alpha'=2, \qquad p=1, \qquad \eta=8, \qquad \eta'=4,$$

so that $p'=2$ and C' is of genus 2.

Hence the double curve of the ruled surface is $R+G+C_2+C_5^2$. The plane of C_2 contains G, while C_5^2 passes through their two intersections. C_5^2 meets G in a third point and meets R in one point.

The bitangent developable is still $6R+G+E_2$.

Similarly, when C is of the type III (D) we have in [3] an elliptic sextic ruled surface whose double curve is $6R+G+C_2$ and bitangent developable $R+G+E_2+E_5^2$.

272. If C is of the type III (E) it meets every plane of Ω through O in three points and has three chords passing through O. We have a surface in [3] with a double curve $3R+C_6$ and a bitangent developable $3R+E_6$.

The planes of either system of Ω which pass through O cut out a g_3^1 on C, this has six double points; of the twelve tangents of C which lie on Ω there are six in each system of planes. The chords of C which lie in either system of planes through O form a ruled surface R_2^9, of order nine, on which C is a double curve; we have thus a (2, 2) correspondence of valency 1 on C, so that there are six points of C at which the two generators of R_2^9 coincide. Then, taking a section C' of R_2^9, there is a correspondence between C and C' for which

$$\alpha=2, \qquad \alpha'=2, \qquad p=1, \qquad \eta=6, \qquad \eta'=6,$$

so that $p'=1$, and C' is of genus 1. Hence C_6 is an elliptic curve C_6^1 and E_6 is an E_6^1.

Of the two trisecants of C one is joined to O by a ϖ-plane and the other by a ρ-plane. The ρ-plane through the first of these trisecants represents a triple plane of E_6^1, while the ϖ-plane through the second trisecant represents a triple point of C_6^1.

R is a trisecant of C_6^1; the three points in which it meets C_6^1 are represented by the ϖ-planes through those three chords of C which pass through O. Similarly there are three planes of E_6^1 passing through R.

273. If C is of the type III (F) it meets every plane of Ω passing through O in three points; two of its chords pass through O and it has a double point P. We now have a surface whose double curve is $3R+G+C_5$ and bitangent developable $3R+G+E_5$.

The chords of C which lie in either system of planes of the cone form a ruled surface R_2^8 on which C is a double curve. The planes of either system cut out a g_3^1 on C; there are six points of C at which the two generators of R_2^8 coincide. Of the twelve tangents of C which lie on Ω there are six in either system of planes. Taking then a section C' of R_2^8 we have for the correspondence between C and C'

$$\alpha=2, \qquad \alpha'=2, \qquad p=1, \qquad \eta=6, \qquad \eta'=6,$$

whence $p'=1$, so that C' is of genus 1. Hence we have a double curve $3R+G+C_5^1$ and bitangent developable $3R+G+E_5^1$.

Since there are two chords of C passing through O there are two points of R at which two of the three generators which meet there lie in a plane with R. These two points are intersections of R and C_5^1; the planes are planes of E_5^1 passing through R.

There are two chords of C passing through P and lying on Ω; one is joined to O by a plane ϖ and the other by a plane ρ. C_5^1 has a double point and a simple point on G; E_5^1 has a double plane and a simple plane through G.

Surfaces with a directrix line which is also a generator

274. If C is of the type IV (A) it passes through O, meeting every plane ϖ of Ω through O in two points other than O and every plane ρ of Ω through O in three points other than O; one of its trisecants passes through O.

An arbitrary plane ρ meets T in a line; the plane ϖ through this line passes through O and contains three points and therefore three chords of C; there are six further chords meeting the line. Thus the surface in [3] has a double curve $3R+C_6$; similarly it has a bitangent developable $6R+E_3$.

To obtain a representation of C_6 we consider a section of the ruled surface formed by the chords of C which lie in ρ-planes through O and do not pass through O. There are ten tangents of C lying on Ω, this being the number of tangents of an elliptic quintic curve on a quadric which lie on the quadric. The planes ϖ cut out a g_2^1 on C (exclusive of O) and thus four tangents of C lie in ϖ-planes; the remaining six lie in ρ-planes. These ρ-planes cut out a g_3^1 on C which is a symmetrical (2, 2) correspondence of valency 1; there are thus six points of C for which the two corresponding points of the g_3^1 coincide.

If then C' denotes a section of the ruled surface formed by the chords of C which lie in the ρ-planes and do not pass through O we have for the correspondence between C and C'

$$\alpha=2, \qquad \alpha'=2, \qquad p=1, \qquad \eta=6, \qquad \eta'=6,$$

so that $p'=1$, and C' is of genus 1.

Thus the double curve is $3R+C_6{}^1$.

Similarly the bitangent developable is $6R+E_3{}^0$; the chords of C which lie in ϖ-planes and do not pass through O form a rational quartic ruled surface.

The second trisecant of C is joined to O by a ρ-plane; this represents a tritangent plane of the surface which passes through R and contains three generators concurrent in a triple point of $C_6{}^1$.

R is itself a generator; through any point of R there pass two other generators, and there is one point of R at which these lie in a plane through R. This point of R is on $C_6{}^1$; R is in fact a trisecant of $C_6{}^1$, the other generators being ordinary chords. There are two planes of $E_3{}^0$ passing through R.

Similarly, if C is of the type IV (B) we have a surface in [3] whose double curve is $6R+C_3{}^0$ and bitangent developable $3R+E_6{}^1$.

275. If C is of the type IV (C) it passes through O, meeting every ϖ-plane of Ω through O in two points other than O and every ρ-plane of Ω through O in three points other than O, and has a double point P.

An arbitrary plane ρ of Ω meets T in a line; the plane ϖ through this line joins it to O and contains three points and therefore three chords of C. There are five further chords of C meeting the line; so that the double curve of the surface in [3] is $3R+G+C_5$. Similarly the bitangent developable is $6R+G+E_2$. Just as in the last article we find that C_5 is an elliptic curve $C_5{}^1$.

There are two chords of C which pass through P and lie on Ω; one of these is PO; let the other be PQ. The plane POQ is a ρ-plane. R and G intersect; their plane contains the generator represented by Q. $C_5{}^1$ has a double point at the intersection of this generator with G and meets G in one other point. R is a chord of $C_5{}^1$. The ρ-plane through the tangent of C at O meets C in two other points; the ϖ-planes which contain the chords of C joining these two points to O represent the two points of intersection of R and $C_5{}^1$.

Similarly, when C is of the type IV (D) we have in [3] a surface whose double curve is $6R+G+C_2$ and bitangent developable $3R+G+E_5{}^1$.

276. If C is of the type V it has a double point at O and meets every plane of Ω passing through O in two points other than O. An arbitrary plane of Ω meets T in a line and the plane of the opposite system through this line joins it to O; this contains three chords of C and there are three others meeting it, the projection of C from the line being a plane sextic with a quadruple point and three double points. Hence the surface has a double curve $6R+C_3$ and a bitangent developable $6R+E_3$; C_3 and E_3 are rational as being represented by the pairs of two series g_2^1 on C. R is not only a directrix but also a double generator; it is a chord of C_3^0 and an axis of E_3^0.

Surfaces whose generators belong to a linear congruence

277. If C belongs to any of the types VI it has two directrices R and R'.

In the type VI (A) we have two double generators G and H; the double curve is $6R+G+H+R'$ and the bitangent developable $R+G+H+6R'$.

In the type VI (B) we have three double generators G, H and J; the double curve is $3R+G+H+J+3R'$ and the bitangent developable $3R+G+H+J+3R'$.

In the type VI (C) we have a triple generator G; the double curve is $3R+3G+3R'$ and the bitangent developable $3R+3G+3R'$.

If C belongs to any of the types VII there is a single directrix R.

In the type VII (A) R is a double generator and there are also two other double generators G and H; the double curve is $7R+G+H$, which gives also the bitangent developable. The curve C is projected from a point of the cone into a plane sextic having two double points and a quadruple point with only three distinct tangents.

In the type VII (B) we have a double curve and bitangent developable $6R+G+H+J$. The curve C is projected from a point of the cone into a plane sextic with three double points and a triple point at which all the branches touch.

In the type VII (C) we have a double curve and bitangent developable $6R+3G$; the curve C is projected from a point of the cone into a plane sextic with an ordinary triple point and a triple point at which all the branches touch.

The normal elliptic ruled surfaces of a given order n

278. In order to carry out the next steps in our investigation we require a knowledge of the properties of the normal elliptic ruled surfaces of the sixth order. We will then take this opportunity of obtaining some of the most fundamental properties of the normal elliptic ruled surfaces of any order n; in particular, we shall investigate how many different types of surfaces there are which are projectively distinct from one another, and give some account of the curves which lie upon them. We shall also obtain methods for generating the surfaces by correspondences between two curves. The results are due originally to Segre*.

* See his paper, "Ricerche sulle rigate ellittiche di qualunque ordine," *Atti Torino*, 21 (1886), 868.

If we have an elliptic ruled surface of order n which is not a cone then, as is seen by an argument precisely similar to that used for a quintic surface in § 160, the surface belongs to a space of dimension $n-1$ at most. If the surface is contained in a space of dimension less than $n-1$ then we take a quadric through one of its generators; this quadric meets the surface again in a curve of order $2n-1$ and genus n which, just as in § 160, is the projection of a normal curve in $[n-1]$. We thus prove, just as for quintic surfaces, that *an elliptic ruled surface of order n is normal in $[n-1]$; and any elliptic ruled surface of order n which belongs to a space of dimension less than $n-1$ is the projection of a normal surface in $[n-1]$.*

279. Consider now a normal elliptic ruled surface F in $[n-1]$. We shall suppose that F is not a cone, that it does not break up into separate surfaces, and that it is not contained in a space of dimension less than $n-1$.

Any space which is contained in $[n-1]$ and meets F in an infinite number of points may contain only a number of generators of F, or else a number of generators together with a directrix curve of F; it cannot contain two directrix curves of F for then it would contain the surface entirely.

If we have on F a curve of order $\nu<n-1$ this curve is contained in a space of dimension less than or equal to $n-2$; it is therefore a directrix curve of F and is elliptic. Also a curve of order $n-1$ must be a directrix curve of F and therefore elliptic; for if it met the generators of F in more than one point it would belong to $[n-1]$ and be a rational normal curve, and Zeuthen's formula shews that we cannot have a $(1, k)$ correspondence between an elliptic curve and a rational curve. Hence *every curve on F of order $\nu\leqslant n-1$ is an elliptic curve and meets each generator in one point.*

A directrix curve of F of order ν cannot be contained in a space of dimension less than $\nu-1$. For if it were contained in a space $[\nu-2]$ this space, together with $n-\nu-1$ arbitrary generators, would determine a space $[n-3]$ meeting F in a composite curve of order $n-1$. Then the pencil of primes through $[n-3]$ would give the generators of F, which is impossible since F is not rational. Hence *every curve of F of order $\nu\leqslant n-1$ is an elliptic normal curve.* This same argument shews that a curve of order $\nu\leqslant n-1$ cannot be contained in a space $[\nu-2]$ when it is composite, i.e. consists of a directrix curve and a certain number of generators. It is true in this case also that the curve belongs to a space $[\nu-1]$ and not to a space of higher dimension; for if it consists of μ generators and an elliptic normal curve of order $\nu-\mu$ this latter lies in a $[\nu-\mu-1]$ and this, together with the μ generators, determines a $[\nu-1]$ containing the whole of the composite curve. Hence any curve of F of order $\nu\leqslant n-1$, whether simple or composite, belongs to a space $[\nu-1]$.

We cannot have on F two directrix curves C_ν, $C_{\nu'}$ of orders ν and ν' such that $\nu+\nu'<n$. For C_ν is contained in a space $S_{\nu-1}$ and $C_{\nu'}$ is contained in a space $S_{\nu'-1}$, so that F is contained in a space $[\nu-1+\nu'-1+1]$ or $[\nu+\nu'-1]$. Hence, since F is not contained in a space of less dimension than $n-1$, $\nu+\nu'\geqslant n$. Hence, *if F contains a curve of order less than $\frac{1}{2}n$ it is the only such curve and is the minimum directrix.*

Similarly, if we have two curves C_ν, $C_{n-\nu}$ on the surface, the sum of whose orders is n, they cannot intersect. For two spaces $S_{\nu-1}$, $S_{n-\nu-1}$ with a common point are contained in a space $[n-2]$, and a prime cannot contain two directrix curves of F.

280. In any space $[n-1]$ we can at once construct a normal elliptic surface F, and indeed several types of surfaces. For take two spaces S_{m-1} and S_{n-m-1} which do not intersect; in S_{m-1} take a normal elliptic curve of order m and in S_{n-m-1} a normal elliptic curve of order $n-m$, these two curves having the same modulus. Then a (1, 1) correspondence between the two curves gives an elliptic ruled surface F of order n. If m is not equal to $\frac{1}{2}n$ we can take the curve of order m to be the minimum directrix; clearly two surfaces F whose minimum directrices are not of the same order cannot be projectively equivalent, and two surfaces F whose minimum directrices are of the same order but have not the same modulus cannot be projectively equivalent.

If n is even and we choose $m=\frac{1}{2}n$ the surface has two minimum directrices. In this case, since the two curves between which there is a (1, 1) correspondence are of the same order, we can obtain a special type of surface by making the correspondence belong to a projectivity* between the two spaces $S_{\frac{1}{2}n-1}$ and $S'_{\frac{1}{2}n-1}$ containing the curves. Then, if a space $[\frac{1}{2}n-2]$ meets the first curve in $\frac{1}{2}n$ points, the generators through these points meet the second curve in $\frac{1}{2}n$ points which also lie in a space $[\frac{1}{2}n-2]$; hence these $\frac{1}{2}n$ generators are contained in a space $[n-3]$. Then, through this $[n-3]$, we have a pencil of primes cutting out ∞^1 curves of order $\frac{1}{2}n$ on F; hence this particular surface has *∞^1 minimum directrices of order $\frac{1}{2}n$*, and *through any point of F there passes one of them.*

Let us then divide the surfaces F into three classes, according to the order m of their minimum directrices:

$$(a)\quad m<\frac{n}{2},$$

$$(b)\quad m=\frac{n}{2},$$

$$(c)\quad m>\frac{n}{2}.$$

* In other words, the (1, 1) correspondence between the two elliptic curves is *special*. Cf. § 164.

We prove that all surfaces of class (*a*) are generated by a (1, 1) correspondence between two elliptic normal curves of orders m and $n-m$ such as we have already mentioned. We prove also that the surfaces of class (*b*) are those already considered, one with two minimum directrices and the other with ∞^1 minimum directrices; as well as a third type of surface with only one minimum directrix. We prove further that in class (*c*) we have only one type of surface—that for which n is odd and $m=\frac{1}{2}(n+1)$; this being the most general type of surface of odd order n. For all surfaces F, $m \leqslant \frac{1}{2}(n+1)$.

These are the only possible types of elliptic normal ruled surfaces for which no two generators intersect.

281. Let us consider now a surface of the class (*a*); there is on the surface a minimum directrix γ^m, where $m<\frac{1}{2}n$. There can be no curve on the surface of order less than $n-m$; we prove that the surface contains an infinity of curves of order $n-m$.

If there is on F a curve C_{n-m} then any prime containing it must meet F further in m generators, and these will meet γ^m in m associated points*. Conversely, any set of m associated points of γ^m is contained in an $[m-2]$, and any curve C_{n-m} is contained in an $[n-m-1]$; hence there is a prime containing any C_{n-m} and any set of m generators which meet γ^m in associated points. Hence, in order to obtain all the curves C_{n-m} on F, it will be sufficient to consider the system of primes which contain the generators of F passing through any given set of associated points of γ^m.

Let us take a set of associated points of γ^m, they lie in an $[m-2]$; thus the m generators which pass through them belong to a $[2m-2]$. They cannot belong to a space $[2m-3]$; for we should then have a $[2m-2]$ containing γ^m and these m generators, i.e. a composite curve of F of order $2m$ lying in a $[2m-2]$, and this we have seen to be impossible if $2m<n$. Hence, through this set of m fixed generators of F there passes a linear system of ∞^{n-2m} primes, so that we have on F a linear system of ∞^{n-2m} curves C_{n-m}; through $n-2m$ points of general position on F there passes one of the curves C_{n-m}.

To make this statement quite accurate we must verify that the curve C_{n-m}, which is the remaining part of the intersection of F with a prime containing the m fixed generators, does not break up. If it does break up it must consist of γ^m and $n-2m$ generators, so that we have a prime containing γ^m, the m fixed generators, and $n-2m$ other generators. But γ^m, the m fixed generators, and $n-2m-1$ other generators arbitrarily chosen, determine a prime which contains them; hence the remaining

* When we have an elliptic normal curve of order s in $[s-1]$ then the set of s points in which it is met by any prime $[s-2]$ is called a set of *associated points*.

generator in which the prime meets F is determined by the choice of the $n-2m-1$ arbitrary generators. This proves that the prime which contains the m fixed generators and $n-2m$ arbitrary points of F meets F in a curve C_{n-m} which does not break up. Through $n-2m-1$ arbitrary points of F there pass ∞^1 curves C_{n-m} forming a pencil, all these curves having also one other point in common.

The surface F can be generated by a (1, 1) correspondence between γ^m and any one of the curves C_{n-m}.

If, in particular, $m=\frac{1}{2}(n-1)$, we have a surface of odd order with a single minimum directrix of order $\frac{1}{2}(n-1)$; there are on this surface ∞^1 curves of order $\frac{1}{2}(n+1)$, which all pass through the same point.

282. Consider now surfaces F of the class (*b*); the surface is of even order n, and there is on it a minimum directrix γ^m of order $m=\frac{1}{2}n$. We enquire whether there are other directrices of this same order. Just as for surfaces of the class (*a*) such a curve is given by a prime containing a set of m fixed generators which meet γ^m in a set of m associated points.

Such a set of generators lies, as before, in a space $[2m-2]$; but we cannot now assert that they do not lie in a $[2m-3]$. However, they certainly cannot lie in a $[2m-4]$; for then we should have a $[2m-3]$ or $[n-3]$ containing the composite curve of order n formed by these generators and γ^m.

If the m generators do lie in an $[n-3]$ then this $[n-3]$ is the base of a pencil of primes; these primes give on F ∞^1 curves C_m of order $\frac{1}{2}n$, one such curve passing through any given point of F. A set of generators which meets any one of these curves in associated points meets any other C_m in associated points also; the surface is that generated by a special (1, 1) correspondence between two normal elliptic curves of the same order.

In general the m generators do not lie in an $[n-3]$; they lie then in a prime, which meets F again in a curve C_m of order $\frac{1}{2}n$. The surface has then *two* minimum directrices; a prime through either of them meets F further in m generators, these generators meeting the other minimum directrix in a set of associated points. This is the most general surface of even order n, and is generated by a (1, 1) correspondence between two elliptic normal curves of the same order. This correspondence is *not* special.

When we take a set of m generators through associated points of γ^m it may happen that the prime which they determine contains γ^m itself. If this happens for one set of associated points of γ^m it must happen for all sets, and we have a surface F with *one* minimum directrix of order $m=\frac{1}{2}n$. Any $m-1$ generators of F determine an $[n-3]$; through this there pass the primes of a pencil, giving thus ∞^1 curves $C_{\frac{1}{2}n+1}$ on F. Each of these curves meets γ^m in one point; for the prime meets γ^m in m points of which $m-1$ are on the generators that we have chosen, the remaining one being on $C_{\frac{1}{2}n+1}$. The prime containing γ^m and the generators through a set of associated points of γ^m meets a curve $C_{\frac{1}{2}n+1}$ in $m+1$ associated points, these including its intersection with γ^m. Hence we have the generation of a surface of this type. We take in $[n-1]$ two spaces $[\frac{1}{2}n-1]$ and $[\frac{1}{2}n]$; these have a common point O. In $[\frac{1}{2}n-1]$ we take a normal elliptic curve of order $\frac{1}{2}n$ and in $[\frac{1}{2}n]$ we take a normal elliptic curve of order $\frac{1}{2}n+1$; these curves must have the same modulus and must both pass through O. We then place the curves in (1, 1) correspondence with O as a united point. The correspondence must be such that any set of $\frac{1}{2}n$ points of the second curve, which correspond to a set of $\frac{1}{2}n$ associated points of the first curve, forms, together with O, a set of $\frac{1}{2}n+1$ associated points.

283. Just as for rational ruled surfaces we investigated the curves of lowest order on the surface by considering primes which contained the greatest possible number of generators, so we can proceed for the elliptic ruled surfaces.

If n is even we take $\frac{1}{2}n-1$ generators; these determine an $[n-3]$ which is the base of a pencil of primes. We have thus on the surface ∞^1 curves of order $\frac{1}{2}n+1$; any two of these curves have two intersections, and these two intersections must be in $[n-3]$. All the ∞^1 curves of order $\frac{1}{2}n+1$ pass through these two points, and the prime containing $[n-3]$ and the generator through either of these points meets the surface further in a curve of order $\frac{1}{2}n$. Hence, if m is the order of the minimum directrix on a surface of even order n, $m \leqslant \frac{1}{2}n$.

Similarly, if n is odd we take $\frac{1}{2}(n-1)$ generators, so determining a prime $[n-2]$. This meets the surface further in a curve of order $\frac{1}{2}(n+1)$. Hence, if m is the order of the minimum directrix on a surface of odd order n, $m \leqslant \frac{1}{2}(n+1)$.

This proves that the only surfaces belonging to the class (*c*) are those for which n is odd and $m = \frac{1}{2}(n+1)$.

284. If we consider now a surface belonging to the class (*c*), for which $m = \frac{1}{2}(n+1)$, any curve C_m on it belongs to a space $[m-1]$. Such a curve determines, together with any $m-2$ fixed generators of F, a prime $[2m-3]$. This prime meets F in one other generator; hence, in order to obtain all the curves C_m on F, it is sufficient to consider the sections of F by primes through $m-2$ fixed generators and one variable generator.

Now $m-2$ fixed generators of F belong to a $[2m-5]$; they cannot be contained in a $[2m-6]$, for then they would lie, together with a C_m, in the same $[2m-6+m-1-(m-3)]$ or $[n-3]$, and no simple or composite curve of F of order $m-2+m=n-1$ can lie in an $[n-3]$. Moreover, the $[2m-5]$ containing these $m-2$ fixed generators does not contain any other generators.

This space $[2m-5]$ and any other generator of F determine a prime $[2m-3]$, and this prime meets F in a curve C_m. We have thus on $F \infty^1$ curves C_m; since, from the way in which we have obtained them, they are in (1, 1) correspondence with the generators of F, they form an elliptic family.

Any two of the curves C_m have one intersection. For consider the prime section of F formed by one curve C_m, the $m-2$ fixed generators, and one other generator. Any other curve of order m meets this prime in m points, of which $m-2$ are on the fixed generators and one on the other generator; the remaining intersection is then on C_m.

Hence, to generate this most general surface F of odd order, we take two elliptic curves of the same order m and the same modulus, and place them in (1, 1) correspondence with a united point.

If this correspondence is special, then a set of $m-1$ points on one of the curves which forms, with the united point, an associated set of points gives, on the other curve, a corresponding set of $m-1$ points which also forms, with the united point, an associated set of points. Thus the $m-1$ generators lie in a $[2m-4]$ or $[n-3]$. Then the pencil of primes through $[n-3]$ gives on $F \infty^1$ curves of order m, and these must all meet $[n-3]$ in the same point, since they all meet it in one point which is not on any of the $m-1$ generators. The generator through this point lies in a prime with $[n-3]$, and this prime gives a curve of order $m-1$ on F. Hence, when we generate the most general surface of odd order $2m-1$ in the way described, the correspondence between the two curves must *not* be special.

285. If we take k generators of the elliptic normal surface F in $[n-1]$ then, to whatever class the surface may belong, a space $[n-3]$ containing these generators meets F, in general, in these generators and a number of isolated points. In order that this may be true it is necessary that the space to which the k generators belong should not contain a directrix curve of F, and this is certainly always true when $k<m$, the order of the minimum directrix. A prime through $[n-3]$ meets F in a curve of order $n-k$, and, of the $n-k$ intersections of this curve with $[n-3]$, k lie on the generators, while the remaining $n-2k$ give isolated intersections of $[n-3]$ with F. Thus, if $k<m$, any S_{n-3} containing k generators of F meets F again in $n-2k$ isolated points.

286. In order to find, for the surface of class (*c*), how many curves C_m pass through a given point P of F, we have to obtain those primes which contain P and $m-2$ fixed generators, and which also contain another generator of F. Now the $m-2$ fixed generators and P determine a $[2m-4]$ or $[n-3]$, and this, as we have just proved, meets F in two other points Q and Q'. Then the prime which contains $[n-3]$ and the generator through Q meets F in a C_m passing through P, and we have a second C_m passing through P if we take the prime which contains $[n-3]$ and the generator through Q'. Hence *through any point of F there pass two of the minimum directrices.*

The following result can also be obtained by arguments similar to those just used. *An elliptic ruled surface of order n with a minimum directrix of order m contains $\infty^{2\mu-n}$ elliptic curves of order μ, for all values of μ for which $n>\mu>n-m$. Through $2\mu-n$ points of general position on the surface there pass two of the curves.* The only exception is for the surface of class (*b*) with ∞^1 minimum directrices, when $\mu=\frac{1}{2}n+1$.

287. Suppose now that we have in $[n-1]$ a normal elliptic ruled surface F of order n, on which two generators intersect. If we project from their point of intersection on to an $[n-2]$ we obtain an elliptic ruled surface of order $n-2$, which is therefore a cone. Hence on F we have a line passing through the intersection of the two generators and meeting all the other generators. Since the surface F is not rational this line λ must be a *double line*. Through every point of λ there must pass two generators of F; for otherwise λ would be a directrix and also a generator, one variable generator passing through each point of λ, or else λ would be a double generator. In the first case F would be rational and in the second case a prime section of F would be a curve C_{n-1} in $[n-2]$, the curve having a double point, which means again that F is rational. We have then a surface F with a double line λ; λ is a double directrix, through each point of it there pass two generators of F.

Such a surface cannot contain a directrix curve of order $\nu<n-2$; for, since such a curve is contained in $[\nu-1]$, the $[\nu+1]$ containing this curve and λ would contain the whole of F. But there is an infinity of curves of order $n-2$ on F; such curves are all obtained by means of primes through two fixed intersecting generators, so that there are ∞^{n-4} such curves. Thus the surface F is generated by a (1, 2) correspondence between a line λ and an elliptic normal curve of order $n-2$. The curves of order $n-2$ on F form a linear system; through $n-4$ points of general position on F there passes *one* such curve. But any two of the curves intersect in $n-4$ points, and through such a set of $n-4$ points there passes a pencil of the curves.

The normal surfaces in [5] with directrix cubic curves

288. We now proceed to study the elliptic sextic ruled surfaces in [3] as projections of normal surfaces in higher space. All elliptic sextic ruled surfaces are projections of normal surfaces in [5]. We project the normal surface F from a line l which does not meet it on to a [3] Σ, and we thus obtain one of the surfaces f. The planes joining l to the points of F meet Σ in the points of f, while the solids joining l to the generators of F meet Σ in the generators of F.

The general surface F has two elliptic plane cubic curves Γ_1 and Γ_2 on it and can be generated by means of a non-special (1, 1) correspondence between Γ_1 and Γ_2*.

The tangents of F form a four-dimensional locus; this can be regarded as the locus of ∞^3 lines, ∞^2 planes or ∞^1 solids †; these ∞^1 solids are, in fact, determined by the pairs of tangents of Γ_1 and Γ_2 at corresponding points. Thus any two tangent solids of F have a line in common meeting the planes of Γ_1 and Γ_2.

We can set up a correspondence between the points B and C of Γ_2 by saying that B and C shall correspond when the solid which is determined by l and the tangent to Γ_1 at the point A on the generator through B meets the plane of Γ_2 on the tangent at C. In this way we have a (6, 6) correspondence of valency zero, the six points C which correspond to a given point B lying on a conic. Now if a point B coincides with one of its corresponding points C there is a [4] through l containing the tangents of Γ_1 and Γ_2 at A and B, and conversely. When this is so the solid containing the tangents to Γ_1 and Γ_2 at a pair of corresponding points meets l. There are therefore twelve such solids; or the locus of tangents of F is an M_4^{12}.

289. Through a general point P of the space [5] there passes a unique line meeting the planes of Γ_1 and Γ_2‡; let the points of meeting be O_1 and O_2. There is a finite number of chords of F passing through P||; let one of these meet F in X and Y.

The solid through O_1O_2P and the generator of F which passes through X meets F further in at least five points, namely, Y, two points of Γ_1 and two points of Γ_2. We therefore conclude ¶ that this solid contains also the generator of F which passes through Y. The lines through O_2 in the plane of Γ_2 cut out a g_3^1 on that curve; the generators of F through a set of this g_3^1 meet Γ_1 in three points forming also a set of a g_3^1; and corresponding to each chord of F passing through P there are two of the three points of a set collinear with O_1. Now the lines through O_1 in the plane of Γ_1 cut out a second g_3^1 on that curve, and there are just three pairs of points on Γ_1 which are common to two linear series g_3^1.**

Hence *there are three chords of F passing through a general point P of the space* [5].

Through any two points X, Y of F there pass two directrix quartic

* § 282.

† § 51.

‡ This line is the intersection of the solid containing O and Γ_1 with the solid containing O and Γ_2.

|| Cf. § 52.

¶ § 285.

** Cf. the footnote to § 134.

curves Q_1 and Q_2*. Through any point P of XY there passes a second chord PX_1Y_1 of Q_1 and a second chord PX_2Y_2 of Q_2; thus the existence of one chord of F through P at once implies the existence of three. The four points X_1, Y_1, X_2, Y_2 lie on another directrix quartic curve.

290. *Elliptic sextic ruled surfaces in* [4]. If we project from P on to a [4] we see that a general elliptic sextic ruled surface in [4] has three double points; it contains two plane cubic curves and three plane quartic curves. Each of the plane quartics has double points at two of the double points of the surface.

If P, instead of occupying a general position, is at the vertex of a quadric cone which contains a directrix quartic Q (there are four such positions of P possible for each directrix quartic, and the locus of such positions will be a surface) we obtain in [4] an elliptic sextic ruled surface with a double conic. It can be obtained by taking two planes in [4] and then a conic in one of the planes and an elliptic cubic curve in the other, both these curves passing through the intersection of the planes; a (1, 2) correspondence between the conic and the cubic with a united point gives the surface.

If P is taken to lie in the plane of Γ_1 or the plane of Γ_2 we obtain in [4] an elliptic sextic ruled surface with a triple line. The surface is given by a (1, 3) correspondence between a line and an elliptic plane cubic, the line not meeting the plane of the cubic curve.

291. We have seen that there are three chords of F passing through a general point of [5]. If the point is such that two of the three chords coincide it will have to lie on some primal V_4. Instead of having three chords PXY, PX_1Y_1 and PX_2Y_2 we shall have only two chords PXY and PX_0Y_0, and one of the two directrix quartics through X_0 and Y_0 is such that its tangents at X_0 and Y_0 intersect. Conversely, if we take two points X_0 and Y_0 on a directrix quartic of F such that the tangents of the quartic at these two points intersect†, then, if any point is taken on X_0Y_0, there is no other chord of the quartic passing through it, the projection of the quartic from this point on to a plane having a tacnode. There is another directrix quartic of F passing through X_0 and Y_0 and there will be a second chord of this second quartic passing through any point on X_0Y_0. Thus any point on X_0Y_0 is such that only two chords of F pass through it. V_4 can therefore be defined as the locus of chords of F such as X_0Y_0.

We shall now examine some of the properties of V_4 which will be of use in the sequel, and this affords an opportunity of introducing an idea

* § 286.

† Each tangent of the quartic is met by four others.

of which we have not availed ourselves before—namely, we can regard the normal surface F as *the projection of another normal surface, in space of one higher dimension, from a point of itself*; the order of this other normal surface being one higher than that of F.

292. Take a general normal elliptic ruled surface F_0 of the seventh order in [6]. There are on this surface ∞^1 elliptic quartic curves; through any point of F_0 there pass two of these curves, while any two of the curves have one intersection*. The chords of F_0 form in [6] a primal M_5 whose order is the number of its intersection with an arbitrary line. But the projection of F_0 from this line is an elliptic ruled surface of the seventh order in [4] which is known, by a general result†, to have seven double points. Hence the chords of F_0 form an M_5^7. Now the projection of F_0 on to [4] from a line meeting it is an elliptic sextic ruled surface, which we have seen to have three double points. Hence such a line meets three chords of F_0 in points other than that in which it meets F_0. Thus F_0 is a quadruple surface on M_5^7.

A general chord of F_0 does not meet any others, because the projection of F_0 from the chord is an elliptic quintic ruled surface in [4] which has no double points. But if the chord of F_0 meets it in two points which are on the same directrix quartic there passes a second chord of F_0 through every point of the first chord; the projection from the chord now gives the elliptic quintic ruled surface in [4] with a double line‡. Thus through any point which lies in a solid containing a directrix quartic of F_0 there pass two chords of F_0; these solids, of which there are ∞^1, form a locus M_4 which is a double locus on M_5^7. It can be shewn that if there is any point, not on F_0 itself, through which there pass two chords of F_0, then the intersections of these chords with F_0 are four points lying on the same directrix quartic of F_0. Thus M_4 is the only double locus on M_5^7.

To find the order of M_4 we take a prime section; this gives the quadrisecant planes of an elliptic curve C_7^1 of the seventh order in [5]. There are

* §§ 284, 286.

† A ruled surface of order n and genus p in [4] has $\frac{1}{2}(n-2)(n-3)-3p$ double points. See Tanturri, *Atti Torino*, 35 (1900), 441. Some of our former work gives particular cases of this general result. For $n=4$ and $p=0$ we see that a rational ruled quartic surface in [4] has one double point and therefore that there is one chord of a rational normal quartic ruled surface passing through a general point of [5] (§ 81). For $n=5$ and $p=0$ the rational quintic ruled surface in [4] has three double points and the chords of the normal surface in [6] form an M_5^3 (§ 124). For $n=5$ and $p=1$ the elliptic quintic ruled surface in [4] has no double points (§ 160). For $n=6$ and $p=0$ the rational sextic ruled surface in [4] has six double points and the chords of the normal surface form an M_5^6 (§ 174). For $n=6$ and $p=1$ the elliptic sextic ruled surface in [4] has three double points and there are three chords of the normal surface through a point of [5] (§ 289).

‡ § 164.

∞^1 such planes, two passing through each point of the curve*; they form an M_3 which is a prime section of M_4, and the order of M_3 is simply the number of quadrisecant planes of $C_7{}^1$ which meet a general plane of [5]. But this number is 7, as is seen on making use of a general result due to Giambelli†. Thus we have an $M_3{}^7$ on which $C_7{}^1$ is a double curve, and so the solids containing the directrix quartics of F_0 form an $M_4{}^7$ on which F_0 is a double surface.

Now let us project F_0 from a point O of itself on to [5]; we obtain the normal elliptic sextic ruled surface F.

A plane through O meets $M_4{}^7$ in five points other than O; it meets $M_5{}^7$ in a curve of the seventh order with a quadruple point at O and these five points for double points; this curve of the seventh order will then be of genus 4. The plane meets [5] in a line, and the fact that any line through O in the plane meets the curve again in three points corresponds to the fact that there are three chords of F passing through each point of the line in which the plane meets [5]. Now the lines through O give a pencil of ∞^1 sets of three points upon a curve of genus 4; thus there are, by a result originally due to Riemann, $2(3+4-1)$ or twelve positions of the line for which two of the three points coincide; which is the same as saying that twelve tangents can be drawn to the curve from the quadruple point. Hence, given any line in [5] there are twelve points on it such that two of the three chords of F, which pass through any one of them, coincide.

Hence the locus V_4 of such points is of order 12; we denote it by $V_4{}^{12}$. It must not be confused with $M_4{}^{12}$, the locus of tangents of F.

293. There are two directrix quartics of F_0 passing through O; these give on projection the cubics Γ_1 and Γ_2 on F. The directrix quartics of F_0 which do not pass through O give ∞^1 of the directrix quartics on F; there are ∞^2 elliptic quintic curves on F_0 which pass through O and these give on projection ∞^2 elliptic quartic curves on F.

Consider now a point U of [5] which is the vertex of a quadric cone containing a directrix quartic of F. In general, this quartic is the projection of a directrix quintic of F_0 which passes through O; then the line OU meets ∞^1 chords of this quintic and so lies on $M_5{}^7$. It meets $M_4{}^7$ in one point other than O‡. Then a plane through OU meets $M_5{}^7$ in OU

* For the projection of $C_7{}^1$ from a point of itself on to a [4] is an elliptic sextic curve having two trisecants (cf. § 253).

† *Memorie Torino* (2), 59 (1909), 489.

‡ Each quartic on F_0 meets the quintic in two points; the [3] containing the quartic meets the [4] containing the quintic in the line joining the two points. We have thus on the quintic a symmetrical (2, 2) correspondence; two points of the quintic corresponding when they lie on the same directrix quartic of F_0. The chords of the quintic meeting OU generate a cubic ruled surface and give a symmetrical (1, 1) correspondence. Both these symmetrical correspondences are of valency one and they have *one* common pair of points, the quintic being elliptic.

and a sextic curve; this sextic has a triple point at O and double points at those four points in which the plane meets M_4^7 and which themselves do not lie on OU. It is therefore of genus 3 and ten tangents can be drawn to it from the triple point. Hence, if in [5] we take a line l which passes through the vertex U of a quadric cone containing a directrix quartic of F, the line will only meet V_4^{12} in ten points other than U.

A similar argument can be used when the quartic on F is the projection of a quartic on F_0 which does not pass through O; the same result is obtained.

Thus the vertices of the quadric cones which contain the directrix quartics of F are *double points* on V_4^{12}; the locus of the vertices will be a *double surface* on V_4^{12}.

The point U is a *quadruple point* of M_4^{12}, since there are *four* tangents of F passing through it.

Take now a line through O lying in the solid containing one of the two directrix quartics of F_0 which pass through O. This line lies on M_4^7 and any plane through the line will meet M_4^7 in four further points*. This same plane meets M_5^7 in the line, counted doubly, and a quintic curve; this quintic curve has a double point at O and four other double points. It is therefore elliptic, and six tangents can be drawn to it from its double point. Hence, if we take a line l meeting the plane of one of the cubic curves on F it will only meet V_4^{12} in six points other than its intersection with the plane; or the planes of Γ_1 and Γ_2 are *sextuple planes* on V_4^{12}.

The planes of Γ_1 and Γ_2 are also sextuple planes on M_4^{12}; through a general point of either plane there pass six tangents of F.

Through any point of V_4^{12} there pass two chords XY and X_0Y_0 of F. The two quartic curves of F which pass through X and Y coincide, while one of those through X_0 and Y_0 is such that its tangents at X_0 and Y_0 intersect; the other quartic through X_0 and Y_0 is the same as the one through X and Y. Now consider a line l which lies in the [3] determined by two generators g and g' of F; there are twelve points of V_4^{12} on l and through each of these there passes a transversal to g and g'. We now enquire how many of these twelve transversals give a pair of points X and Y on g and g'; the remaining ones will give pairs of points X_0 and Y_0.

Consider the quartics of F passing through a point of g; there are ∞^1 of them and any two intersect in one further point. They thus form an elliptic family, since each curve may be put into correspondence with its second intersection with a fixed curve of the family. Now we can regard this family as ∞^1 pairs of curves, since if any point is taken on g' there are two and only two curves of the family passing through it. Thus these

* A solid through O meets M_4^7 in an elliptic curve of the seventh order with a double point at O; but if the solid contains a line through O on M_4^7 it meets it further in an elliptic sextic curve which meets the line in O and in one other point.

pairs, associated with the points of g', form a rational family; there are therefore four double elements, just as a g_2^1 on an elliptic curve has four double points. Hence, given a point X on g there are four points Y on g' such that the two quartics of F which pass through X and Y coincide.

Now we can set up a correspondence between the points P and Q of g', saying that the points P and Q correspond when the two directrix quartics through P and Q' coincide, Q' being the intersection of g with the transversal to g and l from Q. We have thus a (4, 4) correspondence, and therefore eight coincidences. Hence there are eight pairs of points X and Y on g and g' such that XY meets l and the two directrix quartics of F which pass through X and Y coincide.

This argument must be slightly modified if l meets the plane of one of the curves Γ_1, Γ_2. Suppose that l meets the plane of Γ_1 in a point O, we have a line through O meeting g in a point A and g' in a point A', A and A' being the intersections of Γ_1 with g and g'. Then through A and a given point of g' there passes only one directrix quartic of F, the other being the degenerate one consisting of Γ_1 and g'. Hence the four points of g', which are such that the two directrix quartics which are determined by A and any one of them coincide, must all be at the point A'. In the correspondence between the points P and Q of g', when P is at A' the four corresponding points Q are also at A'. Hence A' counts four times among the eight points of g' for which P coincides with one of its corresponding points Q. There are four further coincidences.

We have then the following: if a line l is taken to meet the plane of one of the directrix cubics of F in a point O and to lie in the solid containing a pair of generators g, g' of F (which will meet the cubic in a pair of points collinear with O) l will meet V_4^{12} in six points other than O; if the transversals are drawn from these points to g and g', four of them give pairs of points X, Y on g, g', while the remaining two give pairs of points X_0, Y_0.

294. Take now a line l of general position in [5] and project F from l on to a [3] Σ. A prime through l meets F in an elliptic sextic curve of which nine chords meet l. Thus the chords of F which meet l meet F in a curve C_{18} of order 18. Since the solid containing l and an arbitrary generator of F meets F further in four points*, C_{18} meets each generator in four points.

Thus after projection we obtain in Σ a general elliptic ruled surface f of the sixth order with a double curve C_9 of the ninth order meeting each generator in four points. C_9 is the projection of C_{18} from l.

Now there is a (3, 1) correspondence between the points of C_9 and the points of l, two points corresponding when the line joining them is a chord

* § 285.

of F, and the twelve points in which l meets V_4^{12} are branch-points of the correspondence. Then Zeuthen's formula shews that C_9 is a curve C_9^4 of genus 4. Further, there is a (1, 2) correspondence between C_9^4 and C_{18}, and the correspondence has twelve branch-points on C_9^4, these arising from the twelve intersections of l with M_4^{12} or the twelve points of l which lie on tangents of F. A second application of Zeuthen's formula now shews that C_{18} is a curve C_{18}^{13} of genus 13. Since C_{18}^{13} meets each generator of F in four points it is of genus $19-x$, where x is the number of its double points*. Thus C_{18}^{13} has six double points. Let A be one of these. Then there are two chords AB and AC of C_{18}^{13} passing through A and meeting l; this forces the chord BC to meet l also, and B and C are double points of C_{18}^{13}. Thus the six double points lie in two planes passing through l, each plane containing three of them. On projecting we have two triple points on C_9^4.

The (1, 4) correspondence between Γ_1 and C_{18}^{13} shews that there are twenty-four generators of F touching C_{18}^{13}; hence there are also twenty-four generators of f touching C_9^4 (cf. § 256).

The prime determined by l and the plane of Γ_1 contains three generators of F, as also does that determined by l and the plane of Γ_2. Thus f has two tritangent planes.

f is generated by two elliptic cubics in (1, 1) correspondence.

295. There are ∞^2 directrix quartic curves on F, and through any two points of F there pass two of these. There are four quadric cones through any such curve, and we may specialise the position of l so that it passes through the vertex U of a quadric cone containing a directrix quartic C_4^1. The chords of F which meet l now meet F in the points of C_4^1 and a curve C_{14} which meets every generator of F in three points; when we project from l on to Σ we obtain a surface f whose double curve is C_2+C_7.

Since U is a double point on V_4^{12} there are ten branch-points of the (3, 1) correspondence between C_7 and l; hence C_7 is a C_7^3. The (1, 2) correspondence between C_7^3 and C_{14} only has eight branch-points since U is a quadruple point on V_4^{12}; hence C_{14} is a C_{14}^9.

C_{14}^9 meets each generator in three points and is therefore of genus $11-x$, where x is the number of its double points; it has therefore two double points A and B. Through A there pass two chords AA' and AA'' of C_{14}^9 both meeting l; $A'A''$ will then also meet l, and C_4^1 passes through A' and A''. Similarly we have two intersections B' and B'' of C_4^1 and C_{14}^9. There are in all eight intersections of C_4^1 and C_{14}^9 †, the other four lie

* § 17 *supra*.

† Take a [4] through C_4^1; it meets C_{14}^9 in fourteen points and F in C_4^1 and two generators. Since C_{14}^9 meets each of these generators three times it will have to meet C_4^1 eight times.

in pairs on two lines through U. Hence, projecting on to Σ, C_7^3 has two double points and two simple points on C_2 (cf. § 259).

The (1, 3) correspondence between Γ_1 and C_{14}^9 shews that there are sixteen generators of F touching C_{14}^9; there must then be sixteen generators of f touching C_7^3 (cf. § 257).

This surface is generated by a conic and an elliptic cubic in (1, 2) correspondence with a united point. The pairs of points of the cubic corresponding to the points of the conic form a g_2^1 and are therefore collinear with a fixed point* of the curve. Since one of these lines passes through the point of the conic which gives rise to it the planes joining the points of the conic to the pairs of corresponding points on the cubic touch a quadric cone; this is part of the bitangent developable of the surface.

296. We may further choose l to join the vertex U of a quadric cone containing a directrix quartic C_4^1 to the vertex V of a quadric cone containing a directrix quartic D_4^1. C_4^1 and D_4^1 have two intersections X and Y. The chords of F which meet l meet F in C_4^1, D_4^1 and a curve C_{10} which meets each generator of F in two points. Thus on projection we have a surface f with a double curve $C_2+D_2+C_5$.

U and V are both double points of V_4^{12}, so that l meets V_4^{12} in eight other points which are the branch-points of the (3, 1) correspondence between C_5 and l. Hence C_5 is a C_5^2. Since U and V are quadruple points of M_4^{12} there are four branch-points of the (1, 2) correspondence between C_5^2 and C_{10} so that C_{10} is a C_{10}^5. There are eight generators of F touching C_{10}^5 and eight generators of f touching C_5^2.

The curve C_{10}^5, meeting each generator in two points, has no double points. The lines XU and XV meet C_4^1 and D_4^1 again in points U' and V', the line $U'V'$ meets l and U' and V' must lie on C_{10}^5; we have similarly U'' on C_4^1 and C_{10}^5 and V'' on D_4^1 and C_{10}^5 arising from Y. There are in all six intersections of C_{10}^5 with C_4^1 or D_4^1; the remaining four will lie on two lines through U or V respectively. Thus, on projection, C_2 and D_2 have two intersections through which C_5^2 passes; C_5^2 has two other intersections with each conic (cf. § 261).

To generate this surface take two conics in (2, 2) correspondence with two united points P and Q; to P regarded as a point of one conic correspond two points of the other conic one of which is P, and similarly for Q.

The lines joining the pairs of points of one conic which correspond to the points of the other touch a conic; the planes joining these lines to

* If we use elliptic arguments for the points of the cubic curve it is known that a g_2^1 is given by $\alpha+\beta\equiv c$, where α and β are the arguments for a pair of points of the g_2^1 and c is a constant; different values of c give ∞^1 g_2^1's on the curve. If then we take the point of the curve whose elliptic argument is $\gamma\equiv -c$ we have $\alpha+\beta+\gamma\equiv 0$ and each pair of the g_2^1 is collinear with γ.

the points of the other conic from which they arise touch a quadric cone, two lines passing through the points which give rise to them. Thus this surface has two quadric cones belonging to its bitangent developable.

297. Take now l to lie in the solid determined by a pair of generators g, g' of F. A prime through l meets this solid in a plane containing a transversal of l, g, g'; it meets F in an elliptic sextic curve which meets g and g' at their intersections with the transversal and which has eight other chords that meet l. Hence the chords of F which meet l meet F in g, g' and a curve C_{16} of order 16; this last curve meets each generator of F in four points.

The solid $gg'l$ meets F further in two points X and Y. Through X there passes a transversal of g and l and also a transversal of g' and l, so that X is a double point of C_{16}. Similarly Y is a double point of C_{16}. Associated with X we have intersections of C_{16} with each of g and g', namely, the points in which g and g' are met by the plane Xl. Similarly the plane Yl meets g and g' in points which lie on C_{16}. The remaining points of intersection of C_{16} with g and g', two on each generator, lie on two transversals of l, g, g'. Hence when we project from l on to Σ we obtain a surface f with a double generator G and a double curve C_8, C_8 having two double points and two simple points on G (cf. § 265).

There are twelve points on l for which two of the three chords of F which pass through them coincide; we have seen* that for eight of the twelve points the two chords of C_{16} coincide, while for the remaining four points it is a chord of C_{16} which coincides with the transversal to g and g'. Thus there are eight branch-points of the (2, 1) correspondence between C_8 and l, so that C_8 is a $C_8{}^3$. There are twelve tangents of C_{16} meeting l so that the (1, 2) correspondence between $C_8{}^3$ and C_{16} has twelve branch-points and C_{16} is a $C_{16}{}^{11}$. It has only the two double points X and Y.

There are twenty generators of F touching $C_{16}{}^{11}$ as is seen at once by the application of Zeuthen's formula to the (1, 4) correspondence between Γ_1 and $C_{16}{}^{11}$; there will then be twenty generators of f touching $C_8{}^3$ (cf. § 265).

f is generated by two elliptic plane cubics in (1, 1) correspondence, the correspondence being specialised to give the double generator.

298. Take the two generators g and g' of F; the solid which they determine meets F in two further points X and Y. Take $C_4{}^1$, one of the two directrix quartics through X and Y, meeting g in Z and g' in Z'. Then the four points $XYZZ'$ must be coplanar, since the solid gg' cannot contain $C_4{}^1$.

* § 293.

Through X there passes a transversal of g and g'; but the only lines which are trisecant to F are those lying in the planes of its directrix cubics, hence we may say that X is on Γ_1 and Y on Γ_2.

The lines XZ and YZ' meet in a point U; by suitably selecting the points where g and g' meet Γ_1 we can cause U to be the vertex of a quadric cone through $C_4{}^1$.

This being done, take a line l through U which lies in the solid gg'. The chords of F which meet l meet F in g, g', $C_4{}^1$ and a curve C_{12} meeting each generator of F in three points. Through X there passes a transversal of g' and l meeting g' in X' say, and the lines XZ and $X'Z$ will meet l; C_{12} must pass through X' and X. Similarly, we have a point Y' on g; C_{12} will pass through Y' and Y.

Thus on projecting from l we have in Σ a surface f whose double curve consists of a conic, a double generator meeting the conic in two points and a sextic curve C_6 passing through these two points (cf. § 266). C_6 meets the double generator in two further points, these are projections of pairs of intersections of C_{12} with g and g'.

There are ten points of $V_4{}^{12}$ on l, other than U; six of these give rise to coincidences of the two chords of C_{12} which pass through them, while the remaining four give a coincidence of a chord of C_{12} with a transversal of g and g'. Thus the (2, 1) correspondence between C_6 and l has six branch-points, so that C_6 is a $C_6{}^2$. There are eight tangents of C_{12} meeting l so that the (1, 2) correspondence between $C_6{}^2$ and C_{12} has eight branch-points and C_{12} is a $C_{12}{}^7$. It has no double points, and it touches twelve generators of F.

This surface f is generated by a (2, 1) correspondence between an elliptic cubic and a conic with one united point. The conic is part of the double curve. If P is the united point of the correspondence the plane of the cubic meets that of the conic in a line through P; this line will meet the cubic again in two points P', P'' and the conic in one point Q; the points P' and P'' must be the two points of the cubic which correspond to the point Q of the conic.

The pairs of points of the cubic which correspond to the points of the conic form a $g_2{}^1$ on the curve; thus these pairs must be on lines through a fixed point of the curve, in fact through P. One of them $PP'P''$ passes through its corresponding point Q, so that the planes joining the points of the conic to the corresponding pairs of points on the cubic touch a quadric cone which is part of the bitangent developable of the surface.

299. We shall now suppose the position of l to be specialised so that l lies in a solid K' containing a directrix quartic $C_4{}^1$ of F. Then the projected surface f has a directrix line R, the intersection of Σ and K'. Any plane in K' passing through l meets $C_4{}^1$ in four points, while a prime through

K' meets F further in two generators; hence through any point of R there pass four generators, while any plane through R contains two generators, and f is of the type III (B).

A prime through l meets F in an elliptic sextic curve, nine of whose chords meet l; but this sextic has four intersections with C_4^1 which lie in a plane through l, and six of the nine chords arise from these. Through any point of C_4^1 there pass three of its chords meeting l. Hence the chords of F which meet l meet F in the curve C_4^1 counted three times and in a curve C_6. This curve meets each generator of F in one point; for the solid determined by l and the generator meets F in four further points of which three are on C_4^1. Thus we have an elliptic curve C_6^1, and since there are eight tangents of C_4^1 meeting l there are four tangents of C_6^1 meeting l, and its projection from l is a twisted cubic C_3^0.

To generate this surface we take a line and an elliptic cubic curve, placing them in (1, 4) correspondence with a united point. The sets of four points on the cubic curve which correspond to the points of the line R form a g_4^1; they can therefore be cut out by conics through two fixed points P_1, P_2 of the curve and two other fixed points Q_1 and Q_2 in the plane of the curve. One conic is the line pair Q_1Q_2, P_1P_2, and this gives rise to a tritangent plane of the surface passing through Q_1Q_2. The plane of the cubic curve is a second tritangent plane of the surface. Since a g_4^1 and a g_2^1 on an elliptic curve have two pairs of points in common* there are two planes passing through R which also belong to that part of the bitangent developable other than the planes through R; these join points of R to pairs of points on the cubic.

300. It may happen, however, that the g_4^1 on the cubic curve is such that each of its sets of four points consists of two pairs of a g_2^1; this will happen if l passes through the vertex of a quadric cone containing C_4^1. We can see this geometrically thus: take two points P_1, P_2 of the cubic, the line joining them meeting the curve again in P_3. Then take Q_1 and Q_2 on a line through P_3 so that they separate P_3 and its polar line in regard to the cubic harmonically. Then the conics through P_1, P_2, Q_1, Q_2 cut out on the curve a g_4^1 whose sets of four points consist each of two sets of the g_2^1 given by the lines through P_3. The polar line of P_3 in regard to the cubic curve is also the polar of P_3 in regard to all the conics.

The planes joining the points of R to the corresponding pairs of the g_2^1 touch a quadric cone with vertex P_3 (since there is a united point). This, as well as the planes of the pencil R, is part of the bitangent developable of the surface. The remaining part has two double planes, one is the plane of the cubic and the other passes through Q_1Q_2; these also touch the quadric cone.

* Cf. the footnote to § 134.

301. Now we may further suppose that l passes through the vertices of two quadric cones containing C_4^1. To generate the projected surface in Σ we now take a line and an elliptic cubic in (1, 4) correspondence; but if S, T, U, V are the four points of the cubic corresponding to a point of the line the pairs ST, UV must belong to one g_2^1 and the pairs SU, TV to another g_2^1. The existence of such sets of points on the cubic curve is clear. For take any point X of the curve and draw from X two tangents touching the curve in Y and Z. If a line is drawn through Y meeting the curve again in S and T and ZS, ZT meet the curve again in U, V then Y, U, V are collinear* and the sets of four points S, T, U, V vary in a series such as we require; different sets of the series are given by the different lines YST through Y. There are now two quadric cones belonging to the bitangent developable of the surface.

302. The pencil of [4]'s through the solid K' containing C_4^1 meet F further in pairs of generators; the solids determined by these pairs of generators meet K' in planes forming a developable. In general, no plane of this developable will contain a given line in K'; but we can choose l to lie in one of the planes. Then the projected surface f will have a double generator and will be of the type III (D). The chords of F which meet l now meet F in C_4^1 counted three times, g, g' and another directrix quartic D_4^1.

To generate this surface we again take a line and an elliptic cubic in (1, 4) correspondence with a united point P, but the correspondence must be specialised so that two of the three points of the cubic which correspond to P and do not coincide with it are collinear with it.

303. There is certainly a plane of the developable passing through the vertex of a quadric cone containing C_4^1; hence we can take l to pass through it also. Then the g_4^1 on the elliptic cubic curve is such that each of its sets of four points consists of two sets of a g_2^1, and the surface has a quadric cone as part of its bitangent developable.

304. Now let us take l to meet the plane of Γ_1 in a point O. A prime passing through l meets F in an elliptic sextic curve with a trisecant through O; there are six chords of this curve, besides the trisecant, which meet l. Hence the chords of F which meet l meet F in Γ_1 counted twice and a curve C_{12}. The curve C_{12} meets each generator of F in two points, as is seen at once by considering the solid through l and the generator.

* This follows from the fact that all cubic curves through eight points of a plane have a ninth point in common.

We have, on projection from l, a surface f with a directrix line R, the intersection of Σ with the solid $l\Gamma_1$. Through any point of R there pass three generators, while any plane through R contains three generators; f is of the type III (E). It has a double curve C_6, the projection of C_{12}.

The point O is a sextuple point on V_4^{12}, l having six other intersections with V_4^{12}. Hence the (3, 1) correspondence between C_6 and l has six branch-points, so that C_6 is a C_6^1. O is also a sextuple point on M_4^{12}, there being six tangents of Γ_1 passing through O and six other tangents of F meeting l; hence the (1, 2) correspondence between C_6^1 and C_{12} has six branch-points and C_{12} is a C_{12}^4.

Since C_{12}^4 meets each generator of F twice it must have three double points. These will lie in a plane through l and give on projection a triple point of C_6^1. Also C_{12}^4 meets Γ_1 in six points lying two on each of three lines through O, so that R is a trisecant of C_6^1. C_6^1 has a triple point not lying on R.

This surface is generated by a line and an elliptic cubic in (1, 3) correspondence.

305. Suppose now that l, as well as meeting the plane of Γ_1 in a point O, lies in a solid containing a pair of generators of F. Then the chords of F which meet l meet F in g, g', Γ_1 counted twice and a curve C_{10} which meets every generator of F in two points. The solid gg' meets F further in a point X of Γ_1 and a point Y of Γ_2; C_{10} has a double point at Y, and meets Γ_1 in four points lying two on each of two lines through O.

We thus have on projection a surface f whose double curve is $3R+G+C_5$; C_5 has a double point on G and meets it in one other point, and meets R in two points. R and G intersect (cf. § 273).

The line l meets V_4^{12} in six points other than O; we have seen (cf. the end of § 293) that four of these six points are branch-points of the (2, 1) correspondence between C_5 and l, so that C_5 is an elliptic curve C_5^1. There are six tangents of Γ_1 passing through O, so that there are six other tangents of F meeting l; the (1, 2) correspondence between C_5^1 and C_{10} has six branch-points. Thus C_{10} is a C_{10}^4. It has the one double point Y.

To generate this surface we again take a line and an elliptic cubic in (1, 3) correspondence; but the correspondence must be specialised to give the double generator.

306. Choosing again l to meet the plane of Γ_1 in a point O we can further secure that the solid $l\Gamma_1$ contains a generator g of F. Then the projected surface f has a directrix R—the intersection of this solid with Σ—which is also a generator; through any point of R there pass three other generators, while any plane through R contains two other generators. Thus f is of the type IV (B).

A prime through l meets F in an elliptic sextic curve; there is a trisecant of this curve meeting l and the plane containing l and the trisecant meets the curve in another point. There are three chords of the curve which meet l and do not lie in this quadrisecant plane.

Thus the points of F which lie on chords meeting l and not on g or Γ_1 lie on a curve C_6 of the sixth order. This is an elliptic curve $C_6{}^1$ meeting each generator of F in one point.

To generate the surface in Σ we take a line and an elliptic cubic in (1, 3) correspondence; they have a point of intersection, but it is not a united point.

307. Take now a pair of generators g, g' of F and let the [4] determined by g, g' and Γ_1 meet F further in a generator h. Then the two solids gg' and $\Gamma_1 h$ have a plane of intersection; let us project F from a line l in this plane which does not meet the surface.

The solid $l\Gamma_1 h$ meets Σ in a line R which is a directrix and also a generator of f; through any point of R there pass three other generators, while any plane through R contains two other generators; there is also a double generator—the intersection of Σ with the solid lgg'. Thus f is of the type IV (D).

A prime through l meets F in an elliptic sextic curve; there is a trisecant of this curve meeting l, while the plane of l and the trisecant meets the curve in a fourth point. There is another chord of the curve meeting l, g and g'. There are two other chords of the curve meeting l, and the points of F, not on g, g', h or Γ_1, whichl ie on chords of F meeting l are on an elliptic quartic directrix $C_4{}^1$. This projects into a conic meeting R; the double curve of F is $6R+G+C_2$.

To generate f we take a line and an elliptic cubic in (1, 3) correspondence, the correspondence being specialised to give a double generator. The line meets the cubic but there is no united point. Or we may take a line and a conic in (2, 3) correspondence with a united point, specialising to obtain the double generator.

308. Now suppose that l meets the plane of Γ_1 in a point O_1 and the plane of Γ_2 in a point O_2. Then the projected surface has two directrices R and R', and through any point of either of these pass three generators meeting the other. The lines in the plane of Γ_2 through O_2 meet Γ_2 in sets of a $g_3{}^1$, and the generators of F through these sets of points meet Γ_1 in the sets of a $g_3{}^1$. There is a second $g_3{}^1$ on Γ_1 cut out by lines through O_1, and since two series $g_3{}^1$ on an elliptic curve have three pairs of points in common we conclude that there are three pairs of generators of F which determine solids containing l. The surface f has then three double generators—it is of the type VI (B).

To generate f we take two lines in (3, 3) correspondence; the correspondence being specialised to give three double generators.

309. There is in [5] an elliptic sextic ruled surface F with only one directrix cubic Γ; any three generators which meet Γ in three collinear points lie in a [4] containing Γ and conversely any [4] containing Γ meets F again in three generators which meet Γ in three collinear points*.

Now project this surface on to a solid Σ from a line l meeting the plane of Γ in a point O. The solid $l\Gamma$ meets Σ in a line R which is a directrix of the projected surface f; through any point of R there pass three generators of f lying in a plane through R. Thus f is of the type VII (B).

To generate the surface we take a line and an elliptic quartic in (1, 3) correspondence with a united point P, the three points of the quartic which correspond to a point of the line lying in a plane through the line. The pencil of planes through the line is related to the range of points on the line; to the point P corresponds the plane through the line and the tangent at P.

To a point of the line corresponds a plane through the line meeting the quartic in three points other than P; these three points are joined by three chords meeting the line. Conversely, through any point of the line pass two chords of the quartic, and the planes determined by these and the line give two corresponding points on the line. Thus we have a (2, 3) correspondence between the points of the line; but P counts twice among the five coincidences. There are thus three double generators of f.

310. There exists also in [5] an elliptic sextic ruled surface F with ∞^1 directrix cubics on it. Then the solid determined by any two generators contains a third*.

Take such a solid containing three generators g, g', g''. The planes of the cubic curves meet this solid in transversals of g, g', g'', i.e. in lines of a regulus. An arbitrary line l in the solid will thus meet the planes of two of the cubic curves. The planes of the cubic curves form a V_3^3†.

Projecting from l on to Σ we have a surface f with two directrices and a triple generator; through any point of either directrix there pass three generators meeting the other. To generate it we take a (3, 3) correspondence between two lines specialised to give the triple generator; the surface is of the type VI (C).

If, however, l is chosen to touch the quadric surface determined by the regulus the projected surface will have a triple generator and a single directrix R; through any point of R there pass three generators lying in a plane through R. The surface is of the type VII (C). To generate this surface we take a line and an elliptic cubic in (1, 3) correspondence; to any point of the line correspond the three intersections of the cubic

* § 282.

† The locus formed by the ∞^1 planes which meet three lines in [5] in related ranges of points.

with a plane through the line. The plane of the cubic contains the triple generator.

The normal surface in [5] with a double line

311. There exists in [5] a normal elliptic sextic ruled surface F with a double line λ; through every point of λ there pass two generators of F*.

The tangent solids of F all pass through λ and meet an arbitrary [3] in the tangent lines of an elliptic quartic curve. We have thus ∞^1 solids forming a line-cone M_4^8, so that there are eight tangents of F meeting an arbitrary line l.

There is on F a linear system of ∞^2 directrix quartic curves; through two general points of F there passes one of these curves, while any two of them intersect in two points through which there passes a pencil of the curves*.

There is a finite number of chords of F passing through a general point of [5]; it is at once seen that this number is 2, for if we take one chord of F through a general point of [5] there is a directrix quartic (and in general only one) passing through its two intersections with F, and there will be a second chord of this quartic passing through the point of the first chord with which we started.

There are points of [5] for which the two chords of F coincide; the locus of such points is a primal V_4. To study this primal V_4 we regard F as the projection of a normal elliptic ruled surface F_0 of the seventh order in [6] from a point O of itself. V_4 can be also defined as the locus of the chords of F which are such that the tangents to the directrix quartic, which passes through the two intersections of the chord with F at these two points, intersect.

312. If we take the general ruled surface of the seventh order in [6] we cannot obtain, as a projection, the sextic surface with a double line. But there is in [6] a normal elliptic ruled surface F_0 of the seventh order having an elliptic cubic curve as a directrix†; if we project this on to [5] from a point O of the cubic curve γ we obtain the sextic ruled surface F with a double line.

The chords of F_0 form an M_5^7 on which F is a quadruple surface and γ a quintuple curve.

There is on F_0 a pencil of elliptic quartic curves with a common point of intersection†; the cubic γ taken with the generator g_0 through this intersection belongs to the pencil of curves. If F_0 is projected from a general point of itself we obtain the general elliptic sextic ruled surface which has two directrix cubic curves; one of these is the projection of γ and the other the projection of that quartic curve of F_0 which passes

* § 287. † § 281.

through the centre of projection. If F_0 is projected from the point common to the pencil of quartics we obtain the sextic surface with ∞^1 cubic curves; if F_0 is projected from a point of g_0 we obtain the sextic surface with only one cubic curve. If, however, we project from a point O of γ we obtain the sextic surface F with a double line.

The locus of the solids which contain the quartic curves on F_0 is a V_4^3, the projection on to [5] from the point common to all the solids being the V_3^3 formed by the planes of the ∞^1 cubic curves on the resulting sextic surface*. This is a double locus on M_5^7; it contains F_0, but F_0 is not a double surface on V_4^3.

A plane through a point O of γ meets M_5^7 in a curve of the seventh order with a quintuple point at O. It meets V_4^3 in two points other than O, which are double points of the curve. The curve is therefore of genus 3, and eight tangents can be drawn to it from the quintuple point.

Hence, given an elliptic ruled surface F of the sixth order in [5] which has a double line λ, the primal which is the locus of points of [5] which are such that the two chords of F which pass through them coincide is V_4^8 of order eight.

313. The ∞^1 quartic curves on F_0 give after projection a pencil of quartics on F; this pencil on F has two base-points, one the projection of the single base-point of the pencil on F_0 and the other the intersection of the [5] containing F with the generator of F_0 through O. But, in general, a quartic curve on F is the projection of a quintic curve on F_0 which passes through O; on F_0 there are ∞^3 quintic curves, such that through three general points of F_0 there pass two of them†. Thus through O we have ∞^2 quintic curves on F_0 giving after projection ∞^2 quartic curves on F.

If U is the vertex of a quadric cone containing a directrix quartic of F, the line OU meets ∞^1 chords of F_0 and lies on M_5^7, the quartic being regarded as the projection of a quintic of F_0 which passes through O. The line OU does not meet V_4^3 except in O; thus a plane through OU meets M_5^7 further in a sextic curve having a quadruple point at O and two double points. This curve is of genus 2 and six tangents can be drawn to it from O. Hence if in [5] we take a line l passing through the vertex of a quadric cone which contains a directrix quartic of F this line will only meet V_4^8 in six points other than U; so that U is a *double point* on V_4^8. The same result holds when the quartic on F is the projection of a quartic on F_0.

The point U is a *quadruple point* on the locus M_4^8 formed by the tangents of F, since four tangents of the quartic curve pass through U.

The solids joining γ to the generators of F_0 are, like the solids containing the quartic curves of F_0, double solids on M_5^7. If then we take a line passing through O and lying in one of these solids it is a double line on

* § 310.

† § 286.

M_5^7; a plane through it meets M_5^7 further in a quintic curve with a triple point at O. This curve has also two double points at the intersections, other than O, of the plane with V_4^3. It is therefore of genus 1 and four tangents can be drawn to it from its triple point. Hence if in [5] we take a line which meets the plane containing λ and a generator of F it will only meet V_4^8 in four points other than its intersection with the plane. Hence the planes joining λ to the generators of F are *quadruple planes* on V_4^8.

314. Let us consider now the projection of F from a line l of general position on to a solid Σ. The projection of λ is a line R; through any point of R there pass two generators of the projected surface f, while any plane of Σ passing through R, being the intersection of Σ with a [4] through λ and l, contains four generators of f. This shews that f belongs to the type III (A).

A [4] through l meets F in an elliptic sextic curve with a double point; there are eight chords of this curve which meet l. Hence the chords of F which meet l meet F in the points of a curve C_{16} of order 16.

Take any generator g of F; there is a generator g' which meets it. The [4] determined by l and the plane gg' meets F further in a quartic curve which meets each generator of F in one point; the solid gl meets this curve in three points not on g. We thence conclude that the solid determined by l and any generator of F meets F in three further points. Whence also the curve C_{16} meets each generator of F in three points, and therefore the line λ in four points. These four intersections with λ consist in fact of two double points*.

Hence f has a double curve C_8 meeting each generator in three points, as well as a double directrix R. The chords of F which meet l meet Σ in the points of C_8, so that there is a (2, 1) correspondence between the points of C_8 and the points of l. The eight intersections of l with V_4^8 are the branch-points of the correspondence, so that, by Zeuthen's formula, we have a C_8^3 of genus 3. Further, there is a (1, 2) correspondence between the points of C_8^3 and the points of C_{16}; this also has eight branch-points, since l meets M_4^8 in eight points. Hence we have a C_{16}^9.

Since C_{16}^9 meets each generator of F in three points it must, by Segre's formula for the genus of a curve on a ruled surface, have six double points which are not double points of F. These double points lie three in each of two planes through l, so that C_8^3 has two triple points.

The (1, 3) correspondence between a directrix quartic of F and C_{16}^9

* The planes of pairs of intersecting generators of F are projected from λ by solids forming a quadric line-cone; there are two of these solids meeting l. The pairs of generators contained in these solids meet λ in its intersections with C_{16}; C_{16} has double points at both these points. The plane of the two tangents, at either of these double points, of C_{16} meets l. The points project into the two intersections of R and C_8^3; the two generators of f which pass through either of these points lie in a plane through R, this plane also containing the tangent of C_8^3.

shews that C_{16}^9 touches sixteen generators of F; whence also C_8^3 touches sixteen generators of f (cf. § 267).

To generate this surface we take in Σ a line R and an elliptic quartic in (1, 2) correspondence. The pairs of points of the quartic which correspond to the points of R give the lines of a regulus; neither of the two lines of the regulus which meet R must do so in the point of R which gives rise to it. The planes joining the points of R to the pairs of points of the quartic which correspond to them give a developable E_3^0 which has two planes passing through R; this is part of the bitangent developable of f.

315. Now assume that l, instead of being of general position, passes through the vertex U of a quadric cone containing a directrix quartic C_4^1 of F. Then the chords of F which meet l meet F in C_4^1 and in a curve C_{12} meeting each generator of F in two points and having two double points on λ. After projection we have a surface f whose double curve is $R+C_2+C_6$.

Since U is a double point of V_4^8 there are six branch-points in the (2, 1) correspondence between C_6 and l; thus C_6 is a C_6^2. Then the (1, 2) correspondence between C_6^2 and C_{12} has four branch-points, since there are four tangents of C_4^1 passing through U and therefore four tangents of C_{12} meeting l. Hence C_{12} is a C_{12}^5. It touches eight generators of F.

Since C_{12}^5 meets every generator of F in two points it must have two double points, X and Y, not on λ. Through X there pass two chords XX' and XX'' of C_{12}^5 which meet l; X' and X'' are on C_4^1 and $X'X''$ passes through U, and similarly for Y' and Y''. C_{12}^5 meets C_4^1 in four further points lying on two lines through U. Thus C_6^2 has two double points and two simple points on C_2 (cf. § 268).

To generate this surface we take a line and a conic in (2, 2) correspondence. The pairs of points of the conic which correspond to the points of the line are such that their joins touch another conic; the planes joining the points of the line to their corresponding pairs on the conic form a cubic developable which is part of the bitangent developable of the surface. There are two planes of this developable passing through the line.

316. Now suppose that l passes through the vertex U of a quadric cone containing a directrix quartic C_4^1 and through the vertex V of a quadric cone containing a directrix quartic D_4^1. The chords of F which meet l meet F in C_4^1, D_4^1 and a curve C_8^1 meeting each generator of F once and having two double points on λ.

C_4^1 and D_4^1 intersect in two points X, Y. UX and UY meet C_4^1 again on C_8^1, while VX and VY meet D_4^1 again on C_8^1. Thus the projected surface has a double curve $R+C_2+D_2+C_4^1$; C_2 and D_2 have two intersections through which C_4^1 passes, while C_4^1 meets R in two points. C_8^1 meets each of C_4^1 and D_4^1 in six points of which two are already specified; thus C_4^1 has two intersections with each of C_2 and D_2 other than those already mentioned (cf. § 269). The surface is generated by the lines which meet C_2, D_2 and R.

317. The planes of the pairs of generators which intersect in the points of λ form a three-dimensional locus. Let us choose l to meet a plane of this locus—say the plane which contains two generators g and g' of F. Then projecting from l on to Σ we have a surface f with a directrix line R through every point of which there pass two generators, while a plane through R contains four generators; but here there is also a double generator and f is of the type III (C).

Consider the chords of F which meet l. A prime through l meets F in an elliptic sextic curve with a double point; there are eight chords of this curve meeting l, but one of these is in the plane gg'. There are seven others, so that the chords of F which meet l meet F in g, g' and a curve C_{14} of order 14. C_{14} meets each generator of F in three points.

The [4] $lgg'\lambda$ meets F further in two generators. Hence the solid lgg' meets F further in two points X and Y. Through X there pass transversals to l and g and to l and g', so that X is a double point of C_{14}; similarly for Y. C_{14} has a double point on λ.

After projection we obtain a surface f whose double curve is $R+G+C_7$; R and G intersect, C_7 has two double points and one ordinary point on G and meets R in one point (cf. § 270).

There are eight branch-points in the (2, 1) correspondence between C_7 and l so that C_7 is a C_7^3; also there are eight branch-points in the (1, 2) correspondence between C_7^3 and C_{14} so that C_{14} is a C_{14}^9. It has then just the three double points mentioned. It is touched by sixteen generators of F.

To generate this surface we take a line and an elliptic quartic and place them in (1, 2) correspondence. The correspondence must, however, be specialised to give the double generator; the pairs of points of the quartic which correspond to the points of the line form a g_2^1 and the lines joining them form a regulus; one of the points in which the regulus meets the line must lie on the corresponding line of the regulus. The planes joining the points of the line to the corresponding elements of the regulus touch a quadric cone which is part of the bitangent developable of the surface. There is one tangent plane of the quadric cone passing through the line.

318. Now suppose that l not only meets the plane gg' but also passes through the vertex U of a quadric cone which contains a directrix quartic C_4^1 of F. Then C_4^1 will meet g and g' and pass through X and Y, the line UX meeting g and the line UY meeting g'. There is a [4] containing C_4^1, g and g'. The chords of F which meet l now meet F in g, g', C_4^1 and a curve C_{10} meeting every generator of F in two points. C_{10} passes through X and Y; it has a double point on λ.

Thus on projection we have a surface f with a double curve $R+G+C_2+C_5$; the plane of C_2 contains G and C_5 passes through their two intersections. C_2 and C_5 have two other intersections, these arise from the four points of intersection, other than X and Y, of $C_4{}^1$ and C_{10}. C_5 has a further intersection with G and meets R (cf. § 271).

Since U is a double point of $V_4{}^8$ there are six branch-points in the (2, 1) correspondence between C_5 and l; hence C_5 is a $C_5{}^2$. As there are four tangents of $C_4{}^1$ passing through U there are four tangents of C_{10} meeting l; thus the (1, 2) correspondence between $C_5{}^2$ and C_{10} has four branch-points, so that C_{10} is a $C_{10}{}^5$. It has no double points other than the one on λ, and touches eight generators of F.

To generate this surface we take a line and a conic in (2, 2) correspondence; but the correspondence must be specialised to give the double generator, to the point of the line in the plane of the conic must correspond two points of the conic collinear with it. Then the planes joining the points of the line to the pairs of points of the conic which correspond to them touch a quadric cone which is part of the bitangent developable of the surface.

319. The planes which project the generators from λ form a quartic line-cone of three dimensions. Let us choose l to meet a plane of this cone, the plane joining λ to a generator g. Then the solid $l\lambda g$ meets Σ in a line R which is a directrix and also a generator of the projected surface f; any plane through R contains three other generators, while through any point of R there pass two other generators. Thus f is of the type IV (A).

Any prime through l meets F in an elliptic sextic curve with a double point, the plane of l and this double point meeting the curve again. There are six other chords of the curve meeting l. Hence the points of intersection of F, other than g and λ, with its chords which meet l lie on a curve C_{12}. By considering the intersection of F with a [4] through the solid determined by l and an arbitrary generator we see that C_{12} meets each generator of F in two points; it will then have four intersections with λ, in fact it has a double point on λ and meets it in two other points.

The plane λg is a quadruple plane of $V_4{}^8$, so that there are only four branch-points in the (2, 1) correspondence between C_6 and l; thus C_6 is an elliptic curve $C_6{}^1$. There are six* tangents of C_{12} meeting l, so that the (1, 2) correspondence between $C_6{}^1$ and C_{12} has six branch-points; whence C_{12} is a $C_{12}{}^4$. It touches six generators of F.

Since $C_{12}{}^4$ meets each generator of F in two points it must have three double points not on λ; these lie in a plane through l and give rise on projection to a triple point of $C_6{}^1$.

To generate this surface we take in Σ a line and an elliptic quartic in

* The number of tangents of an elliptic quartic in [3] meeting a line which meets the curve.

(1, 2) correspondence; they have a point of intersection but it is not a united point. The pairs of points of the quartic which correspond to the points of the line form a g_2^1 and the lines joining the pairs form a regulus. When we join the points of the line to the corresponding lines of the regulus we have a developable of the third class which is part of the bitangent developable of the surface. This developable has two planes passing through the line.

320. Now let us choose l to meet the plane of two intersecting generators g and g' and also to meet the plane through λ and a generator h. The solid $l\lambda h$ meets Σ in a line R which is a directrix and also a generator of f; through any point of R there pass two further generators, while any plane through R contains three further generators. Also the surface has a double generator—the intersection of Σ with the solid lgg'.

A [4] through l meets F in an elliptic sextic curve with a double point, the plane through this point and l meeting the curve again. Also there is a chord of the curve meeting g, g' and l. There are five further chords of the curve meeting l. Hence the points of F other than g, g', h which lie on chords of F meeting l are on a curve C_{10}. C_{10} meets each generator in two points and has two intersections with λ. The solid lgg' meets F in two further points, one of which is on h; through the other there pass transversals to l and g and to l and g', so that it is a double point of C_{10}.

The projected surface f is of the type IV (C) and has a double curve $3R+G+C_5$. R meets G and is a chord of C_5; C_5 has a double point on G and meets it in one other point (cf. § 275).

The plane λh being a quadruple plane on V_4^8 the (2, 1) correspondence between C_5 and l has only four branch-points; thus C_5 is an elliptic curve C_5^1. There are six tangents of C_{10} meeting l, so that the (1, 2) correspondence between C_5^1 and C_{10} has six branch-points; whence C_{10} is a C_{10}^4. It has only one double point and touches six generators of F.

To generate this surface we take a line and an elliptic quartic in (1, 2) correspondence. The correspondence must, however, be specialised to give the double generator; one of the points of the line gives rise to the two intersections of the quartic with one of its chords through that point. The line meets the quartic, but there is no united point. The planes joining the points of the line to the pairs of points of the quartic which correspond to them now touch a quadric cone, which is part of the bitangent developable of the surface. There is one tangent plane of the cone passing through the line.

321. If we choose l to lie in the solid through λ and a pair of intersecting generators g and g' this solid meets Σ in a line R which is a directrix and also a double generator of f; through any point of R there pass two further generators, while any plane through R contains two further generators, so that f is of the type V.

To generate f we take an elliptic quartic and one of its chords and place them in (2, 1) correspondence without any united points. The pairs of points of the quartic corresponding to the points of the line give the lines of a regulus and the planes joining the points of the line to the corresponding pairs of points on the quartic form a cubic developable $E_3{}^0$ which is part of the bitangent developable of the surface, two planes of $E_3{}^0$ passing through the line.

322. The directrix quartics of F are all given by primes through two fixed intersecting generators. It is thus clear that an arbitrary line l does not lie in a solid with any one of these quartic curves. Let us, however, choose l to lie in a solid K' containing a directrix quartic.

Then the projected surface f has two directrices; R, the intersection of Σ and K', and R', the intersection of Σ with the solid $l\lambda$. Through any point of R there pass four generators of f all meeting R', while through any point of R' there pass two generators of f meeting R. The pairs of intersecting generators of F give planes meeting K' in the lines of a regulus; l meets two of these lines so that f has two double generators. Thus f is of the type VI (A).

To generate this surface we take two lines R and R' in (2, 4) correspondence, the correspondence being specialised to give two double generators.

323. The quadric line-cone which projects the ∞^1 pairs of intersecting generators of F from λ has another system of generating solids; each solid of this other system contains two generators of F which do not intersect.

If we now choose l to lie in one of these latter solids we have on projection a surface with a directrix R which is also a double generator; through any point of R there pass two generators lying in a plane through R. The surface f is of the type VII (A).

To generate the surface we take in [3] an elliptic quartic and one of its chords. These determine a quadric surface; we place the quartic and the line in (2, 1) correspondence without united points so that the two points of the quartic corresponding to any point of the line are on the same generator of the quadric, this generator belonging to the opposite system to the line. The range of points on the line is related projectively to the system of generators which meet the line. There are two generators of the quadric which meet the line in the points which correspond to them; these are the two double generators of the sextic surface.

324. A table shewing the different types of elliptic sextic ruled surfaces in ordinary space is given on p. 309. There are thirty-four different types. We have already obtained twenty-eight of them; the others will be found at the end of Chapter VI.

SECTION III

SEXTIC RULED SURFACES WHICH ARE NEITHER RATIONAL NOR ELLIPTIC

The normal sextic curve of genus 2

325. The sextic curve of genus 2 is normal in [4] and cannot lie in a space of higher dimension. The pairs of points* of the g_2^1 give ∞^1 chords of the curve forming a rational ruled surface ϕ, the order of ϕ being the number of its generators which meet an arbitrary plane. Now the solids passing through the plane cut out a g_6^1 on the curve C, and on a curve of genus 2 a g_6^1 and a g_2^1 have three pairs of common points †. Hence ϕ is a cubic ruled surface ‡.

The projection of C from one of its chords on to a plane is a quartic with one double point; thus each chord of C is met by one other chord, and there are ∞^2 quadrisecant planes of C.

The projection of C from a point of itself on to a solid is a quintic curve of genus 2; this lies on a quadric surface and its trisecants form a regulus thereon. Hence those quadrisecant planes of C which pass through a point of the curve form one system of planes of a quadric point-cone. The other system of planes of the cone cuts out the g_2^1 on C; thus the generators of ϕ meet all the quadrisecant planes of C. These quadrisecant planes are in fact none other than the planes of the ∞^2 conics on ϕ.

If we take two points P and Q of C we have two quadric point-cones with vertices P and Q; these have in common the quadrisecant plane through PQ and the cubic ruled surface ϕ.

There are ∞^3 trisecant planes of C; through any point of [4] there pass ∞^1 of these. Consider, in particular, a point of [4] which is the intersection of two chords of C; the projection of C from such a point on to a solid is a sextic of genus 2 with two double points. The trisecants of this sextic form both systems of generators of a quadric surface. Hence the trisecant planes of C which pass through an intersection of two of its chords and do not contain either chord are the planes of a quadric point-cone.

There are ∞^3 quadrics containing C; we have noticed already ∞^2 point-cones among these. There is also a line-cone whose vertex is the directrix of ϕ. This directrix is a chord of C, and the quadrisecant planes containing the pairs of points of the g_2^1 all contain this directrix.

326. The projection of C from a line on to a plane is a sextic with eight double points, while the projection from a line which meets it is a quintic with four double points. Hence the chords of C form a locus M_3^8 on which

* There is one, and only one, g_2^1 on a curve of genus 2.

† Cf. the footnote to § 134.

‡ Cf. the footnote to § 19.

C is a quadruple curve. There is also a double surface on M_3^8, the locus of points (∞^2 in aggregate) through which pass two chords of C.

Let us take a plane section of M_3^8 and consider the (5, 2) correspondence between it and C*. There are fourteen tangents of C meeting any plane; thus there are fourteen branch-points on the plane section of M_3^8 and fifty-six branch-points on C. Then Zeuthen's formula† shews that the plane sections of M_3^8 are of genus 14, and they therefore have seven double points. There is thus on M_3^8 a double surface F_2^7 of order 7.

This double surface contains the directrix of ϕ. It also contains C; C is a simple curve on F_2^7, the section of M_3^8 by a quadrisecant plane of C consists of six chords of C and a conic of ϕ.

There are curves C for which ϕ degenerates into a cubic cone. The intersection of a cubic cone in [4] (i.e. a cone projecting a twisted cubic from a point V outside its space) with a quadric threefold not passing through V is a normal sextic curve of genus 2. The g_2^1 is given by the generators of the cubic cone, and there are six tangents of C passing through V. The projection of C from a point of itself gives a quintic curve of genus 2 lying on a quadric cone.

Sextic curves of genus 2 which lie on quadrics

327. Following our usual division of the curves on a quadric Ω in [5] into different classes, we consider five classes of sextic curves of genus 2 as follows:

I. The normal sextic C in [4].

II. C lies on the quadric point-cone in which Ω is met by a tangent prime at a point O.

(A) C meets every ϖ-plane of Ω through O in two points and every ρ-plane of Ω through O in four points, a chord of C passing through O.

(B) C meets every ϖ-plane of Ω through O in four points and every ρ-plane of Ω through O in two points, a chord of C passing through O.

(C) C meets every plane of Ω through O in three points, two chords of C passing through O.

III. C again lies in a tangent prime of Ω but now passes through the point of contact O.

(A) C meets every ϖ-plane of Ω through O in two points other than O and every ρ-plane of Ω through O in three points other than O.

(B) C meets every ϖ-plane of Ω through O in three points other than O and every ρ-plane of Ω through O in two points other than O.

IV. C lies on a quadric surface in a [3] through which pass two tangent primes of Ω.

(A) C meets the generators of one system each in two points and the generators of the other system each in four points, and has a double point.

* Cf. § 262. † § 16.

(B) C meets the generators of both systems each in three points, and has two double points.

V. C lies on a quadric cone; the section of Ω by a [3] which touches it.

(A) C has a double point at the vertex and one other double point, meeting every generator in two points other than the vertex.

(B) C meets every generator in three points and has two double points.

328. We have in fact already met with the classes I, II and III in § 325. Regarding C as the normal curve in [4] we can have non-specialised quadrics containing it, from which arises I. The quadric point-cones which project the surface ϕ from points of itself not on C give II (A) and II (B), while those projecting it from points on C give III (A) and III (B). The quadric point-cones which have their vertices at intersections of two chords of C occur in the type II (C).

The sextic ruled surfaces in [3] *whose plane sections are curves of genus* 2

329. We regard a non-degenerate quadric containing the normal curve C as a prime section of a quadric Ω in [5]. Then C will represent the generators of a ruled surface in [3] belonging to a linear complex.

Through any point of C there pass four of its chords which lie on Ω; the chords of C lying on Ω form a ruled surface of order 16—the intersection of Ω and M_3^8—on which C is a quadruple curve. The complete intersection of Ω and F_2^7 is of order 14; it consists of C and a curve of order eight. Thus the ruled surface of order 16 has a quadruple curve of order six and a double curve of order eight. A section of this ruled surface by a solid will be a curve of order 16 with six quadruple points and eight double points, the curve lying on a quadric and meeting each generator in eight points. Projecting this curve into a plane curve of order 15 we see that its genus is

$$91-2.21-6.6-8=5,$$

so that the double curve and bitangent developable of the ruled surface in [3] are also of genus 5.

Any plane of Ω meets the [4] containing C in a line which is met by eight chords of C; hence the double curve of the ruled surface is C_8^5 and the bitangent developable E_8^5.

There are no triple points or tritangent planes because C has no trisecants.

This ruled surface in [3] of the sixth order and with plane sections of genus 2 cannot contain any directrix lines, conics or cubic curves unless they are multiple curves. But there are on the surface ∞^1 plane quartics of genus 2 each with a double point, these being the intersections of the surface with those planes which contain two intersecting generators.

There is a finite number of these curves passing through a general point A of the surface; this number is simply the number of planes of the bitangent developable which pass through A and do not contain the generator through A. But of the eight planes of $E_8{}^5$ passing through A there are four which contain the generator; hence there are four plane quartics passing through a general point of the surface.

330. Suppose now that C is of the type II (A); we regard the quadric cone containing C as the section of Ω by a tangent prime. Then we have in [3] a sextic ruled surface with a directrix line R; through any point of R there pass two generators, while any plane through R contains four generators.

The chords of C lying in the ϖ-planes join the pairs of the $g_2{}^1$; they form the cubic ruled surface ϕ. The chords lying in the ρ-planes therefore form a ruled surface of order 13 on which C is a triple curve. The intersection of $F_2{}^7$ with the quadric point-cone is made up of C, the directrix of ϕ, and a curve of order seven which is a double curve on the latter ruled surface. The section of ϕ by an arbitrary solid is a twisted cubic lying on a quadric; the other ruled surface gives a curve of order 13 lying on a quadric, meeting all generators of one system in seven points and all of the other system in six points; the curve has six triple points and seven double points. This curve is of genus

$$66-21-15-18-7=5.$$

Hence the chords of C lying in the ϖ-planes form a rational cubic ruled surface ϕ and those lying in the ρ-planes form a ruled surface of order 13, the genus of whose prime sections is 5.

Any arbitrary plane ρ of Ω meets the [4] containing C in a line and the plane ϖ containing this line joins it to O; there are seven other chords of C meeting the line, all of them belonging to the ruled surface of order 13.

Hence the double curve of the ruled surface in [3] is $R+C_7{}^5$; R and $C_7{}^5$ have one intersection, represented on Ω by the plane ϖ which contains the chord of C passing through O. Also the bitangent developable is $6R+E_2$, there being a plane of E_2 containing R.

Similarly, when C is of the type II (B) we have a double curve $6R+C_2$ and a bitangent developable $R+E_7{}^5$; C_2 has one intersection with R, while $E_7{}^5$ has one plane passing through R.

331. If C is of the type II (C) we have in [3] a ruled surface with a directrix line R through any point of which there pass three generators, while any plane through R contains three generators.

The chords of C lying in either system of planes form a ruled surface of order eight on which C is a double curve, and there will be no other double curve. A prime section of this surface gives a curve of order eight lying on a quadric, meeting all generators of one system in three points and all of the other system in five points, the curve having six double points. The genus of such a curve is

$$21 - 3 - 10 - 6 = 2.$$

An arbitrary plane of Ω meets the [4] containing C in a line, and the plane of the opposite system through this line joins it to O. This contains three chords of C; there are five others meeting the line.

Hence the double curve of the ruled surface in [3] is $3R + C_5^2$ and the bitangent developable is $3R + E_5^2$. C_5^2 has two intersections with R represented on Ω by the ϖ-planes containing the two chords of C which pass through O; E_5^2 has two planes passing through R represented by the ρ-planes through the same two chords of C.

332. Let C be of the type III (A). Then we have in [3] a ruled surface with a directrix line R which is also a generator; through any point of R there pass two other generators, while any plane through R contains three other generators.

The ϖ-planes cut out the g_2^1 on C. The ruled surface formed by the chords of C which lie on Ω here splits up into three parts: the quintic cone of genus 2 projecting C from O, the rational cubic ruled surface ϕ and a ruled surface of order eight formed by the chords lying in the ρ-planes and not passing through O; the prime sections of this latter surface are of genus 2 as in § 331.

An arbitrary plane ρ meets the [4] containing C in a line; the plane ϖ through this line joins it to O and contains three chords of C. There are five other chords of C meeting the line and all belonging to the ruled surface of order eight. Hence the double curve of the ruled surface in [3] is $3R + C_5^2$. R and C_5^2 have two intersections: taking that set of the g_3^1 cut out by the ρ-planes which contains O, these intersections are represented on Ω by the ϖ-planes containing the chords of C which join O to the two other points of the set.

An arbitrary plane ϖ meets the [4] containing C in a line; the plane ρ through this line joins it to O and contains six chords of C. There are two other chords of C meeting the line, both belonging to ϕ. Hence the bitangent developable of the ruled surface in [3] is $6R + E_2$. There is one plane of E_2 passing through R: taking the set of the g_2^1 containing O, this plane is represented on Ω by the ρ-plane containing the chord joining the pair of points.

Similarly, if C is of the type III (B) we have in [3] a ruled surface with a double curve $6R + C_2$ and a bitangent developable $3R + E_5^2$. R and C_2 have one intersection, while there are two planes of E_5^2 passing through R.

333. In type IV we have two directrices R and R'.

In IV (A) the double curve is $6R + G + R'$ and bitangent developable

$R+G+6R'$. Through any point of R pass four generators lying in a plane through R', while through any point of R' pass two generators lying in a plane through R.

In IV (B) the double curve is $3R+G+H+3R'$ and bitangent developable $3R+G+H+3R'$. Through any point of either directrix pass three generators in a plane through the other.

In type V we have a single directrix R.

In V (A) this is also a double generator; the double curve is $7R+G$ and bitangent developable $7R+G$; the plane section is a sextic curve with a double point and a quadruple point at which two of the four branches have the same tangent.

In V (B) the double curve and bitangent developable are $6R+G+H$. Through any point of R there pass three generators all lying in a plane through R. The plane sections are sextic curves with two double points and a triple point at which all three branches have the same tangent.

334. The ten different types of sextic ruled surfaces in [3] which we have obtained are shewn in tabular form on p. 310.

A sextic ruled surface in [4] *whose prime sections are curves of genus* 2, *and the ruled surfaces in* [3] *derived from it by projection*

335. Take in [4] a plane and a line R which do not intersect. Take in the plane a quartic with one double point P; then relate the range of points on R to the pencil of lines through P; each of these lines meets the quartic in two further points, and if these pairs are joined to the corresponding points on R the joining lines generate a ruled surface on which R is a double line and P a double point. The ruled surface is of the sixth order and its prime sections are of genus 2*.

The plane of the two generators intersecting in a point of R necessarily passes through P; we have thus ∞^1 planes through P. These planes, as joining the points of a range to lines of a related pencil, generate a quadric point-cone, with vertex P, containing the ruled surface. The plane PR is a plane of the opposite system of this cone.

A solid through the plane of two intersecting generators meets the surface further in a plane quartic with a double point at P; we have thus ∞^1 plane quartics. Through any one of these quartics there pass ∞^1 solids joining it to the points of R, each meeting the surface in two intersecting generators. The planes of these ∞^1 quartics are the opposite system of

* The genus of the prime sections is the same as the genus of the plane quartic. The order of the surface is $1 \cdot 2 + 4 \cdot 1 = 6$; there being a (1, 2) correspondence between the line and the quartic; cf. § 19.

This surface in [4] is mentioned by C. V. Hanumanta Rao, *Proc. Lond. Math. Soc.* (2), 19 (1919), 249.

planes of the quadric point-cone. Through any point of the surface there passes one of the quartic curves.

336. Now project this surface F from a point O on to a [3] Σ. A solid through O meets F in a sextic curve of genus 2 with a double point on R*; there are seven chords of this curve passing through O. There are ∞^1 chords of F passing through O and they meet F in a curve C_{14} of order 14. Since a plane through a generator g of F meets F in three further points† the curve C_{14} meets each generator of F in three points.

A solid through O which contains P meets F in a sextic curve of genus 2 with two double points‡, one at P and one on R. There are six chords of this curve passing through O. We conclude that C_{14} has a double point at P. It has also § a double point on R.

We can now ‖ calculate that C_{14} is of genus 14.

On projecting from O we obtain in Σ a ruled surface whose double curve consists of a directrix and a curve of the seventh order meeting each generator in three points. This curve is in (1, 2) correspondence with C_{14} and its genus can be calculated by Zeuthen's formula when we know the number of branch-points of the correspondence, i.e. the number of tangents of C_{14} which pass through O.

Now the tangent solids ¶ of F all pass through R; there are ten of these solids passing through any point of [4], since a plane quartic of genus 2 is of class ten. Hence there will be ten tangents of C_{14} passing through O. Whence the double curve of the projected surface is of genus 5.

Hence on projection we have a surface of the type II (A) with a double curve $R + C_7^5$. R and C_7^5 have one intersection; the tangent of C_7^5 at this point lies in the plane containing R and the two generators of the surface which intersect there.

To generate the surface in Σ we take a line and a plane quartic with one double point, placing them in (1, 2) correspondence. The bitangent planes of the surface which do not pass through the line join the points of a range

* This curve has ∞^1 quadrisecants; it lies on a quadric, meeting all generators of one system in four points and all of the other system in two points.

† The solid through the plane and the generator which intersects g meets F further in one of the plane quartics; this has three intersections with the plane which do not lie on g.

‡ This curve lies on a quadric cone with vertex P, meeting every generator in two points other than P.

§ The solids joining R to the pairs of intersecting generators of F form a pencil of solids through the plane RP; there will be one of them passing through O. The point of R which is the intersection of the two generators contained in this solid is a double point of C_{14}.

‖ See § 17. Observe that no deduction is made for the double points of C_{14}; this is because the double points of C_{14} are also double points of the ruled surface.

¶ See § 51.

to the lines of a related pencil and therefore touch a quadric cone. There is one tangent plane of this cone passing through the line, viz. the plane joining the line to the double point of the quartic curve.

337. We have projected the surface F from a general point O of [4]; we now proceed to consider the surfaces obtained in Σ by choosing special positions of the centre of projection O. Let us then choose O to lie on the $M_3{}^4$ formed by the planes joining R to the generators of F, i.e. O lies in the plane containing R and a generator g. Then on projection we have in Σ a surface f with a directrix line R which is also a generator. Through any point of R there pass two other generators, while any plane through R contains three other generators. Hence f belongs to the type III (A).

A prime through O meets F in a sextic of genus 2 with a double point on R, and the line joining O to the double point meets the curve again in a point on g. There are five other chords of this curve passing through O, so that the chords of F passing through O meet F in a curve C_{10} of order ten. The plane joining an arbitrary generator of F to O meets g, and meets F only in two further points; hence every generator of F meets C_{10} twice. C_{10} has a double point at P but no other double points, and is of genus 7. R meets C_{10} in two distinct points; the lines joining these points to O meet C_{10} again in its intersections with g.

From a point on a plane quartic of genus 2 we can draw eight tangents to the curve, so that there are eight tangents of C_{10} passing through O. This shews that the projection of C_{10} is a quintic curve of genus 2.

Hence the surface f has a double curve $3R + C_5{}^2$. R and $C_5{}^2$ have two intersections.

To generate this type of surface in Σ we take a plane quartic with one double point and a line which meets it, placing the line and the curve in (1, 2) correspondence without a united point. The bitangent planes of the surface which do not contain the line touch a quadric cone, one of whose tangent planes contains the line.

338. Let us now choose O to lie on the quadric point-cone containing F. Then O lies in the plane of two intersecting generators and also in the plane of a directrix quartic of F. This latter plane will meet Σ in a directrix R' of the projected surface, while we have as before a directrix R. Through any point of R there pass two generators, while through any point of R' there pass four generators. The projected surface has a double generator and is of the type IV (A).

To generate this surface we place two lines R and R' in (4, 2) correspondence, the correspondence being specialised to give the double generator.

Now let us further specialise the position of O and choose it in the plane PR; this plane contains two generators of F. Any solid through this plane meets F further in two generators intersecting in a point of R. Hence on projection we obtain in Σ a surface f with a directrix line R which is also a double generator, any plane through R meeting f further in two generators which intersect on R: f is of the type V (A). The other double generator is the intersection of Σ with the other plane of the point-cone containing O.

To generate this surface we take a plane quartic with a double point P and a line R passing through P; we then set up a (1, 2) correspondence between R and the curve without any united point. There is a double generator passing through P and lying in the plane of the quartic.

The sextic ruled surfaces of genus 2 which are normal in [3]

339. Although we have not obtained all the surfaces in [3] as projections of this surface F in [4], we cannot construct any other ruled surfaces in [4] which are of the sixth order and have prime sections of genus 2. We thus meet abruptly the fact that *the normal space for a ruled surface is not uniquely determined by its order and the genus of its prime sections.* The normal space is uniquely determined for rational and elliptic ruled surfaces of all orders, but for ruled surfaces of given order, whose sections are of genus greater than or equal to 2, there are different normal spaces.

We have obtained ten different kinds of sextic ruled surfaces in [3] whose plane sections are of genus 2; of these four can be obtained as the projections of a single normal surface in [4], but the other six are normal in the space [3] itself. On these latter surfaces the plane sections form a complete linear system of curves; such a system of curves is not contained in any linear system, of greater freedom, of curves of the same order.

340. For those surfaces which are not obtainable by projection from [4] we here give methods of generation.

To obtain a surface of the type I we take two plane quartics of genus 2 and place them in (1, 1) correspondence with two united points, the curves having the same moduli. It is clear that the plane of either curve is met in eight points by the double curve of the ruled surface so generated. The other curve meets this plane in two points which are not united points; through either of these points passes a generator of the surface to the corresponding point on the first curve, this meets the first curve in three further points which are points of the double curve. We thus have six points of the double curve; to these must be added the double point of the quartic and the intersection of the two generators.

For a surface of the type II (B) we take a line and a conic with one intersection and place them in (2, 4) correspondence with a doubly united point. Through any point of the line pass four generators, while any plane through the line contains two generators.

For a surface of the type II (C) we take a line and a plane quartic of genus 2, placing them in (1, 3) correspondence with a united point. Through any point of the line there pass three generators, while any plane through the line contains three generators. The double curve of the ruled surface so generated (apart from the triple line) meets the plane of the quartic in five points; through the united point there pass two lines to corresponding points on the quartic, these meet the quartic each in two other points which are points of the double curve. We have thus four points of the double curve, and to these must be added the double point of the quartic.

For a surface of the type III (B) we take a line and a conic with one intersection, placing them in (2, 3) correspondence with a united point. The ruled surface has the line as a generator, through any point of the line pass three other generators, while any plane through the line contains two other generators.

A surface of the type IV (B) is generated by two lines in (3, 3) correspondence, the correspondence being specialised to give two double generators.

To obtain a surface of the type V (B) we take a line and a plane quartic of genus 2 with one intersection, placing them in (1, 3) correspondence with a united point and so that the triads of points on the quartic corresponding to the points of the line are all collinear with the united point. This is secured by relating the range of points on the line to the pencil of lines through the united point; the united point considered as a point of the range corresponding to the tangent to the quartic. This tangent is a double generator of the ruled surface; there is a second double generator passing through the double point of the quartic.

341. If, on a ruled surface in space of any number of dimensions, we have a curve of order ν and genus π meeting each generator in two points, and having no double points which are not also double points of the ruled surface, then

$$\nu - \pi = n - 2p + 1,$$

where n is the order and p the genus of the ruled surface. If the curve, of order ν and genus π, is the projection of a normal curve in higher space, the ruled surface is also the projection of a normal ruled surface in higher space*; we have already made use of this idea to obtain the normal space for elliptic ruled surfaces.

If the ruled surface is a sextic ruled surface whose prime sections are of genus 2 we have

$$\nu - \pi = 3,$$

* Cf. Segre, *Math. Ann.* 34 (1889), 1.

so that the curve is certainly normal in [3] if $\nu > 2\pi - 2$, i.e. if $\pi < 5$ and $\nu < 8$. Hence, *if a ruled surface in* [3], *of order* 6 *and genus* 2, *is the projection of a normal ruled surface in* [4], *there cannot be on the surface a curve of order less than* eight (*and of genus less than* 5) *meeting each generator in two points.*

If we attempt to obtain such a curve, e.g. by means of a quadric containing at least five generators, the attempt is bound to fail. If the surface has a directrix R the quadric must not contain R, for then the residual curve of intersection would not meet each generator twice.

The sextic ruled surfaces whose plane sections are of genus greater than 2

342. A sextic ruled surface in [4] whose prime sections are of genus 3 is necessarily a cone*; thus such a ruled surface is normal in [3] and the question of projection from higher space will not arise, nor will it arise *a fortiori* for the surfaces with prime sections of genus greater than 3. It remains then to consider such surfaces as curves on the quadric Ω.

The sextic curve of genus 3 is necessarily contained in [3], so that the sextic ruled surface will have two directrices—distinct or coincident. Now the sextic curves of genus 3 lying on a quadric surface are of two kinds:

(A) the curve meets all generators of one system in four points and all of the other system in two points;

(B) the curve meets every generator in three points and has a double point.

In the first case we have a ruled surface with a fourfold directrix and a double directrix; the double curve is $6R + R'$ and the bitangent developable is $R + 6R'$. The surface is generated by two lines R and R' placed in (2, 4) correspondence.

In the second case we have a ruled surface with two triple directrices and a double generator; the double curve and bitangent developable are both $3R + G + 3R'$. The surface is generated by two lines R and R' in (3, 3) correspondence, the correspondence being specialised to give the double generator.

In either case the two directrices may coincide. We can have on a quadric cone:

(A) a curve with a double point at the vertex, meeting every generator in two other points;

(B) a curve meeting every generator in three points and having a double point.

In (A) the double curve and bitangent developable are both $7R$; the directrix itself being a double generator. Through any point of R there pass two other generators lying in a plane through R. The surface is

* Cf. § 160.

generated by a line and a plane quintic in (1, 2) correspondence with a united point, the quintic having a triple point on R.

In (B) the double curve and the bitangent developable are both $6R+G$; through any point of R there pass three generators lying in a plane through R. To generate this surface we take a line and a plane quartic without double points and place them in (1, 3) correspondence with a united point, the three points of the quartic which correspond to any point of the line lying on a line through the united point. The tangent to the quartic at this point is a double generator of the surface.

343. On a quadric in [3] we can have a sextic of genus 4; this is the complete intersection of the quadric with a cubic surface and meets every generator in three points. We can thus have in [3] a sextic ruled surface with plane sections of genus 4; the surface has two directrices R and R', through any point of either there pass three generators lying in a plane through the other. The double curve and bitangent developable are both $3R+3R'$. The surface is generated by two lines R and R' in (3, 3) correspondence.

Here also we can have a surface for which the two directrices coincide; this is represented by the sextic curve which is the intersection of a cubic surface and a quadric cone. The double curve and bitangent developable are both $6R$; through any point of R there pass three generators lying in a plane through R.

The surface is generated by a plane quintic with a tacnode and a line passing through the tacnode, these being in (3, 1) correspondence with a doubly united point. The three points of the quintic corresponding to any point of the line are collinear with the tacnode, and the tangent at the tacnode is a generator of the ruled surface.

CHAPTER V
DEVELOPABLE SURFACES

Introduction

344. We have already mentioned the construct in three-dimensional space which is known as a *developable**. It is formed by a singly infinite system of planes and can thus be regarded as the dual of a twisted curve; for this reason many properties of developables have been known for a long time. The *class* of the developable is the number of its planes which pass through an arbitrary point.

We may regard the developable in another way. Just as the line joining two points of a curve is called a chord of the curve, so the line of intersection of two planes of a developable is called an *axis* of the developable. As the two points of the curve tend to coincide, the chord tends to a limiting position called a tangent of the curve, so, when the two planes of the developable tend to coincide, the axis tends to a limiting position called a *generator* of the developable. Just as there is a tangent at every point of the curve, so there is a generator in every plane of the developable, leaving aside for the moment the consideration of possible singular planes. We have thus ∞^1 generators forming a *developable surface*. It then appears that a developable surface is merely a particular case of a ruled surface; except for a finite number of generators which are torsal the tangent planes to a ruled surface are different for different points of the same generator, but on a developable surface all the generators are torsal with the same tangent plane at different points of the same generator. We shall in future use the same term developable to denote either the singly infinite system of planes or the surface formed by the generators.

Further, just as we derive osculating planes of a curve, so we can derive a singly infinite system of points forming a curve Γ on the developable. If we consider the generator g in the plane α, then the limiting position of the point of intersection of g with another plane β of the developable, as β approaches α, is a point of Γ. The generators of the developable touch Γ and the planes of the developable osculate Γ; Γ is called the "edge of regression" or the "cuspidal edge" of the developable.

Every developable is formed by the osculating planes of some curve Γ, and conversely the osculating planes of every curve Γ form a developable. Any numerical relation connecting singularities of a developable gives another numerical relation connecting corresponding singularities of a

* See e.g. § 21.

twisted curve and *vice versa*; these relations have been well known since Cayley's generalisation of Plücker's formulae for plane curves to curves in space *.

345. If we project a twisted curve Γ on to a plane from an arbitrary point O we obtain a plane curve, and every osculating plane of Γ passing through O gives on the plane a tangent at a point of inflection on the plane curve; the number of these is equal to the class of the developable formed by the osculating planes of Γ. If O lies on a tangent of Γ the plane curve loses two of these inflections and acquires a cusp.

The section of a developable by an arbitrary plane ϖ gives a system of lines enveloping a curve; this curve is the locus of points in which ϖ is met by the generators of the developable and has cusps at the points where ϖ meets the cuspidal edge. If, however, ϖ contains a generator the curve loses two of these cusps and acquires an inflection; this inflection is at the point of contact of the generator in ϖ with the cuspidal edge and the generator is itself the inflectional tangent. If there are r generators of the developable meeting an arbitrary line in space, the section by a plane ϖ containing a generator is a curve of order $r-1$; this will meet the generator in $r-4$ points other than the inflection. Thus given a skew curve Γ of which r tangents meet an arbitrary line any one tangent is met by $r-4$ others. We say that Γ is of rank r.

We have then on a developable surface not only a cuspidal edge but a nodal curve; this nodal curve meets every generator in $r-4$ points if r is the order of the surface. Any plane through a generator meets the surface further in a curve of order $r-1$ passing through these $r-4$ points (which are fixed for all positions of the plane) and having an inflection at the point of contact of the generator with the cuspidal edge; but when the plane is the tangent plane the residual intersection will only be of order $r-2$; it passes through the $r-4$ points in which the generator meets the nodal curve and touches the generator at its point of contact with the cuspidal edge.

346. Suppose that we have in [3] a curve Γ of order n and genus p; then it can be proved, either by means of a correspondence between the planes of a pencil or by projecting Γ on to a plane and using Plücker's equations, that the rank of Γ is $r=2n+2p-2$. A reduction may have to be made for certain singularities of Γ; in particular we must subtract 1 for each cusp.

The curves that we shall meet with will have three kinds of singularities:

(*a*) cusps, or stationary points;

(*b*) inflections, or points at which the tangent is stationary;

(*c*) points at which the osculating plane is stationary.

The last two types of singularity do not affect the rank of the curve; so

* *Papers*, 8 (1871), 72.

that for a curve of order n and genus p the rank is $r = 2n + 2p - 2 - \kappa$, where κ is the number of cusps of the curve.

The tangents at the inflections are stationary generators of the developable of which Γ is the cuspidal edge; a plane meets the developable in a curve having cusps not only at the intersections of the plane with Γ but also at the intersections of the plane with the tangents to Γ at its inflections.

Each tangent of Γ is met by $r - 4$ other tangents, so that we have a nodal curve on the developable. Hence the double curve of the developable surface may consist of three parts: the cuspidal edge, the nodal curve and the tangents at the inflections of the cuspidal edge. Similarly the bitangent developable may also consist of three parts: the original developable itself, the nodal developable and the pencils of planes through the inflectional tangents of the cuspidal edge.

347. The simplest curve in [3] is the twisted cubic; the tangents of this form a developable surface of the fourth order and no other curve can give a developable of so low an order. For a developable of the fifth order the only possible cuspidal edge is the rational quartic with one cusp*. For a developable of the sixth order the cuspidal edge must be such that

$$2n + 2p - \kappa = 8,$$

and there are three possible curves:

(*a*) A rational quartic,
(*b*) A rational quintic with two cusps,
(*c*) A rational sextic with four cusps.

Thus all developables of the sixth order are rational, and the cuspidal edge lies on a quadric surface.

It may be remarked in passing that for an elliptic curve of order n with κ cusps the order of the developable of tangents is $2n - \kappa$. Thus the lowest order possible for an elliptic developable is eight, this developable being formed by the tangents of the curve of intersection of two quadrics. Hence all developables of order less than eight are rational, or, to use Cayley's expression, planar developables†.

348. The expression

$$r = 2n + 2p - 2 - \kappa$$

for the rank of a curve of order n and genus p with κ cusps is true whatever the dimension m of the space in which the curve lies; it gives the number of tangents of the curve which meet an arbitrary $[m - 2]$ of general position.

If the cuspidal edge Γ of a developable in [3] is not normal we can consider a normal curve Γ_0, in higher space, of which Γ is the projection; the developable surface formed by the tangents of Γ is then the projection

* The number of cusps of a rational curve of order n in [3] cannot exceed the integral part of $\frac{4}{3}(n - 3)$; Veronese, *Math. Ann.* 19 (1882), 209.

† Cf. Schwarz, "De superficiebus in planum explicabilibus primorum septem ordinum," *Journal für Math.* 64 (1865), 1.

of the developable surface formed by the tangents of Γ_0, the centre of projection meeting as many tangents of Γ_0 as there are cusps of Γ.

Since a rational quartic in [3] is the projection of a normal rational quartic in [4] it follows that the developable of tangents of a rational quartic in [3] is the projection of the developable of tangents of a normal rational quartic in [4]. By selecting different positions for the point of projection in [4] we are able to obtain different types of developable surfaces of the sixth order in [3], while if we take the point of projection to lie on a tangent of the normal curve we obtain in [3] the developable of the fifth order formed by the tangents of a rational quartic with a cusp.

A very complete investigation of the properties of a rational quartic in [3] as derived by projection from the normal curve is given by Marletta*. When, however, he is examining the details of the nodal curves of some sextic developables he simply obtains the results by geometry in three dimensions; we shall try to obtain all our results systematically by projection.

For a normal rational quartic curve C in [4] the order, or the number of points of C which lie in an arbitrary solid, is 4. The first rank, or the number of tangents of C which meet an arbitrary plane, is 6; the second rank, or the number of osculating planes of C which meet an arbitrary line, is 6; the class, or third rank, or the number of osculating solids of C which pass through an arbitrary point, is 4. These numbers are well known†. If then we take the section by a solid Σ of the surface formed by the tangents of C we obtain a rational curve of the sixth order with cusps at the four points where Σ meets C. The tangents of this curve are the lines in which Σ meets the osculating planes of C, and they form a developable surface of the sixth order. By selecting different positions of the cutting solid Σ we obtain different types of sextic developables in ordinary space.

We shall give subsequently a complete list of the developables of the sixth order with their double curves, bitangent developables and cuspidal edges. Of the ten different classes which we finally obtain all but one are obtainable from the rational normal quartic curve by projection and section. The surfaces have been considered by Chasles, Schwarz and Cayley; but no complete account of them seems to have been published.

We must mention, for completeness, two other methods of studying developables, although we shall not pursue these lines of investigation here.

The generators of a developable form a ruled surface which may be the projection of a normal ruled surface, not itself developable, in higher space. For example: all developable surfaces of the sixth order are rational and can therefore be obtained by projection from the normal rational sextic ruled surfaces in [7].

The planes of a developable may be the projections of a system of

* *Annali di Matematica* (3), 8 (1903), 97–128.

† See e.g. Clifford, *Collected Papers* (London, 1882), 314.

planes, in higher space, forming a three-dimensional locus. For example: a rational developable of class n can always be obtained by projection from a rational normal locus, of order n, of ∞^1 planes in $[n+2]$.

349. We know how to represent the generators of a ruled surface of order n and genus p in [3] by the points of a curve C of order n and genus p lying on a quadric primal Ω in [5]. There are $2(n+2p-2)$ torsal generators of the ruled surface*, giving $2(n+2p-2)$ points of C at which the tangents lie on Ω. Hence, since every generator of a developable surface is a torsal generator, the generators of a developable in [3] are represented on Ω by a curve C all of whose tangents also lie on Ω.

Suppose that we have a curve C, of order n, genus p and with k cusps, lying on a quadric primal Ω in space of any number of dimensions. Then the number of tangents of C which lie on Ω is found at once by considering the section of the figure by a prime Π. For the surface formed by the tangents of C meets Π in a curve C', of order $2n+2p-2-k$, which has cusps at the n points of intersection of C with Π. These cusps are all on the section ω of Ω by Π, so that C' and ω have

$$2(2n+2p-2-k)-2n=2(n+2p-2)-2k$$

further intersections.

The tangent of C which passes through any one of these further intersections of C' and ω lies entirely on Ω, since it meets it in two points at its point of contact with C and in one point where it meets ω. Conversely, a tangent of C which lies on Ω must pass through one of these further intersections of C' and ω; it does not pass through a cusp of C', since the choice of Π is arbitrary. Hence the number of tangents of C which lie on Ω is $2(n+2p-2)-2k$.

350. In order to obtain the properties of developable surfaces in [3] we shall make use of properties of curves on a quadric Ω in [5], these curves being such that all their tangents also lie on Ω. We first obtain the number of osculating planes of such a curve which lie on Ω.

Let us suppose that Ω is a quadric primal in space of any number of dimensions, and that on Ω there lies a curve C, of order n, genus p and having k cusps, whose tangents all lie on Ω. The tangents of C form a surface, and the tangent planes of this surface at the different points of a tangent of C all coincide with the corresponding osculating plane of C. But, if we have a surface on a quadric, the tangent plane of the surface at any point is contained in the tangent prime of the quadric at the same point. Hence the tangent primes of Ω, at the different points of a tangent of C, all contain the osculating plane of C. Thus each osculating plane of C touches Ω at every point of the tangent of C, and if it should meet Ω in any points which are not on this tangent it will lie on Ω completely.

* Cf. § 32.

Consider now the section by a prime Π. The surface formed by the tangents of C meets Π, as before, in a curve C' of order $2n + 2p - 2 - k$, but this curve now lies entirely upon ω. Hence, by the result just proved, the number of tangents of C' lying on ω is

$$2\{(2n + 2p - 2 - k) + 2p - 2\} - 2n = 2(n + 4p - 4) - 2k,$$

since C' has n cusps and is of genus p.

Now the tangents of C' are the lines in which Π is met by the osculating planes of C. Hence, if a tangent of C' lies on ω, the corresponding osculating plane of C will lie on Ω, and conversely. Therefore the number of osculating planes* of C which lie on Ω is $2(n + 4p - 4) - 2k$.

351. If Ω is in [5] the points of C represent the generators of a developable in [3]; these generators all touch a curve Γ. A point P of C represents a generator g of the developable; through the tangent of C at P there pass two planes of Ω, one of each system. The point of [3] which is represented on Ω by the ϖ-plane is the point of contact of g and Γ, while the plane of [3] which is represented on Ω by the ρ-plane is the corresponding osculating plane of Γ.

A cusp of Γ is represented on Ω by a ϖ-plane which osculates C, and a stationary osculating plane of Γ is represented on Ω by a ρ-plane which osculates C. The tangent at an inflection of Γ is represented on Ω by a cusp of C.

Suppose that Γ has κ cusps and κ' stationary osculating planes; then the number of osculating planes of C which lie on Ω must be $\kappa + \kappa'$. But, by the Cayley-Plücker formulae for a twisted curve,

$$\kappa + \kappa' = 2(n + 4p - 4) - 2i,$$

where Γ is of order n, genus p and has i inflections. But C is of order n, genus p and has i cusps; thus the number of osculating planes of C which lie on Ω is in agreement with that given by § 350.

352. If we have a quadric primal Ω in space of any number of dimensions, and on it a curve C whose tangents also lie on Ω, then the tangent primes of Ω at the different points of the tangent of C at a point P all contain the osculating plane of C at P. The tangent prime of Ω at P itself contains the osculating solid of C at P, and so meets C in only $n - 4$ other points, if n is the order of C. We have then, corresponding to each point P of C, a set of $n - 4$ points which are the intersections of C, other than P itself, with the tangent prime of Ω at P; if we have a point P such that one of the set of $n - 4$ points is P itself, the osculating plane of C will lie on Ω. The tangent prime of Ω at a point P of C meets C, in general, in four points at P; if it should happen to meet C in five points at P then the osculating plane of C at P lies on Ω†.

* Cf. Baker, *Proc. Edin. Math. Soc.* (2), 1 (1927), 19.

† Baker, *loc. cit.*

The developable surface of the fourth order

353. The tangents of a twisted cubic in [3] form a developable surface of the fourth order. The section by an arbitrary plane is a rational plane quartic with three cusps. A plane through a tangent of the cubic curve meets the curve in one further point; the section of the developable consists of the tangent and a rational plane cubic. This cubic has an inflection with the generator of the developable as the inflectional tangent, and has a cusp at the remaining intersection of the plane with the twisted cubic. An osculating plane of the twisted cubic meets the developable in the tangent counted twice and a conic, the conic touching the tangent at its point of contact with the cubic curve.

No two tangents of the cubic can intersect.

Given a quartic curve C in [4] there is one quadric Q which contains C and all its tangents; if Q is regarded as a prime section of Ω the points of C represent the generators of a developable of the fourth order in [3]. The tangents of a twisted cubic belong to a linear complex.

Any three tangents of C have one transversal; this transversal must lie on Q and Q can, in fact, be defined as the locus of transversals of triads of tangents of C. The tangents of C form a developable surface lying on Q; this is of the sixth order and meets every line of Q in three points. A plane ρ of Ω meets the [4] containing Q in a line which is met by three tangents of C; this means that there are three points of the cuspidal edge of the developable in an arbitrary plane of [3]. A plane ϖ of Ω meets the [4] containing Q in a line which is met by three tangents of C; this means that there are three planes of the developable passing through an arbitrary point of [3].

The fact that any three osculating planes of a twisted cubic meet in a point coplanar with their points of osculation is quite clear on the quadric Ω. Take three tangents t_1, t_2, t_3 of C; then the planes ρ_1, ρ_2, ρ_3 of Ω passing through them represent three arbitrary osculating planes of the twisted cubic. The point of intersection of these three planes is represented on Ω by the unique plane ϖ_0 which meets each of the planes ρ_1, ρ_2, ρ_3 in lines, and this is clearly the plane ϖ_0 which contains the transversal t_0 of t_1, t_2, t_3. Then the plane ρ_0 through t_0 meets the four planes $\varpi_0, \varpi_1, \varpi_2, \varpi_3$ all in lines and so represents a plane passing through the three points where the planes osculate the twisted cubic and also through the point of intersection of the three osculating planes; $\varpi_1, \varpi_2, \varpi_3$ are the ϖ-planes of Ω which contain t_1, t_2, t_3.

354. There is a result due to Brill and Nöther* which states that the curves of order n and genus p in $[r]$ depend upon

$$n\,(r+1) - (p-1)\,(r-3)$$

parameters, provided that

$$n \geqslant r + \frac{rp}{r+1}\,.$$

* Brill and Nöther, *Math. Ann.* 7 (1874), 308. Nöther, *Journal für Math.* 93 (1882), 281. Segre, *Math. Ann.* 30 (1887), 207.

Thus in [4] there are ∞^{21} rational normal quartic curves. Through each of these curves there passes a quadric containing the curve and all its tangents; hence, since there are only ∞^{14} quadrics in [4], there must be, on any given quadric in [4], ∞^7 rational normal quartic curves all of whose tangents also lie on the quadric. Hence, given a quadric primal Ω in [5], there are ∞^5 prime sections Q on each of which there are ∞^7 of these quartic curves. Hence there must be ∞^{12} developable surfaces of the fourth order in ordinary space.

This is also seen at once since a developable surface is completely determined by its cuspidal edge, and Brill and Nöther's result shews that there are ∞^{12} twisted cubics in [3]*.

The developable surface of the fifth order

355. The developable surface of the fifth order is formed by the tangents of a rational quartic curve, in a [3] Σ, having a cusp. Each tangent is met by one other tangent.

The quartic curve Γ is the projection of a normal curve C in [4] from a point O on one of its tangents. The tangent touches C in a point P and meets Σ in the cusp K of Γ. The developable surface of the sixth order formed by the tangents of C is projected, from O, into the developable surface of the fifth order formed by the tangents of Γ.

The tangent solid of Q at O contains the osculating plane of C at P, and therefore meets C in one other point P'. The osculating solid† of C at P' passes through O and meets Σ in a plane which has four-point contact with Γ at the point W which is the projection of P'. Thus there is a point W of Γ at which the osculating plane is stationary. The intersection of Q with its tangent solid at O is an ordinary quadric cone; the line OP is a generator of this cone, the tangent plane of the cone along this generator being the osculating plane of C at P. This plane meets Σ in the cuspidal tangent of Γ at K. The quadric cone also has OP' as a generator. Hence the intersection of Σ with this quadric cone is a conic touching the cuspidal tangent of Γ at K and passing through W. The tangent of this conic at W lies in the stationary osculating plane of Γ.

This conic is the nodal curve of the developable surface of the fifth order, for every generator of the quadric cone on Q meets three tangents of C, and therefore meets two tangents other than OP. Conversely, every

* For this particular result see also Reye, *Die Geometrie der Lage* (2) (Stuttgart, 1907), 200.

† If any point of [4] is taken there are four osculating solids of C passing through it; the four points in which they osculate C are the intersections of C with the polar solid of the point in regard to Q (Clifford, *Papers*, 312–313). For a point O on Q the polar solid is the tangent solid at O; if O is on the tangent at a point P of C the four points of intersection of the solid with C consist of P counted three times and P'. The osculating solids of C are the tangent solids of Q at the points of C.

line through O meeting two further tangents of C must lie on Q and therefore in its tangent solid at O.

The pairs of tangents of C which meet the lines of Q passing through O touch C in pairs of points belonging to an involution. The double points of this involution are P and P'. The joins of the pairs of points form a cubic ruled surface*, and the solids which contain the pairs of tangents of C are the tangent solids of this ruled surface; they touch a quadric line-cone whose vertex is the directrix of the surface, this directrix passing through O. But these solids meet Σ in planes, each of which contains two tangents of Γ; hence the nodal developable consists of the tangent planes of a quadric cone. The osculating planes of Γ at K and W are tangent planes of this cone. The generators of the cone are the intersections of Σ with the planes joining O to the generators of the cubic ruled surface; the tangent of Γ at W is a generator of the cone, and there is a generator passing through K.

356. Given a rational normal quintic curve C in [5] there are three linearly independent quadric fourfolds which contain C and all its tangents. There are ∞^9 linearly independent quadrics containing C, and each such quadric contains six tangents of C. The tangents of C form a developable surface of order eight on which C is a cuspidal curve; if then a quadric is made to contain C and seven tangents it will necessarily contain the developable surface. Thus of the ∞^9 quadrics containing C there are ∞^2 containing all its tangents.

Conversely, given a quadric Ω in [5] there exist rational normal quintic curves on it such that all their tangents also lie on Ω. The rational normal quintic curves C in [5] are ∞^{32} in aggregate, whereas quadrics are ∞^{20} in aggregate; hence, as there are for each curve ∞^2 quadrics containing its tangents, there must be on a given quadric ∞^{14} curves C all of whose tangents also lie on the quadric.

357. Suppose then that we have on the quadric Ω in [5] a normal rational quintic curve C all of whose tangents also lie on Ω. If the points of Ω represent the lines of a space S_3 the points of C represent the generators of a developable surface of the fifth order.

The tangents of C form a developable surface R_2^8 of the eighth order lying on Ω; hence the ruled surface formed by the chords of C which lie on Ω, in all of order 12, breaks up into R_2^8 and a quartic ruled surface R_2^4. There is one† generator of R_2^4 through each point of C, and R_2^4 is formed by the joins of pairs of an involution on C. This involution has two double points x and y; the tangents of C at x and y are common generators of R_2^4 and R_2^8.

* See the footnote to § 19. † See § 352.

The tangent prime of Ω at any point P of C meets C in four points at P and in another point P', the line PP' is the generator of R_2^4 through P. The tangent prime of Ω at P' meets C four times at P', the remaining intersection of C with this tangent prime being P. But at x or y the tangent prime of Ω has five intersections with C and does not meet it elsewhere; the osculating planes of C at x and y lie on Ω*. We must then regard these as the two trisecant planes of C lying on Ω; they are of opposite systems†.

The tangent plane of R_2^4 at a point P of C is the plane containing the tangent of C at P and the generator PP' of R_2^4. Thus at x or y the tangent plane of R_2^4 is the osculating plane of C. The plane of the directrix conic of R_2^4, which passes through x, thus meets Ω in the directrix conic and also in its tangent at x, and so lies on Ω entirely; similarly the plane of the directrix conic of R_2^4 which passes through y also lies on Ω entirely. The planes of the conics on R_2^4 form a V_3^3 whose complete intersection with Ω consists of R_2^4 and these two planes.

Suppose then that Ω contains ϖ_x (the osculating plane of C at x), ρ_y (the osculating plane of C at y), ρ_x (the plane of the directrix conic of R_2^4 which passes through x) and ϖ_y (the plane of the directrix conic of R_2^4 which passes through y). The osculating plane of C at x or y must be of the opposite system to the plane of the directrix conic of R_2^4 passing through that point since they have in common a tangent of this conic.

Any plane of Ω of general position meets R_2^8 in four points and R_2^4 in two points. The developable surface in S_3 is formed by the tangents of a rational quartic Γ of which there are four osculating planes passing through an arbitrary point of S_3. Γ has a cusp, represented on Ω by ϖ_x, and a stationary osculating plane represented on Ω by ρ_y. The nodal curve is a conic whose plane is represented on Ω by ρ_x and the nodal developable is a quadric cone whose vertex is represented on Ω by ϖ_y.

358. We have seen that on a quadric Ω in [5] there are ∞^{14} rational normal quintic curves all of whose tangents lie on Ω. In other words the quintic developables in S_3 are ∞^{14} in aggregate. This can be verified in other ways. For rational quartics in S_3 are ∞^{16} in aggregate and two conditions are necessary for such a curve to have a cusp. If, for example, the curve is regarded as the projection of a normal curve in [4], the point of projection must lie on the surface formed by the tangents of the normal curve, and this imposes two conditions on the point. Hence rational quartics in S_3 which have cusps are ∞^{14} in aggregate, and since a developable is completely determined by its cuspidal edge the result is verified.

Again, any rational quartic in S_3 which has a cusp is the intersection of a pencil of quadrics having stationary contact. Now the quadrics in S_3 are ∞^9 in aggregate, so that pencils of quadrics are ∞^{16} in aggregate,

* Cf. § 350. † Cf. § 88.

just as there are ∞^{16} lines in [9]. Then pencils of quadrics which touch are ∞^{15}, while pencils of quadrics having stationary contact are ∞^{14}; two conditions being necessary for two quadrics to have stationary contact*.

The projections of the developable formed by the tangents of a normal rational quartic curve

359. Any surface in [4] can be projected from a point O on to a solid Σ. There are ∞^1 chords of the surface passing through O, and these form a cone of lines meeting the surface in a curve†. Two points of this curve which are collinear with O may be called associated points; the tangents to the curve at a pair of associated points intersect, their plane passing through O; the osculating planes of the curve at a pair of associated points have a line in common, the solid containing them passing through O.

We can of course project ruled surfaces in this way.

Consider, in particular, the developable formed by the tangents of a curve C in [4]; we have a cone of lines through O, each line meeting two generators of the developable. These lines meet the developable in points lying on a certain curve; the points of this curve lie on the tangents of C, while the tangents of the curve lie in the osculating solids of C.

360. Consider now a rational normal quartic curve C in [4]; its tangents form a rational developable F of order 6. There are ∞^5 quadric threefolds containing C, each of these containing four tangents of C; there is a unique quadric Q containing F. Let us project F on to a solid Σ from a point O.

There are ∞^1 chords of F passing through O; a solid through O meets F in a rational sextic with four cusps and six apparent double points; thus the chords of F passing through O meet F in a curve C_{12} of order 12.

The plane joining O to a tangent of C is met by two other tangents; for the projection of C from one of its tangents on to a plane is a conic, and there are two tangents of this conic passing through any point of the plane. Hence C_{12} meets every generator of F in two points.

361. There are four points of C for which the osculating solids contain O; these are, in fact, the intersections of C with the polar solid of O in regard to Q‡. Take one of these points W, and the tangent w of C at W.

The projection of C from w on to a plane is a conic; the osculating solid at W meets the plane in a tangent of the conic passing through the pro-

* Salmon, *Geometry of Three Dimensions*, 1 (Dublin, 1914), 208.

The quintic developable is studied algebraically by Cayley, *Papers*, 1 (1850), 491; 2 (1864), 275 and 518; Schwarz, *Journal für Math.* 64 (1865), 4–9; Dino, *Giornale di Matematiche* (1), 3 (1865), 100 and 133. For geometrical treatment see Chasles, *Comptes Rendus*, 54 (1862), 322 and 719; Cremona, *ibid.* 604–608; d'Ovidio, *Giorn. di Mat.* (1), 3 (1865), 107, 184 and 214.

† Lines through a point of [4] are ∞^3 and one condition is necessary for a line to meet a surface in [4].

‡ See the footnote to § 355.

jection of O; there is one other tangent passing through the projection of O. Hence the plane wO only meets one tangent of C other than w; suppose that it meets this other tangent in a point A. Then OA meets w in a point B, and A and B are a pair of associated points on C_{12}. The tangents of C_{12} at A and B intersect and they both lie in the osculating solid of C at W.

This osculating solid of C is the tangent solid of Q at W; it meets Q in a quadric cone whose vertex is W and of which WA and WB are generators. The osculating plane of C at W is common to the tangent solids of Q at all the points of w and touches the cone along w*. The solid meets F in w counted three times and in a cubic curve lying on the cone; this cubic touches w at W and passes through A. There is one chord of this cubic passing through O, and we thus have two points of C_{12}; the solid meets C_{12} also in A and B, touching it at each of these points; the remaining intersections of the solid with C_{12} consist simply of W counted six times. The six chords of C_{12} lying in the osculating solid at W consist of the chord of the cubic, the line OAB counted twice and the line OW counted three times. This solid meets Σ in an osculating plane of the nodal curve.

Thus on projection we have in Σ a rational quartic curve C_4; the tangents of C_4 form a developable of the sixth order with a nodal curve C_6 of the sixth order. There are four points W_1, W_2, W_3, W_4 of C_4 at which the osculating plane is stationary; the nodal curve passes through these four points and has there the same osculating planes as C_4. The tangent of C_4 at any one of these points meets C_6 in one further point, the corresponding stationary plane touching C_6 at this point†.

362. There are four planes through O which contain tangents of C and meet C again‡. Consider then a plane through O containing a tangent t which touches C in B and meeting C again in a point S. There are no tangents of C meeting this plane other than t and the tangent at S. OS meets t in a point T and is a stationary generator of the cone of chords of F; it will meet Σ in a point which is a cusp of the nodal curve C_6. S and T are the only points of C_{12} in the plane Ot.

Consider the solid joining O to the osculating plane of C at B. It meets Q in a quadric cone whose vertex is somewhere on t, while it meets F in t counted twice and a rational quartic, this quartic touching t at B and having a cusp at S. There are two chords of this quartic passing through O; the remaining four chords of C_{12} which lie in the solid must then all coincide with OST. The plane in which the solid meets Σ will thus have four intersections with the nodal curve at its cusp, and is therefore the osculating plane of the nodal curve there.

* Cf. Baker, *Principles of Geometry*, 4 (Cambridge, 1925), 38. Also § 350 above.

† Cf. Cremona, *Annali di Matematica* (1), 4 (1861), 92.

‡ The trisecant planes of C passing through O cut out a g_3^1 on C, being one system of planes of a quadric point-cone. This g_3^1 has four double points.

Hence C_4 has four tangents which touch it in points B_1, B_2, B_3, B_4 and meet it again in points S_1, S_2, S_3, S_4. The nodal curve C_6 has four cusps at the points S; the osculating plane of C_6 at a point S osculating C_4 at the corresponding point B.

363. In the preceding work we have projected from a general point O of the [4] containing C. Suppose now that we specialise the position of O so that it lies on the quadric Q. Then the polar solid of O in regard to Q passes through O, being the tangent solid of Q at O. Hence we obtain in Σ a rational quartic C_4 whose four points of superosculation W_1, W_2, W_3, W_4 are coplanar.

Any line of Q is met by three tangents of C, and in fact Q may be defined as the locus of transversals of triads of tangents of C. Thus the tangents of C_4 intersect in threes in the points of a conic*; this conic is the intersection of Σ with the quadric cone in which Q is met by its tangent solid at O, and it passes through W_1, W_2, W_3, W_4.

Hence we have a developable whose nodal curve degenerates into a triple conic; this conic meets the cuspidal edge in the four (coplanar) points at which its osculating plane is stationary.

364. Now let us choose O to lie in an osculating plane α of C; α contains a tangent t of C touching it at a point T. It is common to the tangent solids of Q at all the points of t, and every line in α touches both Q and F at the point where it meets t.

A solid through O meets F in a rational sextic with four cusps; there is a tangent of this curve passing through O, viz. the line in which the solid meets α. Then there must be five chords of the curve passing through O; so that the chords of F through O give on F a curve C_{10} of order 10, and the nodal curve of the developable in Σ is a curve C_5 of the fifth order.

The polar solid of O in regard to Q contains t and therefore meets C in two other points. Hence when C is projected on to Σ from O it becomes a rational quartic C_4 with an inflection I and two points W_1, W_2 at which the osculating plane is stationary. There are only two planes through O which contain tangents of C and meet it again†, so that there are two tangents of C_4 which touch it at points B_1, B_2 and meet it again in points S_1, S_2.

By repeating previous arguments we see that the nodal curve C_5 passes through W_1 and W_2 and has there the same osculating planes as C_4. Further, C_5 meets C_4 in S_1 and S_2; C_5 has, in fact, cusps at S_1 and S_2, the osculating planes of C_5 at these points osculating C_4 in B_1 and B_2.

* See R. A. Roberts, "Unicursal Twisted Quartics," *Proc. Lond. Math. Soc.* (1), 14 (1883), 22, and Marletta, *Annali di Matematica* (3), 8 (1903), 109.

† The $g_3{}^1$ given by the trisecant planes through O includes a set for which all the three points coincide; this triple point counts for two double points. In general, an m-ple point of a $g_n{}^1$ counts for $m - 1$ double points.

365. If we consider now any solid belonging to the pencil of solids through α, it meets Q in a quadric cone whose vertex lies on t and which touches α along its generator t. The same solid meets F in a quartic having a cusp (at the one intersection other than T of the solid with C) and touching t at T. There are two chords of this quartic passing through O; the other three chords of C_{10} which lie in this solid will all coincide with OT. Thus the nodal curve C_5 of the developable in Σ passes through I, and any plane of the pencil determined by the inflectional tangent of C_4 at I meets C_5 in three points at I.

Similarly we can shew that a plane through I which does not contain the inflectional tangent of C_4 meets C_5 in only one point there; a solid containing OT but not t meets F in a rational sextic with four cusps, one of which is at T, the cuspidal tangent of this curve at T passing through O. Thus we conclude that C_5 has an inflection at I with the same inflectional tangent as C_4.

366. We now choose O to be the intersection of two osculating planes of C*. Then on projection we have in Σ a rational quartic C_4 with two inflections I and J. The developable of tangents has a nodal curve D_4 which is also a quartic; D_4 has inflections at I and J with the same inflectional tangents as C_4.

367. Finally, let us choose O to lie on a chord XY of C. The chords of C form a locus $M_3{}^3$, and through any point of $M_3{}^3$ there pass two lines lying on it which are not chords of C. Such lines we shall call axes of C. The chords of C which meet an axis form a cubic ruled surface†.

Through O there pass two axes m and n of C. The cubic ruled surfaces determined by m and n have the chord XY as a common generator, and the solid which contains the tangents of C at X and Y touches both the cubic ruled surfaces along this generator and contains m and n. When we project from O on to Σ we obtain a rational quartic C_4 with a double point; the lines m and n meet Σ in points A and B which are the vertices of quadric cones containing C_4, A and B both lying in the plane of the tangents at the double point.

Now take one of the axes through O, say m. Then through any point of m there passes a chord of C which is a generator of the cubic ruled surface containing m. The solid containing the two tangents of C at the points where this chord meets it is the tangent solid of the ruled surface along this generator; it therefore contains m. Hence there is a transversal from O to these two tangents.

* The locus of intersections of pairs of osculating planes of C is a quartic surface. See § 368.

† See Segre, "Sulle varietà cubiche dello spazio a quattro dimensioni," *Memorie Torino* (2), 39 (1889); in particular p. 35.

Thus either cubic ruled surface gives a cone through O formed by chords of the developable of tangents of C; the nodal curve of the developable in Σ breaks up into two parts.

There are two tangents of C meeting m; these touch C in two points, the osculating solids at which contain m. There are generators of the cone through O which meet C in these two points.

The line OXY is a stationary generator of the cone, meeting a pair of tangents of C at the points where they themselves touch C. The tangent plane of the cone along this stationary generator will lie in the solid joining O to the osculating plane of C at X and also in the solid joining O to the osculating plane of C at Y.

Now the line m is not a generator of the cone of chords through O which it determines; but nevertheless it meets two tangents of C. Hence it must be a generator of the cone of chords determined by n. The tangent plane of this latter cone along m is the intersection of the two solids joining O to the planes which osculate C at the points where it is touched by the two tangents meeting m; but these are none other than the osculating solids of C at these two points. Thus we have in Σ an inflection on the nodal curve.

Thus the developable of tangents of C_4 has a nodal curve consisting of two plane cubics C_3 and D_3*. Each of these cubics has a cusp at the double point of C_4, the cuspidal tangent being for each of them the intersection of the two osculating planes of C_4 at this point. C_3 meets C_4 also in two points W_1, W_2, at each of which the osculating plane of C_4 is stationary. Similarly D_3 meets C_4 also in two points W_3, W_4, at each of which the osculating plane of C_4 is stationary. C_3 has an inflection at B, the inflectional tangent being the intersection of the osculating planes of C_4 at W_3 and W_4, while D_3 has an inflection at A, the inflectional tangent being the intersection of the osculating planes of C_4 at W_1 and W_2†.

The tangent solids of a cubic ruled surface in [4] all pass through its directrix; they meet any solid in the tangent planes of a quadric cone. Thus the two quadric cones with vertices A and B which contain C_4 belong to the bitangent developable of the surface.

The sections of the locus formed by the osculating planes of a normal rational quartic curve

368. Instead of projecting the points of C from a point O (which does not lie on a tangent of C) we can take the sections of the osculating solids of C by a solid Σ (which does not contain an osculating plane

* Cf. Chasles, *Comptes Rendus*, 54 (1862), 718.

† Cf. Brambilla, *Rendiconti della Reale Acc. di Scienze Fis. e Mat. di Napoli*, 24 (1885), 294.

of C). These sections are planes which osculate a rational sextic C_6 with four cusps, and the tangents of this curve, which are the lines in which the osculating planes of C meet Σ, form a developable of the sixth order. The cusps of C_6 are the four points K_1, K_2, K_3, K_4 in which Σ meets C.

The nodal curve of this developable in Σ is given by pairs of non-consecutive intersecting osculating planes of C; hence its order is equal to the number of points of an arbitrary plane through which pass two osculating planes but not a tangent of C. The osculating planes meet the arbitrary plane in the points of a rational sextic with six cusps at the points where the plane is met by tangents of C; this curve has four double points. Hence there are four points of a given plane at which two distinct osculating planes of C intersect, so that the developable in Σ has a nodal curve C_4 of the fourth order.

369. If a plane meets C in a point K then there are four tangents of C which meet the plane in points other than K; for when C is projected from K on to a solid it becomes a twisted cubic, of which there are four tangents meeting an arbitrary line.

Also, if a line meets C in a point K it is met by three osculating planes of C in points other than K; for when C is projected from the line on to a plane it becomes a rational cubic which has three inflections.

Thus a plane which meets C in a point K is met by the osculating planes of C in the points of a rational sextic curve with a triple point at K and four cusps. This curve will have three other double points. We deduce that the nodal curve C_4 of the developable meets the cuspidal edge C_6 in its four cusps K_1, K_2, K_3, K_4.

But we can prove more than this, for the curves C_4 and C_6 have the same osculating planes at K_1, K_2, K_3, K_4. The osculating plane of C_6 at K_1 is the intersection of Σ with the osculating solid of C at K_1. This solid meets the developable F formed by the tangents of C in the tangent at K_1 counted three times and a twisted cubic touching this tangent at K_1*; the osculating plane of C at K_1 being also the osculating plane of this cubic curve. Then the plane of intersection of the osculating solid with Σ meets this osculating plane in a line p; it meets the other osculating planes of C in the points of a rational quartic with three cusps, one of these cusps is at K_1 and p is the cuspidal tangent there. The remaining intersection of p with the quartic curve is the only point of the plane in which two distinct osculating planes of C intersect. Hence the plane osculates C_4 as well as C_6.

370. Instead of choosing Σ to be a general solid we can choose it to be a tangent solid of the quadric Q. Then the tangents of C meet Σ in the

* Cf. § 361.

points of a rational sextic curve C_6 which has four cusps and lies on a quadric cone. It meets every generator of the cone in three points; the tangent planes of the cone are tritangent planes of the developable.

371. Now choose Σ to contain a tangent t of C; it meets C in two other points K_1, K_2. Then the tangents of C other than t meet Σ in the points of a rational quintic curve C_5 with cusps at K_1 and K_2. The osculating planes of C meet Σ in the tangents of C_5, so that t will be a stationary tangent of C_5. C_5 then has an inflection at I, the point of contact of t with C, t being the inflectional tangent.

Using similar arguments to those above we find that the tangents of C_5 form a developable surface with a nodal quartic curve C_4; C_4 passes through K_1 and K_2 and has at these points the same osculating planes as C_5.

Any line meeting a tangent of C will meet four other osculating planes of C; for when C is projected from the line on to a plane we obtain a rational quartic, with one cusp and two double points, which has four inflections. Hence a plane through t meets the locus formed by the osculating planes of C in t counted twice and a rational quartic with cusps at the two other points in which the plane is met by tangents of C*. This quartic will have one other double point.

Hence any plane of Σ passing through t meets C_4 in only one point not on t. In fact C_4 has an inflection at I with t as the inflectional tangent.

372. If we take Σ to be the solid containing the tangents at two points I and J of C it meets the developable of tangents further in a rational quartic curve C_4 with inflections at I and J. The tangents of C_4 form a developable of the sixth order; this has a nodal curve which is also a quartic, having the same two inflections and inflectional tangents as C_4. We obtain the same surface as in § 366.

373. Finally, choose Σ to contain the plane in which two osculating solids of C intersect. Then the developable is formed by the tangents of a rational sextic with four cusps and a plane which osculates it in two different points. It is the dual of the developable formed by the tangents of a rational quartic with a double point.

We have already seen (in § 368) that the locus of the intersections of pairs of osculating planes of C is a quartic surface. If we project the quartic C on to a plane from a line which lies in one of its osculating planes we obtain a plane quartic with a triple point, the three branches at the triple point having a common tangent which meets the curve in four points there. This tangent is the line of intersection of the plane with the

* Cf. § 360.

osculating solid of C. Such a plane quartic has two inflections*, so that a line lying in an osculating plane of C meets two other osculating planes of C, or the osculating planes of C meet the quartic surface in conics.

Consider now an involution of pairs of points on C; the lines joining the pairs form a cubic ruled surface, and the tangent solids of this cubic ruled surface envelop a quadric line-cone. Now, if we reciprocate in regard to the quadric Q which contains the tangents of C, a tangent solid of the ruled surface, as containing two tangents of C, becomes the point of intersection of two osculating planes of C, and the quadric line-cone becomes a conic. Hence, if we take any involution of pairs of points on C, the pairs of osculating planes at these points intersect in the points of a conic. Hence, since there are ∞^2 involutions on C, the quartic surface has ∞^2 conics upon it. The locus of intersections of pairs of osculating planes of C is therefore a projection of Veronese's surface†.

The conics in which two different osculating planes of C meet the quartic surface have one intersection, this being the intersection of the two osculating planes. The plane of the two tangents to the conics at their intersection is the tangent plane of the surface; it is in fact the plane of intersection of the two corresponding osculating solids of C, an osculating solid of C containing the tangent planes of the surface at all the points of the conic in the osculating plane. Now every solid through a tangent plane of the surface meets it in two conics‡. Hence Σ meets the surface in two conics; these make up the nodal curve of the developable. The conics have one intersection; this lies in the plane which osculates the sextic at two different points. Each conic passes through two of the cusps of the sextic.

If the curve C is given by

$$x_0 : x_1 : x_2 : x_3 : x_4 = \theta^4 : \theta^3 : \theta^2 : \theta : 1,$$

then the osculating planes at the two points whose parameters are θ and ϕ intersect in the point

$$\theta^2\phi^2, \qquad \tfrac{1}{2}\theta\phi\,(\theta+\phi), \qquad \tfrac{1}{6}\,(\theta^2+4\theta\phi+\phi^2), \qquad \tfrac{1}{2}\,(\theta+\phi), \qquad 1.$$

If either θ or ϕ is constant the locus of this point is a conic.

The coordinates of the point may be written, putting $\theta+\phi = x$ and $\theta\phi = y$,

$$y^2, \qquad \tfrac{1}{2}xy, \qquad \tfrac{1}{6}\,(x^2+2y), \qquad \tfrac{1}{2}x, \qquad 1,$$

so that prime sections of the surface are represented by conics in a plane. The surface is of the fourth order.

* The Hessian of the quartic is made up of the tangent at the triple point, counted four times, and two other lines through the triple point; the remaining intersections of these two lines with the curve are the two inflections.

† A surface, in space of any number of dimensions, which contains ∞^2 conics, is the surface of Veronese or one of its projections; see Bertini, *Geometria proiettiva degli iperspazi* (Messina, 1923), 393.

‡ Cf. Bertini, *ibid.* 412.

If there is a relation $ax + by + c = 0$ we obtain the points of a conic on the surface, so that the intersections of osculating planes at pairs of points of an involution lie on a conic.

The tangent plane to the surface is the plane of the three points

$$\begin{array}{lllll} \theta^2\phi^2, & \tfrac{1}{2}\theta\phi\,(\theta+\phi), & \tfrac{1}{6}(\theta^2+4\theta\phi+\phi^2), & \tfrac{1}{2}(\theta+\phi), & 1; \\ 2\theta\phi^2, & \tfrac{1}{2}\phi\,(2\theta+\phi), & \tfrac{1}{3}(\theta+2\phi), & \tfrac{1}{2}, & 0; \\ 2\theta^2\phi, & \tfrac{1}{2}\theta\,(\theta+2\phi), & \tfrac{1}{3}(2\theta+\phi), & \tfrac{1}{2}, & 0; \end{array}$$

and is therefore common to the two solids

$$x_0 - 4\theta x_1 + 6\theta^2 x_2 - 4\theta^3 x_3 + \theta^4 x_4 = 0,$$
$$x_0 - 4\phi x_1 + 6\phi^2 x_2 - 4\phi^3 x_3 + \phi^4 x_4 = 0,$$

which are the osculating solids of C at the points whose parameters are θ and ϕ.

Any solid containing a tangent plane of the surface therefore has an equation

$$\lambda\,(x_0 - 4\alpha x_1 + 6\alpha^2 x_2 - 4\alpha^3 x_3 + \alpha^4 x_4) + \mu\,(x_0 - 4\beta x_1 + 6\beta^2 x_2 - 4\beta^3 x_3 + \beta^4 x_4) = 0;$$

and if we substitute in this equation the coordinates of the point on the surface we obtain

$$\lambda\,(\theta-\alpha)^2(\phi-\alpha)^2 + \mu\,(\theta-\beta)^2(\phi-\beta)^2 = 0,$$

which splits up into factors

$$(\theta-\alpha)(\phi-\alpha) \pm k\,(\theta-\beta)(\phi-\beta) = 0.$$

Hence any solid through a tangent plane meets the surface in *two* curves, each curve being given by a relation of the form

$$a\theta\phi + b\,(\theta+\phi) + c = 0$$

between θ and ϕ. The curves are therefore conics.

The developables of the sixth order considered as curves on Ω

374. If we have a rational developable of the sixth order in [3] its generators are represented by the points of a rational sextic curve C lying on the quadric Ω in [5], all the tangents of C also lying on Ω. If, for the moment, we assume that the edge of regression Γ has no inflections, C will have no cusps.

In [5] the rational sextics C are ∞^{38} in aggregate*, while the quadrics Ω are ∞^{20} in aggregate. Since each sextic lies on ∞^7 quadrics we deduce that each quadric contains ∞^{25} sextics.

Now if one of the sextic curves lies on a quadric there are eight of its tangents which lie on the quadric†; the tangents form a surface of order ten on which the curve is cuspidal, and the eight tangents, taken with the curve C counted twice, make up the complete intersection of the surface with the quadric. If a quadric contains C and nine of its tangents it will contain all the tangents. Given the curve C there will not, in general, be a quadric containing C and all its tangents.

But on any given quadric Ω there will be ∞^{25-9} or ∞^{16} curves C all of whose tangents lie on Ω. There are thus ∞^{36} curves C such that quadrics can be taken to contain all their tangents, and a rational sextic curve in

* § 354. † § 349.

[5] will have to satisfy two conditions in order that all its tangents should lie on a quadric.

We conclude that in [3] the aggregate of rational sextic developables without stationary generators is ∞^{16}. This is in accordance with what we should expect, a developable in [3] being completely defined by its cuspidal edge. For rational quartics in [3] are ∞^{16}; rational quintics with two cusps are $\infty^{20-2\cdot 2}=\infty^{16}$ and rational sextics with four cusps are $\infty^{24-4\cdot 2}=\infty^{16}$.

375. Suppose then that on the quadric Ω in [5] we have a curve C whose tangents also lie on Ω; C being rational, of the sixth order and without cusps. No plane of [5] can be met by more than six tangents of C*, so that there are three possibilities:

(*a*) Every ϖ-plane of Ω meets six tangents of C, while every ρ-plane of Ω meets four tangents of C.

(*b*) Every plane of Ω meets five tangents of C.

(*c*) Every ϖ-plane of Ω meets four tangents of C, while every ρ-plane of Ω meets six tangents of C.

In any case there are four osculating planes of C lying on Ω†.

If we project C from one of its osculating planes on to some other plane we obtain a rational plane cubic; this will have a double point, and, for certain particular osculating planes of C, it may have a cusp. But no osculating plane of C can be met by more than one tangent of C, other than the one which it contains. From this we can conclude that in (*a*) the four osculating planes of C which lie on Ω are all ρ-planes, and that in (*c*) they are all ϖ-planes.

If a rational sextic curve lies on Ω there are eight of its trisecant planes lying on Ω‡; thus, besides the four osculating planes of C which lie on Ω there must be four other trisecant planes of C also lying on Ω.

376. When C is in class (*a*) the cuspidal edge of the developable is a rational quartic Γ with four stationary osculating planes; these are represented on Ω by the four ρ-planes which osculate C. The four other planes of Ω which are trisecant to C will all be ϖ-planes; each of these in fact contains a tangent of C and meets C in a further point: they represent the four points in which Γ is met by its own tangents.

The chords of C form a locus M_3^{10} of three dimensions and the tenth order; there being ten chords of C meeting an arbitrary plane of [5]. The chords of C which lie on Ω form a ruled surface which is the intersection of Ω and M_3^{10}; this consists in fact of two surfaces, that formed by the tangents of C and another ruled surface R_2^{10} of order ten meeting every ϖ-plane of Ω in four points and every ρ-plane of Ω in six points.

The tangent prime of Ω at any point of C meets C four times|| at this

* For we cannot have a rational plane sextic with more than six cusps. See the reference to Veronese in § 347. † § 350. ‡ § 35. || § 352.

point, and in two other points; the chords to these other points are generators of R_2^{10}. Thus C is a double curve on R_2^{10}. The generators of R_2^{10} set up a symmetrical (2, 2) correspondence on C; there are four of them which touch C, and these are precisely the tangents of C at the points where its osculating planes lie on Ω; the tangent prime of C at one of these points only meets C in one other point*.

The pairs of intersections of C with those of its chords which generate R_2^{10} represent pairs of intersecting tangents of Γ; the locus of these points of intersection is a nodal curve on the developable; its points are represented on Ω by the ϖ-planes through the generators of R_2^{10} and it is thus of the sixth order. It has four cusps; these are represented on Ω by those four ϖ-planes which contain tangents of C and meet C again. The four cusps of the nodal curve are at the four points where Γ is met by its own tangents. Also the nodal curve meets Γ in the four points where its osculating plane is stationary; these four points are represented on Ω by the ϖ-planes through the tangents of C at the four points where its osculating plane lies on Ω.

The ρ-planes through the generators of R_2^{10} represent planes of pairs of intersecting tangents of Γ; these envelop a nodal developable of the fourth class to which belong the four stationary osculating planes of Γ.

When C is in class (c) we have similarly a developable whose cuspidal edge Γ is a sextic curve with four cusps; the cusps are represented on Ω by the four ϖ-planes which osculate C. The nodal curve is of the fourth order passing through the cusps of Γ.

377. When C is in class (b) the four planes of Ω which osculate C belong two to each system. The developable is thus formed by the tangents of a rational quintic curve Γ which has two cusps and two stationary osculating planes.

There are four other planes trisecant to C which lie on Ω; these will also be two of each system, and each of them contains a tangent of C and meets C in another point. The two ϖ-planes represent points in which Γ is met by its own tangents, while the two ρ-planes represent osculating planes of Γ which contain other tangents.

The chords of C which lie on Ω again form a ruled surface R_2^{10} on which C is a double curve, but now there are five generators of the surface meeting every plane of Ω. The tangents of C, at those four points at which the osculating planes lie on Ω, are generators of R_2^{10}, as also are those chords of C which lie in the four other trisecant planes.

The ϖ-planes through the generators of R_2^{10} represent the points of a nodal curve; this curve is of the fifth order and passes through the cusps of Γ, and it has cusps at the two points where Γ is met by its own tangents.

* § 352.

The ρ-planes through the generators of R_2^{10} represent planes each of which contains two intersecting tangents of Γ; these envelop a nodal developable of the fifth class. The stationary osculating planes of Γ belong to this developable, and the two planes which osculate Γ, and also touch it, are stationary planes of the developable.

The tangents of Γ here form a developable which we did not obtain by the methods of projection and section in [4].

378. We now suppose that we have a rational sextic curve C in [5] with one cusp—the projection of a rational normal sextic from a point on one of its tangents. The tangents of C form a surface of order nine and any quadric containing C contains six of its tangents *. Any quadric through C which contains seven of its tangents must contain them all, and as there are ∞^8 quadrics containing C there will be ∞^1 quadrics containing C and all its tangents.

Four conditions are necessary for a curve in [5] to have a cusp; if, for example, the curve is regarded as the projection of a curve in [6] without singularities the point of projection must lie on the two-dimensional locus formed by the tangents. There will thus be ∞^{34} rational sextic curves in [5] which have cusps. There are ∞^{20} quadrics in [5]; ∞^8 of these contain a given rational sextic with a cusp. Thus on any given quadric Ω in [5] there are ∞^{22} rational sextic curves which have cusps and ∞^{15} of these curves are such that all their tangents lie on Ω. The cuspidal edge Γ of the developable represented by C has an inflection corresponding to the cusp of C; in the next paragraphs we shall see that Γ is either a rational quartic with an inflection or a rational quintic with two cusps and an inflection. In either case the aggregate of curves Γ is ∞^{15}; two conditions are necessary for Γ to have a cusp, one condition for it to have an inflection.

379. Suppose then that we have on the quadric Ω in [5] a rational sextic curve C with a cusp K. The tangents of C form a surface of order nine, and as no plane can be met by more than five tangents of C† there are two possibilities.

(*a*) Every ϖ-plane of Ω is met by five tangents of C and every ρ-plane by four tangents of C.

(*b*) Every ϖ-plane of Ω is met by four tangents of C and every ρ-plane by five tangents of C.

In either case there are two osculating planes of C lying on Ω‡.

If C is projected from one of its osculating planes (other than that at the cusp) on to another plane we obtain a plane cubic with a cusp. Hence no osculating plane of C can be met by any tangent of C other than the one which it contains. This is sufficient to shew that the two osculating planes of C which lie on Ω are both ρ-planes in (*a*) and both ϖ-planes in (*b*).

* § 349.

† Just as in § 375; we cannot have a rational plane sextic with more than six cusps.

‡ § 350.

380. Suppose, to fix ideas, that C is of the type (a). The chords of C form a locus M_3^9 of three dimensions and of order nine; there are nine chords of C meeting an arbitrary plane of [5]. The osculating plane of C at K belongs to M_3^9; for if we regard C as the projection of a rational normal sextic from a point on one of its tangents the osculating solid of C at the point of contact of this tangent touches the M_3^{10} formed by the chords all along this tangent.

The points of C represent the generators of a developable in [3] whose cuspidal edge Γ is a rational quartic with an inflection. Γ has two stationary osculating planes; these are represented on Ω by the two ρ-planes which osculate C.

The intersection of Ω and M_3^9 consists of the surface formed by the tangents of C and of a ruled surface R_2^9 consisting of chords of C which lie on Ω. This latter surface meets every ϖ-plane of Ω in four points and every ρ-plane of Ω in five points. It has two generators passing through K; these are the cuspidal tangent of C and the other line in which the osculating plane of C at K meets Ω. The generators of R_2^9 set up a symmetrical (2, 2) correspondence on C; the four coincidences include K counted twice, so that we have two other tangents of C which are generators of R_2^9, these being the two tangents which touch C at the points where its osculating planes lie on Ω.

The ϖ-planes through the generators of R_2^9 represent the points of the nodal curve of the developable in [3]. This curve is then of the fifth order and meets Γ in the two points at which its osculating plane is stationary, and also in its inflection.

There are two ϖ-planes of Ω which pass through tangents of C and meet C again; these represent the two points in which Γ is met by its own tangents. These points are cusps on the nodal curve.

The ρ-planes through the generators of R_2^9 represent planes of [3] which envelop a nodal developable. This developable is of the fourth class and the two stationary osculating planes of Γ belong to it, as also does the osculating plane of Γ at its inflection.

381. When C is of the type (b) we have a surface dual to the one just discussed. The cuspidal edge Γ is now of the fifth order having two cusps and an inflection; the two cusps are represented on Ω by the ϖ-planes which osculate C, the inflection by the ϖ-plane through the cuspidal tangent of C.

The nodal curve is of the fourth order passing through the cusps and the inflection of Γ. The nodal developable is of the fifth class; the osculating planes of Γ at its cusps and inflection belong to this developable. There are two planes of Γ which both osculate and touch it; these are stationary planes of the nodal developable.

382. Suppose now that we have in [4] a rational sextic with two cusps—the projection of a rational normal sextic from a line meeting two of its tangents. There are ∞^3 quadric threefolds containing the curve, and each of these contains four of its tangents. There will not, in general, be a quadric containing all the tangents of the curve.

The rational sextics in [4] are ∞^{31} in aggregate*, and as three conditions are necessary for a curve in [4] to have a cusp the rational sextics C which have two cusps are ∞^{25} in aggregate. The aggregate of quadrics in [4] is ∞^{14}, while there are ∞^3 quadrics through each curve C; hence each quadric contains ∞^{14} curves C. If a quadric should contain five tangents of C as well as C itself it necessarily contains all the tangents; thus on any given quadric there will be ∞^9 curves C all of whose tangents also lie on the quadric.

Thus in [4] we have ∞^{23} curves C such that there are quadrics which contain all their tangents; hence a general rational sextic in [4] with two cusps must be specialised twice in order that a quadric should contain all its tangents.

383. Suppose now that we have a quadric in [4] and a rational sextic curve C with two cusps K_1, K_2 whose tangents all lie on the quadric. The tangents form a ruled surface of order eight; since no line on the quadric can meet more than four tangents of C every line on the quadric must meet precisely four tangents of C.

Now regard the quadric as a prime section of Ω. Then the points of C represent the generators of a developable surface in [3]; the edge of regression Γ being of the fourth order and having two inflections. The tangents of Γ belong to a linear complex.

The chords of C form a locus $M_3{}^8$, there being eight of them meeting an arbitrary line of [4]. The osculating planes of C at K_1 and K_2 belong to this locus. The quadric meets this locus in the surface formed by the tangents of C and in a ruled surface $R_2{}^8$ also of order eight; this surface also meets every line on Ω in four points and there are two of its generators passing through any point of C. The cuspidal tangents belong also to this surface; there is one other generator of $R_2{}^8$ through each cusp, the other line in which the osculating plane there meets the quadric.

The ϖ-planes through the generators of $R_2{}^8$ represent points of the nodal curve of the developable; this passes through the inflections of Γ and is also of the fourth order. We also have a nodal developable of the fourth class.

384. One condition is necessary for a curve in [3] to have an inflection; if the curve is regarded as the projection of a curve in [4] the point of projection is constrained to lie on the three-dimensional locus formed by

* § 354.

the osculating planes. Thus there are in [3] $\infty^{16-2}=\infty^{14}$ curves of the fourth order with two inflections.

On the other hand, given a quadric Ω in [5] it has ∞^5 prime sections, and on each of these there lie ∞^9 rational sextic curves C which have two cusps, and are such that all their tangents lie on the quadric. Hence we have ∞^{14} curves C on Ω in agreement with the former result.

The classification of the developable surfaces

385. We now give a table of the different developables of the sixth order in [3]. In [4] there is only one developable of the sixth order—that formed by the tangents of a normal rational quartic curve. We have obtained ten different types of surfaces in [3]; in the first column of the table we give the double curve, in the second the bitangent developable and in the third a description of the cuspidal edge. C_n denotes a curve of order n, E_n a developable of class n and T or T' a stationary generator. D_n is also used for a curve, F_n for a developable when necessary. All curves and developables which occur are rational.

When a bar is placed over a part of the double curve it means that the points in which a plane meets this curve are cusps and not ordinary double points on the plane section. Similarly, when a bar is placed over a part of the bitangent developable it means that the planes of this part which pass through a point are stationary planes and not ordinary double planes of the enveloping cone.

There are no developables of the sixth order in spaces of higher dimension than 4.

	Double curve	Bitangent developable	Cuspidal edge
1	$\bar{C}_4 + C_6$	$\bar{E}_6 + E_4$	Rational quartic
2	$\bar{C}_5 + C_5$	$\bar{E}_5 + E_5$	Rational quintic with two cusps
3	$\bar{C}_6 + C_4$	$\bar{E}_4 + E_6$	Rational sextic with four cusps
4	$\bar{C}_4 + 3C_2$	$\bar{E}_6 + E_4$	Rational quartic whose four stationary osculating planes have their points of contact coplanar
5	$\bar{C}_6 + C_4$	$\bar{E}_4 + 3E_2$	Rational sextic with four cusps, the osculating planes at the cusps being concurrent
6	$\bar{C}_4 + C_3 + D_3$	$\bar{E}_6 + E_2 + F_2$	Rational quartic with a double point
7	$\bar{C}_6 + C_2 + D_2$	$\bar{E}_4 + E_3 + F_3$	Rational sextic with four cusps and a doubly osculating plane
8	$\bar{C}_4 + \bar{T} + C_5$	$\bar{E}_5 + \bar{T} + E_4$	Rational quartic with an inflection
9	$\bar{C}_5 + \bar{T} + C_4$	$\bar{E}_4 + \bar{T} + E_5$	Rational quintic with two cusps and an inflection
10	$\bar{C}_4 + \bar{T} + \bar{T}' + C_4$	$\bar{E}_4 + \bar{T} + \bar{T}' + E_4$	Rational quartic with two inflections

386. We can give another table shewing the singularities of the cuspidal edges of these developables. We shall denote the order of a curve by n, the rank by r, the class by n', the number of cusps by κ, the number of inflections by i and the number of stationary osculating planes by κ'. Also let h denote the number of apparent double points and δ the number of actual double points; δ' the number of doubly osculating planes and h' the number of lines in any given plane which are intersections of two osculating planes of the curve. Also let b be the number of planes through any point which are bitangent to the curve and b' the order of the nodal curve of the developable.

Then we can give the following table; we omit the developables (4) and (5) because the table would not distinguish them from (1) and (2).

	n	r	n'	κ	i	κ'	b	b'	h	δ	h'	δ'
1	4	6	6	0	0	4	4	6	3	0	6	0
2	5	6	5	2	0	2	5	5	4	0	4	0
3	6	6	4	4	0	0	6	4	6	0	3	0
6	4	6	6	0	0	4	4	6	2	1	6	0
7	6	6	4	4	0	0	6	4	6	0	2	1
8	4	6	5	0	1	2	4	5	3	0	4	0
9	5	6	4	2	1	0	5	4	4	0	3	0
10	4	6	4	0	2	0	4	4	3	0	3	0

CHAPTER VI

SEXTIC RULED SURFACES (CONTINUED)

Further types of rational sextic ruled surfaces

387. The developable surface of the fourth order has for its cuspidal edge a twisted cubic; it has no nodal curve. It is a particular case of the general rational quartic ruled surface which has a twisted cubic for its double curve.

The developable surface of the fifth order has for its cuspidal edge a rational quartic with a cusp; its nodal curve is a conic passing through the cusp of the quartic and meeting it in two other points. It is a particular case of the rational quintic ruled surface whose double curve breaks up into a rational quartic and a conic; the quartic has a double point through which the conic passes and the two curves have two other intersections (cf. § 92 and § 130).

When we turn to the developable surfaces of the sixth order we at once notice the fact that, except for the two developables that we have numbered (6) and (7), we have not obtained any rational sextic ruled surfaces of which they are special cases. The developable (6) has two nodal plane cubics and, for its cuspidal edge, a rational quartic with a double point; it is a particular case of the rational sextic ruled surface whose double curve consists of two twisted cubics and a rational quartic (cf. § 180). The developable (7) has two nodal conics and, for its cuspidal edge, a rational sextic with four cusps; it is a particular case of the rational sextic ruled surface whose double curve consists of two conics and a rational sextic with four double points (cf. § 179).

This leads us to suspect that there still remain types of rational sextic ruled surfaces other than the sixty-seven types we have already obtained. For example: the existence of the first developable, whose cuspidal edge is a rational quartic and nodal curve a rational sextic, leads us to expect a type of rational sextic ruled surface whose double curve consists of a rational quartic and a rational sextic, and we have not yet obtained such a surface. Since the generators of the developable are tangents of the cuspidal edge and chords of the double curve we expect the generators of the ruled surface to meet each part of the double curve in two points.

This last remark gives the clue to the discovery of these further types of surfaces. For if we consider the double curve of any type of rational sextic ruled surface that we have obtained, and omit any double generators that may occur, the remainder of the double curve consists of a number of components of which all, with at most one exception, are directrices, meeting each generator in one point. The solid S from which we project the normal surface meets an infinity of chords of one or more directrix curves of the normal surface.

388. Let us then take a curve meeting each generator of the normal surface F in two points, the surface having ∞^1 directrix cubic curves. We take first an elliptic curve $C_8{}^1$ of order eight; such a curve is given by a quadric primal containing four generators of F. The chords joining pairs of points of a rational involution on $C_8{}^1$ form a rational sextic ruled surface with, in general, ∞^1 directrix cubic curves each meeting $C_8{}^1$ twice; but there are 16 involutions for which the sextic ruled surface has a directrix conic*, this conic not meeting $C_8{}^1$. Let us choose S to contain the plane of such a conic ϑ_2; it meets the locus $M_5{}^6$ formed by the chords of F in ϑ_2 and a rational quartic $\vartheta_4{}^0$ having four intersections with ϑ_2. The chords of F which meet $\vartheta_4{}^0$ include four tangents and meet F in the points of an elliptic curve $C_{12}{}^1$; $C_{12}{}^1$ meets each generator twice and has four double points. The two chords of F which pass through any one of these double points and meet $\vartheta_4{}^0$ meet F again in intersections of $C_{12}{}^1$ and $C_8{}^1$; this accounts for eight of the sixteen intersections of the two curves. The remaining eight lie in pairs on the chords of F which pass through the four intersections of ϑ_2 and $\vartheta_4{}^0$.

Hence, projecting from S, we obtain a surface f in [3] whose double curve is $C_4{}^0 + C_6{}^0$. $C_6{}^0$ has four double points through all of which $C_4{}^0$ passes, and the two curves have four other intersections.

If we project F from the plane of ϑ_2 on to a [4] we obtain a rational sextic ruled surface with a rational normal quartic double curve. The generators of the surface are chords of the curve, through each point of the curve there pass two of them. The surface is the intersection of the cubic primal formed by the chords of the curve with a quadric containing the curve.

389. The involution on $C_8{}^1$ sets up a symmetrical (2, 2) correspondence between the generators of F. There are four generators g of F for which the two corresponding generators coincide; these are the four generators g which touch $C_8{}^1$. There are four generators of f touching $C_4{}^0$ and four touching $C_6{}^0$.

The (2, 2) correspondence between the generators of F gives a (2, 2) correspondence on any directrix cubic of F; the chords of the cubic which join pairs of corresponding points form a rational quartic ruled surface. Hence the planes which are determined by those pairs of generators of f which meet in the points of $C_4{}^0$ are the projections, from S, of the solids of an $M_4{}^8$. Each solid of $M_4{}^8$ is determined by two corresponding lines in a (1, 1) correspondence, without united elements, between the generators of two rational quartic ruled surfaces. The projection of $M_4{}^8$ from the solid

* Segre, *Math. Ann.* 27 (1886), 296.

S, which contains a conic ϑ_2 meeting each solid of $M_4{}^8$, is a rational developable $E_6{}^0$ of the sixth class. This is part of the bitangent developable $E_6{}^0 + E_4{}^0$ of f.

The solids which contain the directrix cubics of F form a locus $M_4{}^4$; there are four of them which meet S. The [6] containing S and any one of these four solids meets the space on to which we are projecting in a tritangent plane of f. It meets S in a directrix cubic Δ and in three generators; it contains eight points of $C_8{}^1$, two on each generator and two on Δ. Now the pairs of points in which $C_8{}^1$ is met by the directrix cubics of F are the pairs of a $g_2{}^1$, and two $g_2{}^1$'s on an elliptic curve cannot have a common pair of points. Hence the chord of $C_8{}^1$ which joins its intersections with Δ does not meet ϑ_2. The eight points of $C_8{}^1$ which lie in the [6] are joined in pairs by four lines which meet ϑ_2; the [6] meets the space on to which we are projecting in a plane which is a plane of $E_4{}^0$ and a double plane of $E_6{}^0$.

390. We now choose the solid S to contain ϑ_2 and also to meet the solid containing a pair g, g' of generators of F in a line l. It can be shewn that l must meet the plane of ϑ_2 in a point O of ϑ_2 itself, and that the chord of $C_8{}^1$ through O meets F on the generators g and g'. S meets $M_5{}^6$ in ϑ_2, l and a twisted cubic $\vartheta_8{}^0$ which meets l once and ϑ_2 three times.

The chords of F which meet S meet F in $C_8{}^1$, g, g' and an elliptic curve $C_{10}{}^1$; there are four tangents of $C_{10}{}^1$ meeting $\vartheta_3{}^0$, and it meets each generator of F in two points. $C_{10}{}^1$ has two double points.

Let OAA' be the chord of F through O, meeting g in A and g' in A'. $C_8{}^2$ passes through A and A'; let it meet g and g' again in B and B' respectively. We have chords BC, $B'C'$ of $C_8{}^1$ meeting ϑ_2 and chords BD', $B'D$ meeting l; D' is on g' and D on g. The lines CD' and $C'D$ are chords of $C_{10}{}^1$ and meet $\vartheta_3{}^0$; the other intersections of $C_{10}{}^1$ with g and g' lie on the chord of F which passes through the intersection of l and $\vartheta_3{}^0$. There are three pairs of intersections of $C_8{}^1$ and $C_{10}{}^1$ collinear with the three intersections of ϑ_2 and $\vartheta_3{}^0$; there are four other intersections of $C_8{}^1$ and $C_{10}{}^1$, these are associated in pairs with the two double points of $C_{10}{}^1$.

The projected surface f has a double curve $C_4{}^0 + G + C_5{}^0$. G is a trisecant of $C_4{}^0$, $C_5{}^0$ passing through two of their intersections. $C_5{}^0$ has two double points; $C_4{}^0$ passes through both these double points, as well as meeting $C_5{}^0$ in three further points which do not lie on G.

The locus $M_4{}^8$ now meets S in the conic ϑ_2 and the line l; the planes of the pairs of generators of f which intersect in the points of $C_4{}^0$ form a developable $E_5{}^0$ of the fifth class. The bitangent developable of f is $E_5{}^0 + G + E_4{}^0$. The solid S meets four solids which contain directrix cubics of F; two of these four meet S in points on l. Thus f has two tritangent planes which do not pass through G; these are planes of $E_4{}^0$ and double planes of $E_5{}^0$.

391. We can further choose S to contain ϑ_2, a line l lying in the solid containing a pair of generators g, g' of F and a line m lying in the solid containing a pair of generators h, h' of F. l and m meet ϑ_2. S meets M_5^6 in ϑ_2, l, m and a conic ϕ_2; ϕ_2 meets l and m and meets ϑ_2 twice.

The chords of F which meet S meet F in C_8^1, g, g', h, h' and an elliptic curve D_8^1; D_8^1 meets each generator of F twice and has four of its tangents meeting ϕ_2. C_8^1 and D_8^1 have eight intersections.

The projected surface f has two double generators, its double curve being $C_4^0 + G + H + D_4^0$. C_4^0 and D_4^0 have two intersections on G, two on H, and two others. G and H are trisecants both of C_4^0 and D_4^0. The bitangent developable is $E_4^0 + G + H + F_4^0$.

392. A curve of order ten which meets each generator of F twice is elliptic provided that it has two double points. Let us then consider such a curve C_{10}^1; it can be given by a quadric containing two generators of F and touching F twice.

The joins of the pairs of points of a rational involution on C_{10}^1 form an octavic ruled surface; in general this surface has ∞^1 directrix quartic curves, but there are 25 involutions for which the resulting surface has a directrix cubic. The curve C_{10}^1 is the projection of a normal curve in [9] from a line meeting two of its chords. An involution on an elliptic curve is determined when *one* of its pairs of points has been assigned; the normal curve is projected from a line which meets two chords joining pairs of points of the *same* involution. This involution gives an octavic ruled surface which is projected into the sextic surface F.

We choose the solid S, from which F is to be projected, to contain the directrix cubic ϑ_3^0 of the ruled surface determined by one of the 25 special involutions. S meets M_5^6 in ϑ_3^0 and a second twisted cubic ϕ_3^0, the two curves having four intersections. There are four tangents of C_{10}^1 meeting ϑ_3^0; the chords of F which meet S meet F in C_{10}^1 and a second elliptic curve D_{10}^1. There are four tangents of D_{10}^1 meeting ϕ_3^0; it meets each generator of F in two points and has two double points. C_{10}^1 and D_{10}^1 have sixteen intersections; eight of these are collinear in pairs with the four intersections of ϑ_3^0 and ϕ_3^0, the remaining eight fall into four pairs associated with the two double points of C_{10}^1 and the two double points of D_{10}^1.

The double curve of the projected surface f is $C_5^0 + D_5^0$. Each of C_5^0 and D_5^0 has two double points through which the other passes, and the two curves have four further intersections.

The bitangent developable is $E_5^0 + F_5^0$. Either part of this developable is the projection of a locus M_4^8 from a solid S which contains a cubic curve meeting all the solids of M_4^8.

We can also obtain surfaces in [3], with double curves and bitangent developables as above, by projection from the normal surface with a directrix conic. A surface whose double curve is $C_5^0 + D_5^0$ can be obtained by projection from the normal surface with a directrix line; we have a bitangent developable $10R$ and a double curve $C_5{}^0 + D_5{}^0$.

393. The sextic ruled surface whose double curve is $C_4{}^0 + C_6{}^0$ is generated by a symmetrical (2, 2) correspondence* on a rational quartic $C_4{}^0$. If we specialise this correspondence so that the two points corresponding to some point P of the curve are the points Q and R where the curve is met by its trisecant through P, the surface has a double generator and its double curve is $C_4{}^0 + G + C_5{}^0$; $C_5{}^0$ passes through Q and R. We can specialise the correspondence further and obtain two double generators. We cannot specialise the correspondence still further in this way† without it degenerating into the $g_3{}^1$ cut out by the trisecants of the curve; the sextic ruled surface would then degenerate into a quadric counted three times.

If we have a rational quintic $C_5{}^0$ in [3], with two double points, and set up on the curve a symmetrical (2, 2) correspondence in which the two points on the different branches at either double point of $C_5{}^0$ correspond to one another, the chords joining pairs of corresponding points generate a sextic ruled surface whose double curve is $C_5{}^0 + D_5{}^0$. This is the projection of the ruled surface of order eight, generated by a symmetrical (2, 2) correspondence on a rational normal quintic curve in [5], from a line meeting two of its generators.

394. We now give the representation of these ruled surfaces as curves on Ω. Through each point of a rational sextic curve C on Ω there pass four of its chords which lie on Ω; the chords of C which lie on Ω set up a symmetrical (4, 4) correspondence on C. It is characteristic of the types of ruled surfaces that we have just obtained that this correspondence degenerates into the sum of two symmetrical (2, 2) correspondences.

Suppose that C has no double points. The joins of corresponding points in a symmetrical (2, 2) correspondence on C form a ruled surface of order ten; the ruled surface $R_2{}^{20}$ formed by the chords of C which lie on Ω (cf. § 173) here breaks up into two ruled surfaces $R_2{}^{10}$ and $S_2{}^{10}$, both of order ten and both rational.

Suppose that PQR is a trisecant plane of C which lies on Ω. Then the chords QR, RP, PQ of C cannot all belong to the same ruled surface, for then the symmetrical (2, 2) correspondence would be an involution of sets of three points‡, and we should have ∞^1 trisecant planes of C lying on Ω. Hence two of the three chords must belong to one of the two ruled surfaces, the other chord belonging to the other ruled surface. The double curve of the ruled surface in [3] breaks up into two parts; one of these parts has its points in (1, 1) correspondence with the generators of $R_2{}^{10}$,

* See footnote to § 19.

† The symmetrical (2, 2) correspondence and the $g_3{}^1$ given by the trisecants have four common pairs of points and no more. See § 15.

‡ Cf. Baker, *Principles of Geometry*, 2 (Cambridge 1922), 135–6.

the other has its points in (1, 1) correspondence with the generators of S_2^{10}. At each of the four triple points of the sextic ruled surface there is one part of the double curve which has a double point. Similarly each tritangent plane of the surface is a double plane of one of the two parts of the bitangent developable.

The surfaces R_2^{10} and S_2^{10} have four common generators; the two parts of the double curve have four intersections other than at triple points of the ruled surface while the two parts of the bitangent developable have in common four planes which are not tritangent planes of the ruled surface.

Neither of the ruled surfaces R_2^{10} and S_2^{10} can meet a plane of Ω in more than six points. Suppose, first, that R_2^{10} meets every ϖ-plane of Ω in four points and every ρ-plane of Ω in six points; then, since each plane of Ω is met by ten chords of C, S_2^{10} meets every ϖ-plane of Ω in six points and every ρ-plane of Ω in four points. The surface in [3] has a double curve $C_4^0 + C_6^0$ and a bitangent developable $E_6^0 + E_4^0$. The four ϖ-planes of Ω which are trisecant to C contain each two generators of S_2^{10} and one generator of R_2^{10}; C_6^0 has four double points through each of which C_4^0 passes. Also E_6^0 has four double planes, these being also planes of E_4^0.

It may also happen that both R_2^{10} and S_2^{10} meet every plane of Ω in five points. Then the surface in [3] has a double curve $C_5^0 + D_5^0$ and a bitangent developable $E_5^0 + F_5^0$.

395. Suppose now that C has a double point P; and that the points of C on the two different branches at P are corresponding points in both the symmetrical (2, 2) correspondences. These correspondences give rise to two rational ruled surfaces R_2^9 and S_2^9, both of the ninth order. Each of these surfaces must meet the planes of one system each in four points and the planes of the opposite system each in five points; each plane of Ω is met by four generators of one surface and five of the other. The corresponding ruled surface in [3] has a double curve $C_5^0 + G + C_4^0$ and a bitangent developable $E_4^0 + G + E_5^0$.

The plane of the two tangents of C at P meets Ω in two lines which are common generators of R_2^9 and S_2^9; the two surfaces have two other common generators and each surface has a third generator passing through P. There are four trisecant planes of C lying on Ω, two being ϖ-planes and two ρ-planes. Thus C_5^0 has two double points through each of which C_4^0 passes; the curves have two intersections on G in addition to two further intersections, and G is a trisecant of both curves. There are similar statements for the bitangent developable.

We can suppose also that C lies in [4] and has two double points P and Q; and that the points of C on the two different branches at either double point are corresponding points in both symmetrical (2, 2) correspondences. These correspondences give rise to two rational ruled surfaces

R_2^8 and S_2^8, both of the eighth order. Each of these surfaces meets every plane of Ω in four points on the line in which it meets the [4] containing C, and the corresponding ruled surface in [3] has a double curve $C_4^0 + G + H + D_4^0$ and a bitangent developable $E_4^0 + G + H + F_4^0$.

There are two common generators of R_2^8 and S_2^8 in the plane containing the tangents of C at P, and there is a third generator of each surface through P; similarly for Q. There are no other common generators of R_2^8 and S_2^8 other than the two at P and the two at Q, and there are no trisecants of C. Hence C_4^0 and D_4^0 have two intersections on G and two intersections on H; G and H are trisecants both of C_4^0 and of D_4^0.

396. There are two types of rational sextic ruled surfaces which were overlooked in the first section of Chapter IV; we will obtain them now.

Take the rational normal sextic ruled surface F in [7] which has ∞^1 directrix cubic curves, and on this surface two directrix quartics E and E'. These quartic curves have two intersections, and we consider two involutions of pairs of generators of F, the generators through the two intersections of E and E' forming a pair of both involutions. The first involution determines a cubic ruled surface containing E and the second determines similarly a cubic ruled surface containing E'; these two cubic ruled surfaces have directrices λ and λ' respectively, and we choose the two involutions so that λ and λ' intersect on the common chord of E and E'. We take, further, a pair of generators g, g' which belong to the first involution and a line l meeting λ and lying in the solid gg'. We then project F on to a [3] Σ from the solid S determined by λ, λ' and l.

S meets M_5^6 in λ, λ', l and a twisted cubic ϑ_3^0 which meets l and λ and has λ' as a chord. The chords of F which meet S meet F in E, E', g, g' and an elliptic curve C_{10}^1 of which four tangents meet ϑ_3^0; C_{10}^1 meets each generator in two points and has two double points, and meets each of E and E' in six points.

Two of the intersections of C_{10}^1 with E are on the chord of F which passes through the intersection of λ and ϑ_3^0; the remaining four are associated in pairs with the two double points of C_{10}^1. The chord of F which passes through the intersection of ϑ_3^0 and l accounts for an intersection of C_{10}^1 with each of g and g'; the remaining intersections of C_{10}^1 with g and g' are associated with the intersections of E' with g' and g (respectively) and with two of the intersections of E' and C_{10}^1. The remaining intersections of E' and C_{10}^1 are collinear in pairs with the two intersections of λ' and ϑ_3^0.

We obtain, on projection, a surface f in Σ whose double curve is $C_2 + D_2 + G + C_5^0$. G is a chord of D_2 and C_5^0 passes through their intersections, meeting D_2 in two other points and G in one other point. C_5^0 has two double points through each of which C_2 passes; C_2 meets C_5^0 in one other point and meets G and D_2 each in one point.

The surface is generated by a (2, 2) correspondence between two conics C_2 and D_2 with a common point, this being a doubly united point. The correspondence is to be specialised to give the double generator; to the second intersection of C_2 with the plane of D_2 there corresponds a pair of points of D_2 collinear with it. The planes of the pairs of generators which intersect in the points of C_2 envelop a quadric cone E_2; the planes of the pairs of generators which intersect in the points of D_2 envelop a cubic developable $E_3{}^0$. There are two planes of $E_3{}^0$ and one plane of E_2 passing through G. The bitangent developable of the surface is $E_2 + E_3{}^0 + G + E_4{}^0$.

397. There is also a surface dual to the one just mentioned; the double curve of this surface will be $C_2 + C_3{}^0 + G + C_4{}^0$, the bitangent developable $E_2 + F_2 + G + E_5{}^0$.

To obtain this surface by projection we consider, on the normal surface F with ∞^1 directrix cubic curves, a directrix quartic E and a prime section $C_6{}^0$; these have four intersections. We then consider two involutions on F; the first of these determines, by means of E, a cubic ruled surface with a directrix line λ, and the second determines, by means of $C_6{}^0$, a quintic ruled surface with a directrix conic Γ. We choose the involutions so that λ and Γ meet on a chord of F which joins two of the intersections of E and $C_6{}^0$. We can determine a solid S which not only contains λ and Γ but also a line l, meeting λ, which lies in the solid determined by a pair of generators g, g' belonging to the first involution. We project F from S on to Σ.

S meets $M_5{}^6$ in λ, l, Γ and a conic Δ meeting Γ twice and l and λ each once. The chords of F which meet S meet F in E, g, g', $C_6{}^0$ and an elliptic curve $C_8{}^1$ of which four tangents meet Δ; $C_8{}^1$ meets each generator in two points, has no double points, and meets E in four points and $C_6{}^0$ in eight points.

Two of the intersections of $C_8{}^1$ with E are on the chord of F which passes through the intersection of λ and Δ; the remaining two are associated with those two intersections of E and $C_6{}^0$ which do not lie on the chord of F passing through the intersection of λ and Γ and with two of the intersections of $C_8{}^1$ and $C_6{}^0$. There are two other intersections of $C_8{}^1$ and $C_6{}^0$ associated with the intersections of $C_6{}^0$ with g and g' and with intersections of $C_8{}^1$ with g' and g (respectively). The other intersections of $C_8{}^1$ with g' and g lie on the chord of F through the intersection of Δ and l, while the four remaining intersections of $C_8{}^1$ and $C_6{}^0$ are collinear in pairs with the two intersections of Γ and Δ.

We obtain, on projection, a surface f in Σ whose double curve is $C_2 + C_3{}^0 + G + C_4{}^0$. C_2 and $C_3{}^0$ have three intersections through two of which $C_4{}^0$ passes; $C_4{}^0$ meets C_2 in one other point and $C_3{}^0$ in four other points. G joins two of these four points; it meets $C_4{}^0$ again and also meets C_2.

The surface is generated by a (2, 2) correspondence between a conic C_2

and a twisted cubic C_3^0; the curves have three intersections one of which is a doubly united point, the other two being ordinary united points. The correspondence is specialised to give the double generator; there is a point of C_2 to which correspond the two points in which C_3^0 is met by the chord passing through the point. The planes joining the points of C_2 to the pairs of points of C_3^0 which correspond to them touch a quadric cone E_2, while the planes joining the points of C_3 to the pairs of points of C_2 which correspond to them touch a quadric cone F_2. The bitangent developable is $E_2 + F_2 + G + E_5^0$. There are two planes of F_2 and one plane of E_2 passing through G.

398. We now shew how the two surfaces which we have just obtained are represented as rational sextic curves C on the quadric Ω in [5]. Since the surfaces are not self-dual their generators cannot belong to a linear complex; hence C actually belongs to [5] and is not contained in a space of lower dimension. C has a double point P representing the double generator G.

C is the projection of a rational normal sextic curve from a point on one of its chords. The chords which join the pairs of points of an involution on a rational normal sextic curve form a rational normal quintic ruled surface with a directrix conic; we take two such involutions and project from a point on a chord belonging to one of them. We obtain a curve C, with a double point P, in [5]; we have, containing C, a quartic ruled surface and a quintic ruled surface with a common generator. Of the ∞^{20} quadrics in [5] there are ∞^8 which contain C; of these ∞^8 there are ∞^3 containing the quintic ruled surface, ∞^5 containing the quartic ruled surface, and ∞^1 containing both surfaces. We take one of these last quadrics to be Ω.

There is, on the quintic surface, a plane cubic curve with a double point at P (cf. § 191); the plane of this curve lies on Ω. Every plane of Ω of the same system as this meets two generators of the quintic surface; every plane of the opposite system meets three generators of the quintic surface. The quartic ruled surface meets every plane of Ω in two points. The chords of C which lie on Ω form the quartic ruled surface R_2^4, the quintic ruled surface R_2^5, and a rational ruled surface R_2^9 of order nine on which C is a double curve. The plane of the two tangents of C at P meets Ω in two lines one of which is a generator of R_2^4 and the other of R_2^9. There are two generators of R_2^5 passing through P; these are also generators of R_2^9; R_2^5 and R_2^9 have two other common generators while R_2^4 and R_2^9 have one common generator. R_2^4 and R_2^5 have one common generator. A plane of Ω which belongs to the same system as the plane of the cubic curve on R_2^5 is met by five generators of R_2^9; a plane of the opposite system is met by four generators of R_2^9.

Suppose that the plane cubic on R_2^5 lies in a ρ-plane of Ω. Then the surface in [3] has a double curve $C_2 + D_2 + G + C_5^0$ and a bitangent developable $E_2 + E_3^0 + G + E_4^0$. If, on the other hand, the plane cubic on R_2^5 lies in a ϖ-plane of Ω the surface has a double curve $C_2 + C_3^0 + G + C_4^0$ and a bitangent developable $E_2 + F_2 + G + E_5^0$.

Sextic ruled surfaces with a triple curve

399. One of the developables of the sixth order which we have obtained has a triple conic; in order to obtain a sextic ruled surface with a triple curve by projection we must choose, for the centre of projection, a space which is met in lines by ∞^1 trisecant planes of the normal surface.

Consider a prime section C_6^0 of the rational normal sextic ruled surface F in [7] which has ∞^1 directrix cubics. Let us consider the planes which contain the triads of points which form sets of a g_3^1 on C_6^0; they form a three-dimensional locus whose order is the number of planes which meet an arbitrary solid, Π say, in the prime which contains C_6^0. Now the trisecant planes of C_6^0 are the intersections of corresponding primes of four projectively related triply infinite systems*; to obtain the planes which contain the sets of a g_3^1 we consider four corresponding pencils of primes belonging to the four systems. The solid Π meets these pencils in four projectively related pencils of planes; and it is a well-known result that there are *four* points which are intersections of corresponding planes of the four pencils†. Hence the planes which contain the sets of a g_3^1 on C_6^0 form a three-dimensional quartic locus V_3^4.

This locus V_3^4 is normal in [6]; it can be generated by the planes which join triads of corresponding points of two lines and a conic, projectively related to each other‡. It therefore contains the quadric surface Q determined by the projective relation between the lines; there is a generator of Q in each plane of V_3^4. We select the solid S which contains Q as the centre of projection, and project F from S on to a [3] Σ.

400. The curve C_6^0 does not meet Q; the chords of C_6^0 which lie in the planes of V_3^4 form a ruled surface of order ten which meets Q in a rational quartic curve ϑ_4^0, the generators of Q which lie in the planes of V_3^4 being the trisecants of ϑ_4^0. Since the g_3^1 on C_6^0 has four double points there are four tangents of C_6^0 which meet ϑ_4^0. The solid S meets the locus M_5^6 formed by the chords of F in ϑ_4^0 and a conic ϑ_2, ϑ_2 meeting ϑ_4^0 in four

* The bases of the four systems may be taken to be any four fixed trisecant planes of C_6^0.

† If l_1, l_2, l_3, l_4 denote the axes of the four pencils, the two pencils whose axes are l_2 and l_3 generate, by means of the lines of intersection of corresponding planes, a regulus. This regulus contains the cubic curve generated by the pencils l_1, l_2, l_3 and also that generated by the pencils l_2, l_3, l_4; these two cubic curves have four intersections.

‡ Segre, *Atti Torino*, 21 (1885), 95.

points. The chords of F which meet S meet F in the curve $C_6{}^0$ counted twice (since two of them pass through each point of $C_6{}^0$) and an elliptic curve $C_8{}^1$, four of whose tangents meet ϑ_2, meeting each generator twice. The eight intersections of $C_8{}^1$ and $C_6{}^0$ are collinear in pairs with the four intersections of ϑ_2 and $\vartheta_4{}^0$.

On projection we obtain a surface f in Σ whose double curve is $3C_2 + C_4{}^0$, C_2 and $C_4{}^0$ having four intersections. The surface is generated by a conic C_2 and a twisted cubic in (1, 3) correspondence with three united points. The planes of pairs of generators which intersect in the points of C_2 envelop a developable $E_4{}^0$; the bitangent developable of the surface is $E_4{}^0 + E_6{}^0$.

The surface is also generated by the chords of $C_4{}^0$ which meet C_2.

There is also a dual surface whose double curve is $C_4{}^0 + C_6{}^0$ and bitangent developable $3E_2 + E_4{}^0$.

401. We can choose the $g_3{}^1$ on $C_6{}^0$ so that S meets $M_5{}^6$ in $\vartheta_4{}^0$ and two lines l and m; these lines are chords of $\vartheta_4{}^0$ and intersect. They are axes of two directrix quartics E and E', the common chord of E and E' passing through the intersection of l and m. On projection from S we obtain a surface f whose double curve $3B_2 + C_2 + D_2$ consists of a triple conic and two double conics; C_2 and D_2 have one intersection and each of them meets B_2 in two points. The surface is generated by two conics, B_2 and C_2, in (2, 3) correspondence with two doubly united points. The planes of the pairs of generators which intersect in the points of C_2 or D_2 envelop a developable of the third class. The bitangent developable of the surface is $E_4{}^0 + E_3{}^0 + F_3{}^0$.

The surface is generated by the lines which meet the three conics.

There is also a dual surface whose double curve is $C_4{}^0 + C_3{}^0 + D_3{}^0$ and bitangent developable $3E_2 + F_2 + G_2$.

402. The planes which contain the triads of points of a $g_3{}^1$ on a rational sextic curve C in [5] form a locus $v_3{}^4$ which is the projection of the normal locus $V_3{}^4$ formed by the planes containing the triads of points of a $g_3{}^1$ on the normal curve. We obtain different types of loci $v_3{}^4$ according as to the position we select for the point of projection; the only locus $v_3{}^4$ which lies on a non-degenerate quadric Ω of [5] is obtained by projecting $V_3{}^4$ from a point which lies in the solid containing the quadric Q. We thus obtain a locus $v_3{}^4$ with a double plane, the ∞^1 generating planes of $v_3{}^4$ meeting this double plane in the tangents of a conic.

The generating planes of $v_3{}^4$ are all of the same system on the quadric Ω, the double plane being of the opposite system. If the points of Ω represent the lines of [3] then the points of C represent the generators of a rational sextic ruled surface f. If the double plane of $v_3{}^4$ is a ρ-plane f has a triple conic C_2 whose plane is represented on Ω by this ρ-plane. If the double plane of v_3^4 is a ϖ-plane f has as tritangent planes the tangent planes of a quadric cone E_2 whose vertex is represented on Ω by the ϖ-plane.

403. The four types of sextic ruled surfaces that we have just obtained can be derived by projection either from the normal surface with ∞^1 directrix cubics or from the normal surface with a directrix conic Γ. On the latter surface C_6^0 and Γ have two intersections; these belong, in general, to different sets of the g_3^1 on C_6^0.

We now proceed to consider the particular case when the two intersections, a_1 and a_2 say, of C_6^0 and Γ belong to the same set of the g_3^1; the third point of this set is some other point b on C_6^0. The line a_1a_2 meets the quadric Q on V_3^4, so that we are projecting from a solid S which meets the plane of Γ in a point O. Moreover, the [5] $S\Gamma$ contains the plane a_1a_2b, and therefore also the generator g_0 of F which passes through b. Hence the projected surface f has a directrix line R which is itself a generator; through any point of R there pass two other generators while any plane through R contains three other generators.

The generators which meet C_6^0 in the sets of the g_3^1 give also sets of a g_3^1 on Γ; since a g_3^1 and a g_2^1 on Γ have two common pairs of points there is one pair of points, other than a_1 and a_2, which belong to a set of the g_3^1 on Γ and have their join passing through O. The two generators g and g' of F which pass through this pair of points lie in a solid which meets S in a line l passing through O. S meets M_5^6 in l, m and ϑ_4^0, where m is the line of intersection of S with the solid Γg_0 and ϑ_4^0 is the quartic curve on Q. l, m and ϑ_4^0 all pass through O.

The chords of F which meet S meet F in C_6^0, Γ and g_0 each counted twice, and in g and g'. On projection from S we obtain a surface f whose double curve is $3R + G + 3C_2$; R and C_2 have one intersection and G meets both R and C_2.

The surface is generated by a line R and a conic C_2 in (3, 2) correspondence with a doubly united point; the correspondence must be specialised to give the double generator. The joins of the pairs of points of C_2 which correspond to the points of R envelop a rational curve of class three, one point of R lying on the tangent of the curve to which it gives rise. Hence the planes of the pairs of generators which intersect in the points of R touch a developable E_3^0 which has two planes passing through R and one through G. The bitangent developable of f is $6R + G + E_3^0$.

There is also a dual surface whose double curve is $6R + G + C_3^0$ and bitangent developable $3R + G + 3E_2$.

404. In order to obtain a rational sextic ruled surface f in [3] which has an infinity of tritangent planes we must project the normal surface F, in [7], which contains ∞^1 directrix cubics from a solid S which meets every solid K that contains one of the directrix cubics.

The solids K form* a locus $M_4{}^4$. This locus has ∞^3 linear directrices, one of these passing through any given point of the locus; it can in fact be generated by a projectivity between any two of its solids K, the lines which join corresponding points of the two solids being the directrices. The generators of F are themselves directrices of $M_4{}^4$; the cubic curves in which the two solids K meet F correspond to each other in the projectivity.

Suppose now that we project F on to a [3] Σ from a solid S which contains a directrix d of $M_4{}^4$. Each point of d lies in a solid K, and through it there passes a chord of the corresponding cubic curve on F. These chords all meet F on the same pair of generators† g and g', and d lies in the solid gg'. Hence on projection we obtain a surface F, with a double generator G, whose bitangent developable is $G + 3E_3{}^0$; the solids K when projected from S become the osculating planes of a twisted cubic. The double curve of the surface is $G + C_9{}^2$.

There is also the dual surface whose double curve is $G + 3C_3{}^0$ and bitangent developable $G + E_9{}^2$. We take a curve of order nine lying on the normal surface and meeting each generator in two points; this curve is of genus 2, and the planes which contain the sets of a $g_3{}^1$ on the curve form a locus $V_3{}^5$. There is a quadric‡ Q which has a generator in each plane of $V_3{}^5$, and we project from the solid S which contains Q. The chords of the curve which lie in the planes of $V_3{}^5$ form a ruled surface of order fourteen§, meeting Q in a curve of order five which is trisecant to the generators of Q which lie in the planes of $V_3{}^5$. This quintic curve forms part of the intersection of S with the locus $M_5{}^6$ formed by the chords of the ruled surface; the residual intersection is a line which lies in a solid containing a pair of generators of the ruled surface.

In order to obtain by projection the surfaces which have as tritangent planes the tangent planes of a quadric cone we project from a solid S which contains a directrix conic of $M_4{}^4$.

405. We have seen that the surface which is generated by means of a (3, 2) correspondence, with a doubly united point, between a line R and a conic C_2 is a rational sextic ruled surface, provided the correspondence

* p. 143 *supra*.

† Each directrix of $M_4{}^4$ lies in a solid containing two generators of F. Each solid which contains two generators of F meets $M_4{}^4$ in a quadric surface, on which lie ∞^1 directrices of $M_4{}^4$.

‡ There are two types of locus $V_3{}^5$; a locus of the first type is generated by means of two lines and a cubic curve, a locus of the second type by a line and two conics. We are concerned with a locus of the first type here. $V_3{}^5$ is normal in [7].

§ The ruled surface is generated by the joins of pairs of corresponding points in a symmetrical (2, 2) correspondence of valency 1 on a curve of genus 2. See the footnote to § 19.

is specialised to give a double generator. If the correspondence is not specialised to give a double generator the resulting ruled surface is elliptic. We therefore proceed to enquire whether we can obtain an elliptic sextic ruled surface with a triple conic by projection; the surface must be the projection of a normal surface in [5] from a line l which lies in ∞^1 of its trisecant planes. The triple conic must be the projection from l of the section of the surface by a prime through l, there being ∞^1 trisecant planes of this prime section passing through l and forming a quadric line-cone.

Suppose we have an elliptic normal sextic curve in [5]; through a point of general position there pass two of its trisecant planes. There are four Veronese surfaces containing the curve*, and through a point of any of these surfaces there pass not two but an infinity of trisecant planes of the curve. The surfaces may be defined by this property. The tangent planes of any one of the Veronese surfaces form a cubic primal, and the four cubic primals so obtained belong to a pencil whose base is the M_3^9 formed by the chords of the curve. The four cubic primals together form the locus of points which are such that the two trisecant planes of the curve which pass through them coincide†.

Take now a point O on one of the Veronese surfaces. The ∞^1 trisecant planes of the sextic which pass through O meet the Veronese surface in conics; if the sextic is projected from O on to a [4] it becomes a curve lying on a cubic ruled surface, meeting every generator in three points. The tangent plane π of the Veronese surface at O meets all the trisecant planes through O in lines; the projection from any point of π on to a [4] gives an elliptic sextic curve such that ∞^1 of its trisecant planes pass through a line. The trisecant planes through O form a cubic cone; so that, after projection from a point of π, we obtain ∞^1 trisecant planes of an elliptic sextic curve in [4] which generate a quadric line-cone.

The chords of the normal curve which lie in the trisecant planes through O meet π in the points of a cubic curve; we can either project from a general point of π or from a point of this cubic curve.

406. Suppose first that we project from a general point of π. We obtain, in [4], an elliptic sextic curve with only one trisecant; there are ∞^1 trisecant planes of this curve all passing through a line, this line being met also by the trisecant. We therefore consider a prime section C_6^1 of the normal surface F which has only one directrix cubic Γ. We have on C_6^1 a g_3^1 cut out by trisecant planes through a line l; the three points of intersection of C_6^1 and Γ lie on a line meeting l in a point O. The chords of F

* Rosati, *Rend. Ist. Lomb.* (2), 35 (1902), 407.

† There are four quadric cones which contain an elliptic quartic curve in [3]; the two chords of the curve which pass through a point of any of the cones coincide. There is an analogous result for a normal elliptic curve of any even order; that for the sextic is as above.

which meet l meet F in $C_6{}^1$ and Γ each counted twice; on projection we obtain a surface with a triple directrix line R and a triple conic C_2. The double curve is $3R + 3C_2$; R and C_2 intersect. The surface is generated by a (3, 3) correspondence between R and C_2 with a trebly united point; to the point of intersection regarded as a point of either curve there correspond three points of the other curve which all coincide with it. The triads of points of C_2 which correspond to the points of R are such that their joins envelop an elliptic curve of the sixth class; the tangent of C_2 at the united point is a stationary tangent of this envelope, which has three other tangents passing through the point. The bitangent developable of the surface is $3R + E_6{}^1$, there being three planes of $E_6{}^1$ passing through R.

407. If we project from a point of π which lies on a chord of the normal curve we obtain an elliptic sextic curve with a double point in [4]. There is on this curve a $g_3{}^1$ cut out by the planes of a quadric line-cone; the two points on the different branches at the double point belong to the same set of the $g_3{}^1$ and the line joining them to the remaining point of the set meets the vertex of the line-cone. We therefore consider a prime section $C_6{}^1$ of the normal surface F with a double line λ. $C_6{}^1$ has a double point; the plane joining this to the vertex l of the line-cone meets $C_6{}^1$ again, and the generator g through this other intersection lies in the solid $l\lambda$. We obtain, on projection from l, a surface in [3] with a directrix line R which is itself a generator; through each point of R there pass two other generators while each plane through R contains three other generators. R is the projection of g and λ; there is also a triple conic C_2, the projection of $C_6{}^1$. R and C_2 have one intersection; the surface is generated by a (3, 2) correspondence, with a doubly united point, between R and C_2. The joins of the pairs of points of C_2 which correspond to the points of R form a rational envelope of the third class, one of whose tangents passes through the point of R which gives rise to it. The planes which contain the pairs of generators which intersect in the points of R therefore form a developable $E_3{}^0$ two of whose planes pass through R. The bitangent developable of the surface is $6R + E_3{}^0$.

408. If we project the normal elliptic surface F which has ∞^1 directrix cubic curves from a line l we obtain a surface f in [3] which has ∞^1 tritangent planes. The planes of the cubic curves on the normal surface form a locus $V_3{}^3$, and are projected into the planes of a developable of class three, there being three of them which pass through an arbitrary point of [3]. Hence we obtain a surface whose bitangent developable is $3E_3{}^0$. The double curve is $C_9{}^4$.

The dual surface whose double curve is $3C_3{}^0$ is obtained by projection from the normal surface which has two directrix cubic curves; the bitangent developable is $E_9{}^4$. This surface is generated by a symmetrical (3, 3) correspondence between the points of a twisted cubic $C_3{}^0$.

When we represent these surfaces on Ω we obtain an elliptic sextic curve with ∞^1 trisecant planes on Ω; these planes are all of the same system, two of them passing through any point of the curve. They form a three-dimensional sextic locus with a double Veronese surface.

When we project the surface F which contains ∞^1 directrix cubics from a line which meets one of the planes which contain the cubic curves we obtain a surface f which has as tritangent planes the tangent planes of a quadric cone. These planes are the projections of the planes of a locus $V_3{}^3$ from a line l which meets one of them.

In general the line l, meeting the plane of a directrix cubic Γ, is not such that the solid which joins it to the plane of Γ contains also a generator of F. The chords of F which meet l meet F in Γ counted twice and a curve $C_{12}{}^2$, six of whose tangents meet l, meeting each generator in two points. The projected surface has a double curve $3R + C_6{}^1$ and a bitangent developable $3R + 3E_2$, R being the projection of Γ.

If we choose l to lie in the solid which contains Γ and a generator g then the chords of F which meet l meet F in Γ and g each counted three times and a prime section $C_6{}^1$. We obtain a surface f with a directrix R which is also a generator. The double curve is $6R + C_3{}^0$ and the bitangent developable $3R + 3E_2$.

409. The following three surfaces were overlooked in the third section of Chapter IV.

The chords of a normal sextic curve C of genus 2 in [4] which lie on a quadric containing C set up on C a symmetrical (4, 4) correspondence. If this breaks up into the sum of two (2, 2) correspondences we have in [3] a ruled surface, normal in [3], whose double curve is $C_4{}^1 + D_4{}^1$ and bitangent developable $E_4{}^1 + F_4{}^1$. $C_4{}^1$ and $D_4{}^1$ have four common points; $E_4{}^1$ and $F_4{}^1$ have four common planes.

Suppose that we take a prime section $C_6{}^2$ of the normal surface F (§ 335) which lies on a cubic cone* and project F on to a [3] from the vertex O of this cone. There are two tangents of $C_6{}^2$ through O; the remaining chords of F through O meet F in a curve $C_8{}^5$ having two intersections with each generator, eight tangents of $C_8{}^5$ passing through O. We obtain in [3] a surface whose double curve is $R + C_3{}^1 + C_4{}^1$ and bitangent developable $6R + E_2$; it is generated by a (2, 2) correspondence between R and $C_3{}^1$ with a doubly united point. $C_4{}^1$ meets $C_3{}^1$ four times but does not meet R.

There is also the dual surface, normal in [3], whose double curve is $6R + C_2$ and bitangent developable $R + E_3{}^1 + E_4{}^1$.

* The intersection of an elliptic cubic cone with a cubic surface containing three of its generators and touching it is a $C_6{}^2$ with a double point.

TABLES SHEWING THE DIFFERENT TYPES OF RULED SURFACES IN [3] UP TO AND INCLUDING THOSE OF THE SIXTH ORDER

We give here a set of tables shewing the different kinds of ruled surfaces in [3] that we have studied. In the first two columns of a table we give the double curve and bitangent developable of the surface, following the model of the table at the end of Cremona's paper on quartic ruled surfaces.

The symbols $B_n{}^p, C_n{}^p, D_n{}^p$ denote curves of order n and genus p, while $E_n{}^p, F_n{}^p, G_n{}^p$ denote developables of class n and genus p. R is used for a directrix, G and H for generators.

We shall not give here the developable surfaces, since a table of these is on p. 284.

Cubic Ruled Surfaces

The cubic ruled surfaces are of only two kinds, both are rational and are projections of a normal surface F in [4] with a directrix line λ. They can be exhibited as follows:

Double curve	Bitangent developable
$2R$	$2R'$
$2R$	$2R$

Quartic Ruled Surfaces

When we consider quartic ruled surfaces there are ten rational surfaces and two elliptic surfaces. Of the ten rational surfaces six are projections of the normal surface in [5] with directrix conics, while the remaining four are projections of the normal surface in [5] with a directrix line.

We give also in the table the type of rational quartic C on Ω from which any rational ruled quartic surface arises (the list of these curves C is found in § 58) and also the numbers attached to the surfaces by Cremona and Cayley. The last two surfaces in the table are elliptic.

Double curve	Bitangent developable	Type of curve C on Ω	Order of minimum directrix on normal surface F	Cremona's type	Cayley's type
C_3^0	E_3^0	I	2	1	10
$3R$	E_3^0	II (A)	2	8	9
C_3^0	$3R$	II (B)	1	7	8
$R + C_2$	$R + E_2$	II (C)	2	2	7
$3R$	$R + E_2$	III (A)	2	3	—
$R + C_2$	$3R$	III (B)	1	4	—
$3R$	$3R'$	IV (A)	1	9	3
$R + G + R'$	$R + G + R'$	IV (B)	2	5	2
$2R + G$	$2R + G$	V (A)	2	6	5
$3R$	$3R$	V (B)	1	10	6
$R + R'$	$R + R'$	—	—	11	1
$2R$	$2R$	—	—	12	4

Quintic Ruled Surfaces

Of quintic ruled surfaces in [3] there are twenty-four kinds of rational surfaces, six kinds of elliptic surfaces, and two surfaces whose plane sections are of genus 2.

Of the rational surfaces seventeen are projections of the normal surface in [6] with a directrix conic and seven are projections of the normal surface in [6] with a directrix line.

For the purpose of classifying the rational quintic surfaces we distinguished nineteen different types of rational quintic curves C on Ω. We give the type of curve corresponding to each surface (a list of the curves is given in § 85) and also the number associated with the surface by Schwarz*.

The table is divided into four sections by horizontal lines drawn across it. The surfaces in the first section have not a directrix line; those in the second section have a directrix line which is not a generator; those in the third section have a directrix line which is also a generator, while those in the fourth section are surfaces whose generators belong to a linear congruence.

* *Journal für Math.* 67 (1867), 57.

Double curve	Bitangent developable	Type of curve C on Ω	Order of minimum directrix on normal surface F	Schwarz's type
C_6^1	E_6^1	I, II (A)	2	II
$C_2 + C_4^0$	$E_2 + E_4^0$	I, II (A)	2	VIII
$B_2 + C_2 + D_2$	$E_2 + F_2 + G_2$	I, II (A)	2	IX
$G + C_5^0$	$G + E_5^0$	II (B)	2	X
$6R$	E_6^1	III (A)	2	I
$6R$	$E_2 + E_4^0$	III (A)	2	I
$6R$	$E_2 + F_2 + G_2$	III (A)	2	I
C_6^1	$6R$	III (B)	1	II
$C_2 + C_4^0$	$6R$	III (B)	1	VIII
$B_2 + C_2 + D_2$	$6R$	III (B)	1	IX
$3R + G + C_2$	$R + G + E_4^0$	III (C)	2	IV
$R + G + E_4^0$	$3R + G + E_2$	III (D)	2	VII
$3R + C_3^0$	$R + E_5^0$	III (E)	2	III
$R + C_5^0$	$3R + E_3^0$	III (F)	2	VI
$6R$	$R + E_5^0$	IV (A)	2	I
$R + C_5^0$	$6R$	IV (B)	1	VI
$3R + G + C_2$	$3R + G + E_2$	IV (C)	2	IV
$3R + C_3^0$	$3R + E_3^0$	IV (D)	2	III
$6R$	$3R + E_3^0$	V (A)	2	I
$3R + C_3^0$	$6R$	V (B)	1	III
$6R$	$6R'$	VI (A)	1	I
$3R + G + H + R'$	$R + G + H + 3R'$	VI (B)	2	V
$4R + G + H$	$4R + G + H$	VII (A)	2	V
$6R$	$6R$	VII (B)	1	I

To classify the elliptic quintic ruled surfaces in [3] we divided the elliptic quintic curves C on Ω into six classes (§ 151). Of the six types of surface two are projections of the normal surface with directrix cubic curves, while four are projections of the normal surface with a double line.

We have the following table:

Double curve	Bitangent developable	Type of curve C on Ω	Order of minimum directrix on normal surface F	Schwarz's type
$C_5{}^1$	$E_5{}^1$	VIII	3	I
$3R + C_2$	$R + E_4{}^1$	IX (A)	3	II
$R + C_4{}^1$	$3R + E_2$	IX (B)	2	IV
$3R + C_2$	$3R + E_2$	X	2	II
$3R + G + R'$	$R + G + 3R'$	XI	2	II
$4R + G$	$4R + G$	XII	2	III

There are only two types of quintic ruled surface in [3] whose plane sections are of genus 2; they are not projections of quintic surfaces in higher space. They are given by

Double curve	Bitangent developable	Type of curve C on Ω
$3R + R'$	$R + 3R'$	XIII
$4R$	$4R$	XIV

Sextic Ruled Surfaces

Proceeding now to the sextic ruled surfaces we have eighty-three kinds of rational surfaces, thirty-four kinds of elliptic surfaces, thirteen kinds of surfaces whose plane sections are of genus 2, four kinds of surfaces whose plane sections are of genus 3 and two kinds of surfaces whose plane sections are of genus 4.

As a basis for the classification of the rational surfaces we have thirty-eight types of rational curves C on Ω (§ 171).

Corresponding to curves C of types I and II we have twenty-seven different kinds of ruled surfaces; twelve of these are without multiple generators. We have the following table:

Double curve	Bitangent developable	Type of curve C on Ω
C_{10}^{3}	E_{10}^{3}	I (A) II (A)
$C_5^0 + D_5^0$	$E_5^0 + F_5^0$	I (A)
$C_4^0 + C_6^0$	$E_6^0 + E_4^0$	I (A)
$C_2 + C_8^1$	$E_3^0 + E_7^1$	I (A)
$C_3^0 + C_7^1$	$E_2 + E_8^1$	I (A)
$C_2 + D_2 + C_6^0$	$E_3^0 + F_3^0 + E_4^0$	I (A)
$C_3^0 + D_3^0 + C_4^0$	$E_2 + F_2 + E_3^0$	I (A)
$C_2 + C_3^0 + C_5^0$	$E_3^0 + E_2 + E_5^0$	I (A)
$3C_2 + C_4^0$	$E_4^0 + E_6^0$	I (A)
$3B_2 + C_2 + D_2$	$E_4^0 + E_3^0 + F_3^0$	I (A)
$C_4^0 + C_6^0$	$3E_2 + E_4^0$	I (A)
$C_4^0 + C_3^0 + D_3^0$	$3E_2 + F_2 + G_2$	I (A)
$G + C_9^2$	$G + E_9^2$	I (B) II (B)
$C_2 + G + C_7^1$	$E_2 + G + E_7^1$	I (B) II (B)
$C_2 + D_2 + G + C_5^0$	$E_2 + F_2 + G + E_5^0$	I (B) II (B)
$C_4^0 + G + C_5^0$	$E_5^0 + G + E_4^0$	I (B)
$C_2 + G + C_7^0$	$E_3^0 + G + E_6^0$	I (B)
$C_3^0 + G + C_6^0$	$E_2 + G + E_7^0$	I (B)
$C_2 + D_2 + G + C_5^0$	$E_2 + E_3^0 + G + E_4^0$	I (B)
$C_2 + C_3^0 + G + C_4^0$	$E_2 + F_2 + G + E_5^0$	I (B)
$G + 3C_3^0$	$G + E_9^2$	I (B)
$G + C_9^2$	$G + 3E_3^0$	I (B)
$G + H + C_8^1$	$G + H + E_8^1$	II (C)
$C_4^0 + G + H + D_4^0$	$E_4^0 + G + H + F_4^0$	II (C)
$C_2 + G + H + C_6^0$	$E_2 + G + H + E_6^0$	II (C)
$C_2 + D_2 + G + H + C_4^0$	$E_2 + F_2 + G + H + E_4^0$	II (C)
$3G + C_7^0$	$3G + E_7^0$	II (D)

The remaining types of curves C on Ω give rise to fifty-six kinds of surfaces; each of these surfaces is the projection of a unique surface in [7], twenty-seven are projections of the normal surface with directrix cubic curves, twenty are projections of the normal surface with a directrix conic and nine are projections of the normal surface with a directrix line. They are exhibited in the following table. The table is divided into three sections; the surfaces in the first section have a directrix line which is not itself a generator, those in the second section have a directrix line which is also a generator and those in the third section are such that their generators belong to a linear congruence.

Double curve	Bitangent developable	Type of curve C on Ω	Order of minimum directrix on normal surface F
$10R$	$E_{10}{}^{3}$	III (A)	3
$10R$	$E_5{}^0 + F_5{}^0$	III (A)	3
$C_{10}{}^{3}$	$10R$	III (B)	1
$C_5{}^0 + D_5{}^0$	$10R$	III (B)	1
$6R + C_4{}^0$	$R + E_9{}^1$	III (C)	3
$6R + C_4{}^0$	$R + E_3{}^0 + E_6{}^0$	III (C)	3
$6R + C_4{}^0$	$R + E_3{}^0 + F_3{}^0 + G_3{}^0$	III (C)	3
$R + C_9{}^1$	$6R + E_4{}^0$	III (D)	2
$R + C_3{}^0 + C_6{}^0$	$6R + E_4{}^0$	III (D)	2
$R + B_3{}^0 + C_3{}^0 + D_3{}^0$	$6R + E_4{}^0$	III (D)	2
$6R + G + C_3{}^0$	$R + G + E_8{}^1$	III (E)	3
$6R + G + C_3{}^0$	$R + G + E_2 + E_6{}^0$	III (E)	3
$6R + G + C_3{}^0$	$R + G + E_3{}^0 + E_5{}^0$	III (E)	3
$6R + G + C_3{}^0$	$R + G + E_2 + E_3{}^0 + F_3{}^0$	III (E)	3
$R + G + C_8{}^1$	$6R + G + E_3{}^0$	III (F)	2
$R + G + C_2 + C_6{}^0$	$6R + G + E_3{}^0$	III (F)	2
$R + G + C_3{}^0 + C_5{}^0$	$6R + G + E_3{}^0$	III (F)	2
$R + G + C_2 + C_3{}^0 + D_3{}^0$	$6R + G + E_3{}^0$	III (F)	2
$6R + G + H + C_2$	$R + G + H + E_7{}^1$	III (G)	3
$6R + G + H + C_2$	$R + G + H + E_2 + E_5{}^0$	III (G)	3
$6R + G + H + C_2$	$R + G + H + E_3{}^0 + E_4{}^0$	III (G)	3
$6R + G + H + C_2$	$R + G + H + E_2 + F_2 + E_3{}^0$	III (G)	3
$R + G + H + C_7{}^1$	$6R + G + H + E_2$	III (H)	2
$R + G + H + C_2 + C_5{}^0$	$6R + G + H + E_2$	III (H)	2
$R + G + H + C_3{}^0 + C_4{}^0$	$6R + G + H + E_2$	III (H)	2
$R + G + H + C_2 + D_2 + C_3{}^0$	$6R + G + H + E_2$	III (H)	2
$3R + C_7{}^0$	$3R + E_7{}^0$	III (I)	3
$3R + G + C_6{}^0$	$3R + G + E_6{}^0$	III (J)	3
$3R + G + H + C_5{}^0$	$3R + G + H + E_5{}^0$	III (K)	3
$3R + 3G + C_4{}^0$	$3R + 3G + E_4{}^0$	III (L)	3

Double curve	Bitangent developable	Type of curve C on Ω	Order of minimum directrix on normal surface F
$10R$	$R + E_9{}^1$	IV (A)	3
$10R$	$R + E_3{}^0 + E_6{}^0$	IV (A)	3
$10R$	$R + E_3{}^0 + F_3{}^0 + G_3{}^0$	IV (A)	3
$R + C_9{}^1$	$10R$	IV (B)	1
$R + C_3{}^0 + C_6{}^0$	$10R$	IV (B)	1
$R + B_3{}^0 + C_3{}^0 + D_3{}^0$	$10R$	IV (B)	1
$6R + C_4{}^0$	$3R + E_7{}^0$	IV (C)	3
$3R + C_7{}^0$	$6R + E_4{}^0$	IV (D)	2
$6R + G + C_3{}^0$	$3R + G + E_6{}^0$	IV (E)	3
$6R + G + C_3{}^0$	$3R + G + 3E_2$	IV (E)	3
$3R + G + C_6{}^0$	$6R + G + E_3{}^0$	IV (F)	2
$3R + G + 3C_2$	$6R + G + E_3{}^0$	IV (F)	2
$6R + G + H + C_2$	$3R + G + H + E_5{}^0$	IV (G)	3
$3R + G + H + C_5{}^0$	$6R + G + H + E_2$	IV (H)	2
$10R$	$3R + E_7{}^0$	V (A)	3
$3R + C_7{}^0$	$10R$	V (B)	1
$6R + C_4{}^0$	$6R + E_4{}^0$	V (C)	2
$6R + G + C_3{}^0$	$6R + G + E_3{}^0$	V (D)	2
$10R$	$6R + E_4{}^0$	VI (A)	2
$6R + C_4{}^0$	$10R$	VI (B)	1
$10R$	$10R'$	VII (A)	1
$6R + G + H + K + R'$	$R + G + H + K + 6R'$	VII (B)	2
$3R+G+H+J+K+3R'$	$3R+G+H+J+K+3R'$	VII (C)	3
$10R$	$10R$	VIII (A)	1
$7R + G + H + K$	$7R + G + H + K$	VIII (B)	2
$6R + G + H + J + K$	$6R + G + H + J + K$	VIII (C)	3

Of the thirty-four types of elliptic sextic ruled surfaces in [3] sixteen are projections of the general normal surface which has two directrix cubic curves and eleven are projections of the normal surface with a double line. Five types are projections of the normal surface with ∞^1 plane cubics on it (denoted in the table by 3_∞) and the two remaining types are the projections of the normal surface with only one cubic curve on it (denoted in the table by 3_1).

There are twenty different types of elliptic sextic curves C on Ω (§ 255).

The table of the elliptic sextic ruled surfaces is divided into four sections by horizontal lines drawn across it. The surfaces in the first section have not a directrix line; those in the second section have a directrix line which is not itself a generator; those in the third section have a directrix line which is also a generator; those in the fourth section belong to a linear congruence.

Double curve	Bitangent developable	Type of curve C on Ω	Order of minimum directrix on normal surface F
C_9^4	E_9^4	I, II (A)	3
$C_2 + C_7^3$	$E_2 + E_7^3$	I, II (A)	3
$C_2 + D_2 + C_5^2$	$E_2 + F_2 + E_5^2$	I, II (A)	3
$3C_3^0$	E_9^4	I	3
C_9^4	$3E_3^0$	I	3_∞
$G + C_8^3$	$G + E_8^3$	II (B)	3
$C_2 + G + C_6^2$	$E_2 + G + E_6^2$	II (B)	3
$R + C_8^3$	$6R + E_3^0$	III (A)	2
$R + C_2 + C_6^2$	$6R + E_3^0$	III (A)	2
$R + C_2 + D_2 + C_4^1$	$6R + E_3^0$	III (A)	2
$6R + C_3^0$	$R + E_8^3$	III (B)	3
$6R + C_3^0$	$R + E_2 + E_6^2$	III (B)	3
$6R + C_3^0$	$R + E_2 + F_2 + E_4^1$	III (B)	3
$R + G + C_7^3$	$6R + G + E_2$	III (C)	2
$R + G + C_2 + C_5^2$	$6R + G + E_2$	III (C)	2
$6R + G + C_2$	$R + G + E_7^3$	III (D)	3
$6R + G + C_2$	$R + G + E_2 + E_5^2$	III (D)	3
$3R + C_6^1$	$3R + E_6^1$	III (E)	3
$3R + 3C_2$	$3R + E_6^1$	III (E)	3_1
$3R + C_6^1$	$3R + 3E_2$	III (E)	3_∞
$3R + G + C_5^1$	$3R + G + E_5^1$	III (F)	3
$3R + C_6^1$	$6R + E_3^0$	IV (A)	2
$3R + 3C_2$	$6R + E_3^0$	IV (A)	2
$6R + C_3^0$	$3R + E_6^1$	IV (B)	3
$6R + C_3^0$	$3R + 3E_2$	IV (B)	3_∞
$3R + G + C_5^1$	$6R + G + E_2$	IV (C)	2
$6R + G + C_2$	$3R + G + E_5^1$	IV (D)	3
$6R + C_3^0$	$6R + E_3^0$	V	2
$6R + G + H + R'$	$R + G + H + 6R'$	VI (A)	2
$3R + G + H + J + 3R'$	$3R + G + H + J + 3R'$	VI (B)	3
$3R + 3G + 3R'$	$3R + 3G + 3R'$	VI (C)	3_∞
$7R + G + H$	$7R + G + H$	VII (A)	2
$6R + G + H + J$	$6R + G + H + J$	VII (B)	3_1
$6R + 3G$	$6R + 3G$	VII (C)	3_∞

We give now the list of the sextic ruled surfaces in [3] whose plane sections are of genus 2, classified according to their double curves and bitangent developables.

Double curve	Bitangent developable	Type of curve C on Ω
C_8^5	E_8^5	I
$C_4^1 + D_4^1$	$E_4^1 + F_4^1$	I
$R + C_7^5$	$6R + E_2$	II (A)*
$R + C_3^1 + C_4^1$	$6R + E_2$	II (A)*
$6R + C_2$	$R + E_7^5$	II (B)
$6R + C_2$	$R + E_3^1 + E_4^1$	II (B)
$3R + C_5^2$	$3R + E_5^2$	II (C)
$3R + C_5^2$	$6R + E_2$	III (A)*
$6R + C_2$	$3R + E_5^2$	III (B)
$6R + G + R'$	$R + G + 6R'$	IV (A)*
$3R + G + H + 3R'$	$3R + G + H + 3R'$	IV (B)
$7R + G$	$7R + G$	V (A)*
$6R + G + H$	$6R + G + H$	V (B)

The list of curves C on Ω of order 6 and genus 2 is found in § 327.

The five surfaces marked with an asterisk are the projections of a normal surface in [4], but the others are not the projections of a sextic ruled surface in higher space, and are themselves normal.

For surfaces whose plane sections are of genus 3 we have

Double curve	Bitangent developable
$6R + R'$	$R + 6R'$
$3R + G + 3R'$	$3R + G + 3R'$
$7R$	$7R$
$6R + G$	$6R + G$

and for surfaces whose plane sections are of genus 4

Double curve	Bitangent developable
$3R + 3R'$	$3R + 3R'$
$6R$	$6R$

NOTE

THE INTERSECTIONS OF TWO CURVES ON A RULED SURFACE

1. Suppose that we have in space $[r]$ a ruled surface of order n and on this surface two curves of orders m and m'. A curve will meet all the generators of the surface in the same number of points; suppose then that the curve of order m meets each generator in k points and that the curve of order m' meets each generator in k' points. We wish to find an expression for the number of intersections of the two curves.

In the first instance we shall assume that each curve is a simple curve on the ruled surface; this means that through each point of a curve, with possibly a finite number of exceptions, there passes only one generator of the surface.

Take then an arbitrary $[r-2]$; this will meet the surface in n points. We establish a correspondence between primes P and P' passing through this $[r-2]$; two primes P and P' correspond when P joins $[r-2]$ to a point of the first curve and P' joins $[r-2]$ to a point of the second curve, these two points being on the same generator of the surface. Then any prime P meets the curve of order m in m points through each of which there passes a generator of the surface, so that we have mk' corresponding primes P'. Similarly, given a prime P', we have $m'k$ corresponding primes P. Hence, by Chasles' principle of correspondence, there will be $mk'+m'k$ coincidences of pairs of corresponding primes.

The prime joining $[r-2]$ to an intersection of the two curves clearly counts among these coincidences. But there are also other coincidences; for $[r-2]$ meets the surface in n points, and the prime joining $[r-2]$ to the generator of the surface through any one of these points contains k points of the first curve and k' points of the second curve, all on this same generator. This prime in fact counts kk' times among the coincidences. There are no other coincidences than those already mentioned.

Hence we conclude that, if i is the number of intersections of the two curves*,

$$mk' + m'k = i + nkk',$$

or

$$i = mk' + m'k - nkk'.$$

For example, if we consider two prime sections we have $m = m' = n$ and $k = k' = 1$, so that they have n intersections. These are, of course, the n points in which the $[r-2]$ common to the primes meets the surface.

* Segre, *Rom. Acc. Lincei Rend.* (4), 3^2 (1887), 3.

We have assumed implicitly in the above proof that none of the intersections of the two curves is a multiple point on the ruled surface; for if one of the i points is at an intersection of two or more generators of the ruled surface we should have to count it more than once among the coincidences, although both the curves might only have simple points there. In such a case the number i given by the formula would have to be modified.

2. Let us consider now the intersections of two multiple curves on a ruled surface. We take as before a ruled surface of order n in $[r]$ and on it two curves of orders m and m', meeting each generator of the surface in k and k' points respectively. But now the curves are of multiplicities s and s' upon the surface; through a general point of the curve of order m there pass s generators, while through a general point of the curve of order m' there pass s' generators. The preceding is the particular case of this when $s = s' = 1$.

We set up just as before a correspondence between the primes P and P' of a pencil; but now to any given prime P there will correspond msk' primes P', while to any given prime P' there will correspond $m's'k$ primes P. We thus have

$$msk' + m's'k - nkk'$$

coincidences of pairs of corresponding primes which are to be accounted for by intersections of the two curves.

The question then remains to be answered, "How many times does each intersection count among this number of coincidences?"—and at first sight it seems as though the answer cannot be given without some difficulty. There may be points of the first curve through which there pass more than s generators of the surface just as there may be points of the second curve through which there pass more than s' generators of the surface. It seems as though we ought to know the number of generators which meet at any given intersection of the two curves before we can tell how many times this intersection should count among the coincidences, and we may have to know more than this.

3. It will help to explain some of the difficulties if we illustrate them by one or two examples.

(A) Suppose that we take a line and a conic with one intersection and place them in (2, 2) correspondence with a doubly united point. The joining lines will then generate a ruled surface of the fourth order on which the line and the conic are double curves. For the line $m = 1$, $s = 2$, $k = 1$, while for the conic $m' = 2$, $s' = 2$, $k' = 1$, and $n = 4$. Hence

$$msk' + m's'k - nkk' = 2,$$

and the single intersection is counted twice.

(B) If we consider the number of intersections of a prime section and a double curve the formula for the number of coincidences gives twice the order of the double curve, whereas the number of intersections is actually equal to the order of the double curve. Each intersection then must be counted twice.

(C) Let us take a rational quartic with a double point and a conic which passes through the double point and meets the quartic in two other points. Then the chords of the quartic which meet the conic generate a quintic ruled surface on which the two curves are double curves. The double point of the quartic curve is, in fact, a triple point of the ruled surface, there being three generators passing through this point.

Then for the quartic

$$m = 4, \quad s = 2, \quad k = 2,$$

and for the conic $$m' = 2, \quad s' = 2, \quad k' = 1,$$

while $n = 5$. Hence $$msk' + m's'k - nkk' = 6.$$

But the number of actual intersections of the two curves is four, if we count the double point as two intersections, and the relation between the number of intersections and the number of coincidences does not seem clear without further investigation.

Now it is known, from the general theory of ruled surfaces, that on this quintic ruled surface there is a simple conic; through each point of this conic not on the double curve there passes one generator of the surface, while each generator (with three exceptions) meets the conic in one point. Then for this conic $m'' = 2$, $s'' = 1$, $k'' = 1$, so that, considering the two conics,

$$m's'k'' + m''s''k' - nk'k'' = 1.$$

It certainly cannot be maintained that any coincidence has been counted twice in this result, and there is in fact precisely one intersection of the two conics. Hence in this particular case the formula gives the correct result without modification.

Also $$m''s''k + msk'' - nk''k = 2,$$

which is also correct; the simple conic does, in fact, meet the double quartic in two points.

But if we were to calculate the number of intersections of either the double conic or the double quartic with a plane section we should get twice the correct result, as in (B).

Thus it appears that when we have two curves of given multiplicities on a ruled surface we cannot, without further examination, state the number of times that each intersection counts among the coincidences. We certainly cannot for two double curves, or for a double curve and a simple curve.

4. It may be that the ruled surface which we are considering is the projection of a normal ruled surface in higher space. When this is so it may happen further that the curves of orders m and m' and multiplicities s and s' are the projections of simple curves of orders ms and $m's'$ on the normal surface. Then, since the order of the surface and the number of points in which a curve meets a generator are unaltered by projection, the formula

$$i = msk' + m's'k - nkk'$$

gives the number of intersections of these two simple curves on the normal surface*. Thus if an intersection of the multiple curves is the projection of only one of the intersections of the simple curves it will count only once among the coincidences; if, however, it is the projection of two intersections of the simple curves it will count twice, and so on.

We can thus clearly explain the fact that the formula, when applied to a prime section and a double curve, gives twice the correct number of intersections. We assume that the surface in $[r]$ is the projection of a normal surface of the same order in $[R]$ from a space $[R - r - 1]$ not meeting this normal surface. Then we suppose that the double curve of the surface in $[r]$ is the projection from $[R - r - 1]$ of a simple curve C on the normal surface; there will be ∞^1 chords of C meeting $[R - r - 1]$, each of these chords being joined to $[R - r - 1]$ by an $[R - r]$ meeting $[r]$ in a point of the double curve. A prime section of the surface in $[r]$ is joined to $[R - r - 1]$ by a space $[R - 1]$ which gives the corresponding prime section S of the normal surface; then through any intersection of S and C there must pass a chord meeting $[R - r - 1]$; the other intersection of this chord with C then necessarily lies also on S. Hence each intersection of the double curve and the prime section on the surface in $[r]$ is the projection of two intersections of S and C.

5. It will be advisable now to elaborate at some length the account of the curves on the quintic surface in our third example; the whole theory of the quintic ruled surfaces has been fully investigated, and this process of elaboration will throw much light on more general examples†.

We had a rational quartic C_4 with a double point and a conic C_2 passing through this double point and meeting C_4 in two other points. The quintic ruled surface formed by the chords of C_4 which meet C_2 has both C_4 and C_2 for double curves; it is rational since its plane sections have six double points. It can therefore be regarded as the projection of a normal quintic ruled surface F in $[6]$.

The centre of projection will be a plane ϖ. The surface F will have a directrix conic Γ, and the projection of Γ from ϖ gives the simple conic c_2 on the projected surface. The surface F has ∞^4 directrix quartic curves lying on it, and we choose ϖ to contain an axis p of one of these quartics E (§ 130).

* By § 1.

† See § 130.

It is known that the chords of F form a locus $M_5{}^3$ of five dimensions and the third order; thus ϖ will meet this locus in the line p and a conic ϑ. Through every point of p there passes a chord of E, while through every point of ϑ there passes a chord of F; for different points of ϑ the different chords of F trace out on F a curve C_8 of the eighth order meeting each generator in two points. It can be proved that C_8 has one double point A. Through A there will then pass two chords AB and AC of C_8 which both meet ϑ; the line BC is then also a chord of F meeting ϖ, its intersection with ϖ lies on p, and B and C lie on E as well as on C_8. Also through the intersections of p and ϑ there pass lines which are common chords of E and C_8.

When we project from ϖ on to a solid the curve E becomes a conic C_2 and the curve C_8 becomes a quartic C_4; both C_2 and C_4 are double curves on the projected surface. The solid through ϖ containing A, B, C meets the solid on to which we are projecting in a point which lies on C_2 and is a double point on C_4, this being the projection of two intersections, viz. B and C, of E and C_8. C_2 and C_4 have two other intersections each of which is the projection of two intersections of E and C_8.

We now see clearly how to reckon the intersections of C_2 and C_4; the double point of C_4 lies on C_2 and counts twice among the coincidences, while each other intersection of C_2 and C_4 counts twice among the coincidences. The curves C_8 and E on the normal surface have six intersections and no more.

The curve E, meeting each generator of F in one point, will meet the conic Γ in one point, while the curve C_8, meeting each generator of F in two points, will meet Γ in two points. Through the intersection of Γ and E there passes a chord of E meeting p, but the other intersection of this chord with E is not on Γ nor does the solid through ϖ which contains it meet Γ again. Hence, on the quintic surface in [3], the double conic C_2 and the simple conic c_2 have one intersection, and this is the projection of the single intersection of Γ and E. Similarly the double quartic C_4 meets the simple conic c_2 in two points each of which is the projection of one intersection of Γ and C_8.

If, however, we were to consider intersections of either C_4 or C_2 with a plane section each would be the projection of two intersections of C_8 or E with a prime section of F. The prime would contain ϖ, two chords of E meeting p and four chords of C_8 meeting ϑ.

6. It is usual to assume that a general ruled surface has no singularities unless it lies in three or four-dimensional space; a ruled surface in [4] will have a finite number of double points, while a ruled surface in [3] has a double curve with a finite number of triple points which are also triple points of the ruled surface. This is, of course, a statement which is only true in very general instances; we can have many ruled surfaces with multiple curves in any space. For example, if a curve of order n lies on a quadric then the chords of the curve which lie on the quadric form a ruled surface on which the curve is a multiple curve of multiplicity $n-2$. Also any ruled surface generated by any correspondence other than a (1, 1) correspondence between two curves has necessarily one or both of the curves as multiple curves.

Let us, however, for the present confine our attention to surfaces in [3] with only double curves. It may happen, as in the case of the quintic ruled surface which we have been discussing, that the double curve is composite, consisting of two or more parts. We shall examine in detail how the intersections of two of these parts are given in the expression

$$msk' + m's'k - nkk'.$$

7. Suppose that the surface f in [3] is the projection of a normal surface F in $[r]$ from a space $[r-4]$ not meeting F. Then a point of the double curve of f is the intersection with [3] of an $[r-3]$ containing $[r-4]$ and meeting F in two points; the chord of F joining these two points will meet $[r-4]$. There are, in fact, ∞^1 chords of F meeting $[r-4]$; of the $\infty^{2(r-1)}$ lines in $[r]$ there are ∞^{2r-5} meeting $[r-4]$ and $r-3$ conditions are necessary for one of these to meet F. The curve in which these chords of F meet $[r-4]$ (if $r > 4$) is in birational correspondence with the double curve of f.

If the double curve of f has a triple point we shall have an $[r-3]$ containing $[r-4]$ and meeting F in three points; thus we have a trisecant plane of F meeting $[r-4]$ in a line. Of the $\infty^{3(r-2)}$ planes of $[r]$ there are $\infty^{3(r-4)}$ meeting $[r-4]$, and $r-4$ conditions are necessary for one of these to meet F. We thus expect f to have a finite number of triple points. In general, F will not have any trisecant lines, and, even if it had, none of them would meet a general $[r-4]$.

The chords of F meeting $[r-4]$ will then meet F in the points of a curve. If a trisecant plane meets F in points A, B, C and also meets $[r-4]$ in a line the chords BC, CA, AB will all meet $[r-4]$ so that the curve on F has double points at each of A, B, C.

If now the double curve of f is composite this curve on F will also be composite. It is then at once clear that *if the two parts of the double curve on f have an intersection which is a simple point on both of them and not a triple point of f then this intersection is the projection of two distinct intersections of the corresponding curves on F*, the common chord of the two curves meeting $[r-4]$.

It remains to consider the intersection of the two parts at a triple point of f. Suppose that the first component of the double curve has a double point here, then the second component will only have a simple point. Then, the triple point being the intersection of [3] with an $[r-3]$ meeting F in three points A, B, C, the first component of the curve on F will have a double point at one of these points, say A, and pass through the other two, while the second component passes through B and C. Thus *the intersection of the two curves at the triple point of f is the projection of two intersections B and C of the corresponding curves on F.* The quintic ruled surface in § 5 is an example of this.

On the other hand, it may happen that both components of the double curve pass simply through the triple point, there being a third component also passing through the triple point. When this happens the three components must be projections of three curves on F one of which passes through B and C, another through C and A and another through A and B. Then *the intersection of the two components is the projection of only one intersection of the two corresponding curves on F.*

We can then state the following rule.

Suppose that we have on a ruled surface f, in [3], *two double curves of orders m and m' meeting each generator in k and k' points respectively. Then the mutual intersections of the two curves are of three possible kinds:*

I. A simple intersection at a point which is not a triple point of the ruled surface.

II. An intersection at a triple point of the ruled surface, one curve having a double point and the other a simple point.

III. An intersection at a triple point of the ruled surface, both curves having only simple points.

Then, if we count each intersection under I or II as two intersections and each intersection under III as one intersection, the total number of intersections so obtained will be

$$2\,(mk' + m'k) - nkk'$$

where n is the order of the surface.

Both the quartic and quintic ruled surfaces in the examples in § 3 illustrate this rule.

8. An abundance of other examples could be given to illustrate the rule; we give only a few:

(A) Take three conics circumscribing the triangles of three faces of a tetrahedron. Then the lines which meet all three conics form a quintic ruled surface on which the conics are double curves; the point common to the three conics is a triple point of the ruled surface. Then, for any pair of the conics, $m = m' = 2$, $s = s' = 2$, $k = k' = 1$, while $n = 5$, so that

$$msk' + m's'k - nkk' = 3,$$

the intersection of the two conics at the triple point only counting once in this result, while the other intersection counts twice.

(B) Let us take an elliptic quartic curve and a line meeting it once.

Then the chords of the curve which meet the line form a ruled surface of the fifth order on which the line and the curve are both double. For the curve $m = 4$ and $k = 2$, while for the line $m' = 1$ and $k' = 1$. Thus, since $n = 5$, $2(mk' + m'k) - nkk' = 2$; the single intersection counting twice.

(C) If we take a conic C_2 and a twisted cubic and place them in (1, 2) correspondence with a united point we obtain a ruled surface of the sixth order on which C_2 is a double curve. The surface has also a double curve C_8 of the eighth order meeting each of its generators in three points; C_8 has two triple points. It has also two double points through which C_2 passes and has three simple intersections with C_2 (cf. §§ 175, 176). $n = 6$.

For C_8 $\quad m = 8, \quad s = 2, \quad k = 3.$

For C_2 $\quad m' = 2, \quad s' = 2, \quad k' = 1.$

$$msk' + m's'k - nkk' = 10 = 2 \cdot 2 + 3 \cdot 2.$$

(D) Take two twisted cubics and place them in (1, 2) correspondence with three united points. Then the joins of corresponding points give a ruled surface of the sixth order on which one of the cubics C_3 is a double curve. On this surface there is also a double curve C_7 meeting each generator in three points. C_7 has four double points through all of which C_3 passes; it has also three simple intersections with C_3 (cf. §§ 175, 177). $n = 6$.

For C_7 $\quad m = 7, \quad s = 2, \quad k = 3.$

For C_3 $\quad m' = 3, \quad s' = 2, \quad k' = 1.$

$$msk' + m's'k - nkk' = 14 = 4 \cdot 2 + 3 \cdot 2.$$

(E) Take two conics C_2 and D_2 with one intersection and place them in (2, 2) correspondence with a doubly united point. Then the joins of pairs of corresponding points form a ruled surface of the sixth order on which C_2 and D_2 are both double curves. There is also on this surface a double curve C_6 of the sixth order meeting each generator in two points. This curve has four double points, two of which are on C_2 and two on D_2, while it has two simple intersections with each of C_2 and D_2 (cf. §§ 178, 179). $n = 6$.

For C_6 $\quad m = 6, \quad s = 2, \quad k = 2.$

For C_2 $\quad m' = 2, \quad s' = 2, \quad k' = 1.$

For D_2 $\quad m'' = 2, \quad s'' = 2, \quad k'' = 1.$

$$m's'k'' + m''s''k' - nk'k'' = 2 = 2 \cdot 1,$$
$$m''s''k + msk'' - nk''k = 8 = 2 \cdot 2 + 2 \cdot 2,$$
$$msk' + m's'k - nkk' = 8 = 2 \cdot 2 + 2 \cdot 2.$$

(F) Take two twisted cubics C_3 and D_3 with five intersections and place them in (2, 2) correspondence with four ordinary united points and one doubly united point. Then the joins of pairs of corresponding points generate a ruled surface of the sixth order on which C_3 and D_3 are double curves. There is further on this surface a quartic double curve C_4 meeting each generator in two points; this passes through the four ordinary united points of the correspondence and meets each cubic in two other points (cf. §§ 178, 180). $n = 6$.

For C_4 $\quad m = 4, \quad s = 2, \quad k = 2.$

For C_3 $\quad m' = 3, \quad s' = 2, \quad k' = 1.$

For D_3 $\quad m'' = 3, \quad s'' = 2, \quad k'' = 1.$

$$m's'k'' + m''s''k' - nk'k'' = 6 = 2 \,.\, 1 + 4,$$

$$m''s''k + msk'' - nk''k = 8 = 2 \,.\, 2 + 4,$$

$$msk' + m's'k - nkk' = 8 = 2 \,.\, 2 + 4.$$

(G) Take a conic C_2 and a twisted cubic C_3 which has three intersections with the conic. Then place these in (2, 2) correspondence with two ordinary united points and one doubly united point. Then the joins of pairs of corresponding points form a ruled surface of the sixth order on which C_2 and C_3 are double curves. On this surface there is also a double curve C_5 of the fifth order which meets each generator in two points and passes through the two ordinary united points of the correspondence. C_5 has two double points through which C_3 passes; it has two intersections with C_3 other than these double points and the united points already mentioned. Also it has two intersections with C_2 other than these united points (cf. § 181). $n = 6$.

For C_5 $\quad m = 5, \quad s = 2, \quad k = 2.$

For C_3 $\quad m' = 3, \quad s' = 2, \quad k' = 1.$

For C_2 $\quad m'' = 2, \quad s'' = 2, \quad k'' = 1.$

$$m's'k'' + m''s''k' - nk'k'' = 4 = 2 \,.\, 1 + 2,$$

$$m''s''k + msk'' - nk''k = 6 = 2 \,.\, 2 + 2,$$

$$msk' + m's'k - nkk' = 10 = 2 \,.\, 2 + 2 \,.\, 2 + 2.$$

9. At a triple point of the ruled surface there are three generators meeting; we may have part of the double curve with a triple point, or one part with a double point and another part with a simple point, or three parts all with simple points. In any case we have three distinct branches of the double curve; let P_1, P_2, P_3 be points of the different branches at the triple point. Then we can regard the three generators of the surface which pass through the triple point as the lines P_2P_3, P_3P_1, and P_1P_2; each generator joining the points on two of the branches of the curve. This statement is obscure without further elucidation; but is made much clearer when the triple point is regarded as the projection of three different points of the normal surface, at each of which the curve which projects into the double curve has a double point. It can also be elucidated in another way—by regarding the generators as points of a curve on a quadric in [5]*.

Suppose then that at the triple point we have two parts of the double curve, one having a double point P_1P_2 and the other a simple point P_3. Then given an arbitrary line the plane joining it to P counts for two among the coincidences; for it joins the point P_3 of the second curve to the point P_1 of the first on the same generator P_1P_3 and also joins the point P_3 of the second curve to the point P_2 of the first on the generator P_2P_3.

If, however, there are three parts of the double curve each passing simply through P they have there simple points P_1, P_2, P_3. If we consider intersections of the first two curves, the plane joining an arbitrary line to P only counts once among the coincidences, as joining the point P_1 of the first curve to the point P_2 of the second on the same generator.

But if two parts of the double curve intersect at a point which is not a triple point of the ruled surface the plane joining an arbitrary line to this intersection counts for two among the coincidences as joining the line to an intersection of the curves which lies on two different generators.

10. We know that we can represent the generators of a ruled surface f of order n in [3] by the points of a curve C of order n on a quadric fourfold Ω in [5]. Thus we can enquire how the intersections of different parts of the double curve of f are represented on Ω. The points of the double curve of f are in (1, 1) correspondence with the chords of C which lie on Ω; these chords form a ruled surface R_2.

If there is a triple point on f we shall have a plane of Ω, representing this point, which is trisecant to C; the points of the plane representing all the lines of [3] which pass through the triple point. Then the three points X, Y, Z in which this plane meets C represent the three generators of f which pass through the triple point; while the three lines YZ, ZX, XY which are all generators of the ruled surface formed by the chords of C lying on Ω are all, in the (1, 1) correspondence between the generators of R_2 and the points of the double curve, in correspondence with the triple point of the double curve.

If the double curve of f breaks up into component parts then R_2 will have to break up into corresponding component ruled surfaces. If two parts of the double curve both pass through a triple point then the corresponding ruled surfaces will have to have generators in the same plane of Ω which is trisecant to C; if, however, two parts of the double curve both pass through a point which is not a triple point of the surface the corresponding ruled surfaces on Ω must have a common generator. For the points of the double curve are in correspondence with the generators of R_2, and the same point cannot be in correspondence with two different

* See § 10 below.

generators unless these lie in a plane which lies on Ω and is trisecant to C*. Thus we see that there is a sharp distinction to be drawn between the intersections of two double curves on the surface according as the intersections do or do not lie at triple points of the surface.

If, at a triple point of the ruled surface, one part of the double curve has a double point and another a simple point then, in the corresponding trisecant plane XYZ of C, two of the three chords are generators of one ruled surface, while the remaining chord is a generator of another. If, however, three different parts of the double curve of f pass through the triple point then the three chords YZ, ZX, XY of C belong to three different ruled surfaces.

Also we now obtain a new aspect of the statement made above that at a triple point P of the ruled surface where we have three points P_1, P_2, P_3 on three different branches of the double curve, we regard the generators as the lines P_2P_3, P_3P_1, P_1P_2. The points P_1, P_2, P_3 of the double curve are represented by the generators YZ, ZX, XY respectively of R_2, and to say that one generator is the line P_2P_3 and does not (strictly) pass through P_1 is the same as saying that X lies on ZX and XY but not on YZ.

11. Suppose now that we have on a ruled surface f in a space $[r]$ a double curve and a triple curve. We shall assume that this surface is the projection of a normal ruled surface F of the same order in a space $[R]$; the centre of projection being a space $[R-r-1]$ which does not meet F. Then there will be ∞^1 trisecant planes of F which meet $[R-r-1]$ in lines; the spaces $[R-r]$ containing $[R-r-1]$ and these planes meeting $[r]$ in the points of the triple curve on f. Also there will be ∞^1 chords of F which meet $[R-r-1]$; the spaces $[R-r]$ containing $[R-r-1]$ and these chords meeting $[r]$ in the points of the double curve on f.

If Q_1, Q_2, Q_3 denote the three intersections of F with one of its trisecant planes which meets $[R-r-1]$ in a line, then the points Q describe a curve on F whose order is three times that of the triple curve on f, and which meets each generator of F in the same number of points as the triple curve on f meets the generators of f. Also, if P_1, P_2 denote the two intersections of F with one of its chords which meets $[R-r-1]$ in a point then the points P describe a curve on F whose order is twice that of the double curve on f and which meets each generator of F in the same number of points as the double curve on f meets the generators of f.

Now an intersection of the double curve and the triple curve on f is joined to $[R-r-1]$ by an $[R-r]$ which contains two points P and three points Q on F. Unless, then, we are to have a quadrisecant solid of F meeting $[R-r-1]$ in a plane, two of the points Q must coincide with the points P, and the intersection on f will be the projection of two inter-

* We may here refer to § 66, § 92 and § 100.

sections of the corresponding curves on F. There are two possibilities in which a quadrisecant solid of F could meet $[R-r-1]$ in a plane; either the intersection of the two curves on f could be a multiple point on one or both of them or a third multiple curve on f might pass through this same point.

We can therefore state the following:

If on a ruled surface f we have a double curve of order m meeting each generator in k points and a triple curve of order m' meeting each generator in k' points and if all their intersections are simple points on both curves, and if, further, none of their intersections lies on a third multiple curve of f, then the number of these intersections is

$$\tfrac{1}{2}(2mk' + 3m'k - nkk'),$$

where n is the order of the surface. In obtaining this we have assumed that the multiple curves are projections of simple curves on a normal surface.

And similarly we have the following:

If on a ruled surface f we have a curve of order m and multiplicity s meeting each generator in k points and also a curve of order m' and multiplicity s' meeting each generator in k' points, and if all their intersections are simple points on both curves, and if, further, none of their intersections lies on a third multiple curve of f, then the number of these intersections is

$$\frac{1}{s_0}(msk' + m's'k - nkk'),$$

where n is the order of the surface and s_0 is the smaller of s and s'. The result holds if $s = s' = s_0$.

12. We can illustrate these last statements by examples:

(A) If we take a line R and a conic and place them in (1, 3) correspondence the joins of pairs of corresponding points will generate a ruled surface of the fifth order on which R is a triple line. This surface has also a double curve; this is a twisted cubic C_3 which has R for a chord. A plane through R meets the conic in two points and contains two generators of the surface; their intersection is a point of C_3 (cf. §§ 139, 140). $n = 5$.

For C_3 $\quad m = 3, \quad s = 2, \quad k = 1.$

For R $\quad m' = 1, \quad s' = 3, \quad k' = 1.$

$$msk' + m's'k - nkk' = 4 = 2 \,.\, 2.$$

The ruled surface is rational, the plane sections being quintic curves each with a triple point and three double points. It can therefore be obtained by projection from a rational normal quintic ruled surface F in [6]. We project from a plane ϖ, and for this particular surface we choose ϖ to meet a solid K containing a directrix cubic Δ of the normal surface in a line p*. Then the pencil of planes through p in K gives a system of trisecant planes of F which all meet the centre of projection in lines (in this case the same line). The plane ϖ meets $M_5{}^3$, the locus of the chords of F, in p and a conic ϑ. Through each point of ϑ passes a chord of F, and these chords will meet F in the points of a rational sextic curve C_6 meeting each generator of F once. Then C_6 and Δ have four intersections, these being the points of F on the two chords which pass through the intersections of p and ϑ.

Each intersection of R and C_3 is the projection of two intersections of Δ and C_6.

The conic which we put in correspondence with R is a simple conic on the surface; it does not meet R but it meets C_3 three times.

For the conic $\quad m'' = 2, \quad s'' = 1, \quad k'' = 1,$

so that
$$m''s''k' + m's'k'' - nk'k'' = 0,$$
$$m''s''k + msk'' - nkk'' = 3.$$

The three intersections of the conic with C_3 are the projections of three distinct intersections of C_6 and the directrix conic of the normal surface.

(B) If we take a line R and a twisted cubic in (1, 3) correspondence the joins of pairs of corresponding points form a ruled surface of the sixth order on which R is a triple line. This surface has also a double curve C_7 of the seventh order which meets every generator in two points and R in four points (cf. § 222). $n = 6$.

For C_7 $\quad m = 7, \quad s = 2, \quad k = 2.$

For R $\quad m' = 1, \quad s' = 3, \quad k' = 1.$

$$msk' + m's'k - nkk' = 8 = 2 \cdot 4.$$

The ruled surface is rational and is obtained by projection from a normal surface in [7]. The normal surface has ∞^1 directrix cubic curves on it; we project from a solid S meeting the solid K containing one of these cubic curves in a line p. The chords of F meeting S do so in p and a rational quintic $\vartheta_5{}^0$ of which p is the quadrisecant. The chords of F through the intersections of p and $\vartheta_5{}^0$ give four pairs of points on F; each of these pairs of points projects into one intersection of R and C_7.

(C) Finally, we will give an example in which the conditions required do not hold, there being three different multiple curves on a ruled surface with points common to all of them.

Let us take a rational quintic curve C in [4]; this has a trisecant chord t meeting it in three points P, Q, R. Suppose that we have a quadric Ω containing C; this quadric will also contain t.

* There are ∞^2 curves Δ on F with corresponding solids K. These solids K generate the $M_5{}^3$ formed by the chords of F, and a general plane of [6] will not meet any of them in a line.

Then the chords of C which lie on Ω form a ruled surface of order 12 on which C and t are both triple curves. There is also on this surface a double curve of the sixth order meeting each generator in one point and passing through P, Q and R*. $n = 12$.

For C $\qquad m = 5, \qquad s = 3, \qquad k = 2.$

For the double curve

$$m' = 6, \qquad s' = 2, \qquad k' = 1.$$

$$msk' + m's'k - nkk' = 15.$$

The number of intersections of C with the sextic curve other than P, Q, R is known to be six, and each of these will be counted twice according to our rule. Hence *the three intersections which are on t are only counted once.*

We have here an example in which a triple curve and a double curve intersect, three of their intersections being on another triple curve of the ruled surface. It appears that these last three intersections of the triple curve and the double curve only give rise to one coincidence each.

The ruled surface can be shewn to be elliptic; it can therefore be obtained by projection from an elliptic ruled surface of order 12 in [11]; the centre of projection is a [6] not meeting the surface.

* See § 96.

CAMBRIDGE: PRINTED BY W. LEWIS, M.A., AT THE UNIVERSITY PRESS